A Metric Manual of
Specifications and Quantities
for Civil Engineers

also of interest

Introduction to Structural Mechanics
Trefor J. Reynolds and Lewis E. Kent
with David M. Lazenby

A Metric Manual of Specifications and Quantities for Civil Engineers

W. H. King, BA, BSc, MSc, PhD, FICE
Associate Professor, Department of Civil Engineering
University of Capetown

D. M. R. Esson, BSc(Eng), MICE
Of the Inner Temple, Barrister
Fellow of the Institute of Arbitrators
Lecturer in Civil Engineering, University of Glasgow

The English Universities Press Ltd

ISBN 0 340 12377 X (boards edition)
0 340 12376 1 (paperback edition)

based on the fifth edition of *A Manual of Specifications and Quantities for Civil Engineers* by A. Johnson and W. H. King

First published 1975

The English Universities Press Ltd
St. Paul's House, Warwick Lane, London EC4P 4AH

Printed in Great Britain by
Elliott Bros. & Yeoman Ltd, Liverpool L24 9JL

CONTENTS

LIST OF FIGURES

LIST OF FIGURES—(*continued*)

* *See envelope inside back cover.*

PREFACE

THE scarcity of books on Civil Engineering Contracts, Specifications and Quantities is the reason for the appearance of this book.

It embodies the result of extensive experience in the preparation of specifications and quantities for engineering work, and in lecturing on the subject to students.

Textbooks on the Law of Contract frequently present great difficulty to engineering students unacquainted with legal terms. The chapters on contracts have therefore been written with the object of explaining in simple language the essential principles of the Law relating to contracts, and for this reason all references to decided cases have been omitted.

Students making their first acquaintance with the Conditions of Contract are inclined to regard this document as a collection of verbose clauses which no memory, however good, can possibly retain. By grouping these clauses according to the subject to which they relate it is hoped that the task of memorising their contents for examinations will, at least, be lightened.

Only the main principles of specification writing have been dealt with. Space would not allow for more than references to British Standards, and it is left to the reader to consult the relevant specifications, a list of which is found at the end of each chapter.

The object in compiling the sections on quantities has been to provide a graded course of original worked examples beginning with simple exercises and working up to more difficult examples illustrating a variety of engineering work. Sketches have been prepared in a few cases to illustrate how difficult examples, which are not easily visualized, should be treated, and the appendix on the use of duodecimals for "squaring" should prove useful to readers wishing to understand the old method of computing areas and volumes.

In the transitional stages of converting to the Metric system, some anomalies and inconsistencies have appeared. The authors have taken a practical view of these, and have endeavoured to predict the probable course of British industry in the solution of such problems. Undoubtedly some alterations will be necessary in future editions, but it is hoped these will be minimal.

Whilst the book has been written primarily for University students in

Civil or Municipal Engineering and for candidates preparing for the examinations of the Institution of Civil Engineers and the Institution of Municipal Engineers, it is hoped that it may prove useful to assistants and others whose work involves the preparation of specifications and quantities.

Our thanks are due to the British Standards Institution, 2 Park Street, London W1A 2BS for permission to refer to British Standards and to reproduce extracts from BS 4466:1969, 'Bending Dimensions and Scheduling of Bars for the Reinforcement of Concrete' and CP 114 'The Structural Use of Reinforced Concrete in Buildings', Part 2:1969, to the Council of the Institution of Civil Engineers for permission to consult the Report of the Committee on Engineering Quantities, to them, the Association of Consulting Engineers and the Federation of Civil Engineering Contractors for consent to reproduce their Conditions of Contract, and to the latter for consent to reproduce their Form of Sub-Contract.

Cape Town W. H. K.
Glasgow D. M. R. E.

CHAPTER I

CONTRACTUAL RELATIONSHIP. FORMS OF A CONTRACT

1.01 It is a common experience, particularly in commercial transactions, to find two or more persons agreeing as to their future relations. One person may give money or goods on condition that he receive from some other person money or goods in return; he may do, or refrain from doing, some act in consideration of some act or forbearance of another, or he may agree to give services in return for wages or a lump sum, either specified or to be determined at a future date. All such agreements, if complying with certain conditions to be discussed later, are called Contracts.

1.02 It is not necessary, except in certain special cases, for a Contract to be in writing, although some written evidence is desirable to establish the terms of the agreement. An oral contract will depend upon oral testimony of the parties and any witnesses, as to the circumstances in which it was made, and as such evidence, particularly if a dispute arises, is likely to be conflicting, the desirability of having written evidence is obvious.

1.03 For the purpose of classification contracts are divided into two classes:—

(1) Speciality or sealed contracts.
(2) Simple contracts.

1.04 Contracts under seal are necessarily in writing, and a characteristic of all such contracts is that they do not require consideration for their validity. Nevertheless, lawyers almost invariably introduce into such agreements consideration in one form or another in order to remove suspicions of fraud.

1.05 Consideration is the benefit which each party to a contract derives from its operation. It is what one party gives or receives in return for something given or received by the other party. Such consideration must not be valueless, but on the other hand the law is not concerned with the amount of the consideration so long as it has some value or is capable of having value. The parties are quite free to make what agreement they please and for one of the parties to make what might appear to a disinterested person to be a bad bargain, but such lack of business acumen would not affect the validity of the contract.

1.06 A simple contract, which may be oral, written or implied from conduct, requires consideration for its validity. The rule appears to be based on the theory that a simple contract not under seal, whereby one party receives no benefit from the transaction, gives rise to suspicions of fraud, hence the law lays down the principle that contracts devoid of consideration can be made in one way only, that is under seal.

1.07 It need hardly be emphasised that the object of a valid contract must be legal, otherwise the contract will be void from the outset. Also both parties must clearly understand the implications of the agreement, and they must be legally competent to make a contract, as for example, neither party may be under 18 years of age or insane.

1.08 The proper understanding of the terms of a contract is particularly important when dealing with illiterate persons. In such cases the contract should be read to them clause by clause and the meaning of each elucidated. Where this procedure is impossible, as where transactions must be conducted by post, it is important that the contract when sent for signature should be accompanied by a request that the party signing should first read it, or have it read through to him, and satisfy himself as to the meaning of the whole document.

1.09 The steps in the making of a valid contract are:—

(1) An offer.

(2) An acceptance.

Both offer and acceptance must be made with the intention that they shall have legal effect. An invitation to dinner, for example, even if made and accepted in writing is not a contract, as the parties concerned do not contemplate any legal consequences in the event of a breach. Such an arrangement could not be the subject of an action for damages even though one party suffered considerable inconvenience and perhaps loss.

1.10 It is essential that the offer be definite and refer exclusively to the subject of the contract; the acceptance must be equally definite and unconditional.

1.11 An offer may contain conditions referring to its acceptance; if it does, they should be followed carefully. If any parts of the conditions are not fulfilled, the party in question should ascertain whether the other party considers himself bound. Until both parties are fully agreed, the contract has not come into being and either party may withdraw. Accordingly an offer may be cancelled at any time before acceptance, unless consideration has been given for its acceptance before a specified time. Exceptionally, in Scotland a written undertaking to keep an offer open for a period can be enforced.

1.12 Occasionally contracts occur where there has been no formal offer and acceptance, as for example where one person supplies goods or services to another without any prior formality. These implied contracts carry with them the obligation to pay a reasonable price for the goods or services. No engineering works of any magnitude would be carried out on this basis, but such arrangements are not uncommon where the value of the work is small, where sub-contracting is concerned, and where extreme urgency requires immediate action without waiting for the preparation of a written document.

1.13 Certain contracts are required by statute to be in writing. These include contracts of guarantee and of employment. The more important of those affecting the engineer are the Statute of Frauds, 1677, and the Law of Property Act, 1925 which apply only in England, the Sale of Goods Act, 1893, the Law Reform (Enforcement of Contracts) Act, 1954, the Contracts of Employment Act, 1972, and the Hire Purchase Act, 1965. Engineering contracts, whether between the Engineer and the Employer or the Employer and the Contractor, do not come within the terms of these Statutes, but the Engineer should, for his own protection, make it his business to see that contracts for works for which he is to be responsible are in writing.

1.14 Written agreements to the value of £5 and upwards formerly required stamping. A contract by deed, however, still requires a 50p impressed stamp. An unstamped agreement is neither void nor invalid, but it cannot be produced as evidence in the Courts until it has been stamped. After the fourteen day period has expired, the Inland Revenue are entitled to demand payment of £10 in addition to the stamp duty.

CHAPTER II

ENGINEER'S CONTRACT WITH THE EMPLOYER

2.01 An Engineer commissioned to carry out an engineering project is in a contractual relationship with his Employer, and although disputes between Engineer and Employer are not likely to arise except on the question of fees, it is desirable that the contract should be in writing. Formal contracts are not common, except where major works are concerned. In this case the Model Agreement of the Association of Consulting Engineers is generally used: this defines the duties of the parties and states the terms under which they are to be discharged. It also makes clear what are extras, such as hotel bills, preparation of Parliamentary plans, etc., and delineates the property in the works documentation. For minor works, or where the Engineer is being engaged by unincorporated bodies such as tenants' associations, the contract is usually contained in an interchange of letters. This correspondence must contain the offer, the acceptance, a sufficient exposition of what is required, and a statement of what the fee shall be, either by fixing it or by laying down how it shall be computed.

2.02 Contracts with Corporations.—When an Engineer has to do important work for a Local Authority, a nationalised industry or a limited company, he should insist on a written contract. At Common Law, such a contract with a body corporate was unenforceable unless made under seal, but there were three exceptions to this rule, as follows. If by the terms of its constitution a corporation could enter into simple contracts, then a suitable agent could act for it, and over the years this was specially written into the various Companies Acts. If the impressment of the seal would lead to an unreasonable interference with the smooth running of a corporation where routine contracts of frequent occurrence or trifling importance were involved, then a further exception was permitted. If the contract, important or trivial, was incidental to the objects and purposes of a trading company, then, too, sealing was immaterial. These relaxations were further extended by the Corporate Bodies' Contracts Acts, 1960, which assimilated bodies corporate with natural persons for the purposes of the law of contract.

2.03 It is equally important for the Engineer to see that his instructions are within the scope of the Authority giving them. This means that in the case of a Local Authority or Statutory Undertaker the instructions are within the scope of the Act of Parliament or Statutory Instrument under which the Authority operates. In the case of a Limited Liability Company, which derives its authority from its Memorandum, the Engineer should satisfy himself that the proposed work is within its scope. Copies of the Memorandum can be had from Companies House, London, or the Companies' Registration Office, Edinburgh, on payment of a small fee. There are many instances on record where Engineers have failed to recover their fees through neglect of this precaution.

2.04 Disputes between Engineer and Employer.—Disputes between the Engineer and the Employer will usually be on the question of fees payable if the work is abandoned. The Engineer should guard against such a contingency by stating beforehand the fee payable in this event. Failing any such agreement, the work will be paid for according to value, which is usually determined by the custom and practice of the profession.

2.05 It need hardly be pointed out that an Engineer should not agree to the payment of his fee being contingent upon a future event, as, for example, the approval of his scheme by the Employer, for until such an event happens, and it may never happen, the Engineer will not be entitled to his remuneration.

2.06 Ownership of Drawings.—There is little doubt that the copyright of the drawings prepared by the Engineer for the purpose of carrying out contract works remains vested in the Engineer. Two copies are usually provided free for the Contractor under the terms of the contract, and he may purchase further copies if he requires them; but at the conclusion of the work, the the Contractor must return to the Engineer the drawings supplied, after marking thereon any alterations which were effected. Since the Employer is paying for the work, he too is entitled to a copy of the drawings for his own use, but he is generally contractually required to refrain from using them for "any additional or similar work".

2.07 Engineer as Agent of Employer.—During the period of his commission the Engineer is the legal agent of the Employer and as such has all the rights and obligations of an agent. Normally a principal is responsible for the acts of his agent so long as the latter acts within the scope of his actual authority. But a principal may be bound by the acts of his agent if it is within the agent's apparent or implied authority, even though the principal did not authorise the act, and third parties are always entitled to assume, unless they have notice to the contrary, that an agent has all the powers usually exercised by a person in his position.

2.08 It is important that an Engineer, in carrying out the wishes of his Employer, does not in any way make himself personally liable. If the Engineer enters into a contract or incurs a liability in his own name, but as agent for the Employer, without disclosing the name of the Employer, the former may be held liable for payment. It follows, therefore, that in giving orders and instructions, particularly to sub-contractors who are not parties to the principle contract, the Engineer should make it clear that he is acting for the

Employer. An agent contracting without authority is liable to the other party to the principal contract for a breach of an implied warranty of authority, and this is so even if the agent believes at the time that he possesses such authority.

2.09 It need hardly be said that an agent is liable for any fraudulent misrepresentation of his authority, and that he must not make any secret profit from his position. An Engineer receiving any reward or bribe which might conflict with his duty to his Employer, must account for such reward to the Employer, who has the right to sue for its recovery if necessary.

2.10 Negligence of Engineer.—An Employer is entitled to expect that a person holding himself out to be an Engineer is competent to perform his professional duties and that he will carry out those duties with skill, care and diligence.

2.11 If, through serious lack of skill or the carelessness of the Engineer, the Employer suffers loss, he is entitled to be compensated by the Engineer. But an Engineer is not expected to show exceptional skill over and above the average skill of a member of his profession. He is bound to exercise all ordinary care and forethought in the interests of the Employer but, should he make an unfortunate mistake, he will not be liable for negligence in the legal sense unless the Employer can show that in carrying out his duties he failed to exercise the reasonable skill and care to be expected of Engineers of average ability. Far more serious than any legal liability is the injury to the Engineer's reputation by reason of any discoverable mistake, particularly if other engineers feel that it could have been avoided.

2.12 Death of the Parties.—The contract between the Employer and the Engineer is one of personal service; it is thus terminated by the death of either party. If the Employer should die during the course of the contract, the Engineer should seek fresh instructions from the personal representatives of the Employer. On the other hand, if the Engineer is a Partnership, it is usual in all documents to provide that, at the death of any partner, the survivors will accept all further responsibility.

2.13 The Engineer's authority is also terminated by the bankruptcy or insanity of the Employer, or the winding-up (whether compulsory or voluntary) or other dissolution of the Employing corporation. But these events do not affect the Engineer's rights to payment for the work he had already done.

CHAPTER III

CONTRACT BETWEEN EMPLOYER AND CONTRACTOR

3.01 Engineering contracts between Employers and Contractors have certain characteristics which distinguish them from ordinary contracts.

The Employer, who is the party contracting for work to be done, has usually little or no technical knowledge to enable him to specify the work which is to be the subject of the contract. He therefore employs an Engineer to advise him and to prepare the necessary Drawings, Specifications and Quantities which are to form the basis of the contract, and although the Engineer is not legally a party to the contract, he obviously occupies a very important position as between the Employer and the Contractor, and he is usually given complete power to ensure that his Drawings and Specifications are followed faithfully.

3.02 Engineering contracts also differ from ordinary contracts in that the Engineer, who, as explained in the last chapter, is the agent of the Employer, is frequently made the arbiter between the Employer and the Contractor in the event of disputes arising between them on certain matters. The parties may even agree, if they wish, that the Engineer be sole arbitrator, but it is more common in large contracts to find these functions limited to certain specified matters of dispute and for all other disputes to be submitted to an independent arbitrator. The Engineer may, therefore, find himself acting in a dual capacity. He is paid by the Employer to see that the latter obtains proper work and full value for his money, but on the other hand he may be called upon to adjudicate fairly between the Employer and the Contractor should one of the disputes arise of which he is the sole arbitrator. It is most important if an Engineer should have to act in this second capacity that he give his decisions without bias or prejudice, and so long as he holds the balance fairly between the parties it is unlikely that any decision of his will be upset by a Court of Law.

3.03 Documents in an Engineering Contract.—One must understand clearly the importance and purpose of the various documents used in the completion of an engineering contract. Such contracts are invariably in writing, but they may or may not be under seal.

3.04 The document to which the parties put their signatures and, in the case of sealed contracts, their seals, is the contract proper. If under hand, it is usually termed an Agreement; if under seal, a Deed. This document merely recites the names of the parties, including in some cases the Sureties, and sets out the terms of the agreement by which the Contractor agrees to perform all the work in accordance with the Drawings, Specifications, Quantities and Conditions of Contract. If the Conditions of Contract are properly drawn up this agreement is usually quite short, as there is no need to repeat the clauses of the Conditions of Contract. It is as a rule, drawn up by the Employer's lawyer, who retains custody of it after attending to the formalities of stamping.

3.05 The Drawings, Specifications, Quantities and Conditions of Contract are therefore important items in an Engineering Contract as it is upon them that the Contract is founded. It is the function of the Drawings to show the form and construction of the work; the Specification describes all materials and workmanship, whilst the Conditions of Contract lay down in detail the relations between the Employer, the Engineer and the Contractor, from the moment the agreement is signed to the time when the Works are completed and paid for.

3.06 The drafting of the Conditions of Contract is normally the work of the Employer's lawyer, the Engineer merely giving such assistance on technical matters as the lawyer may require. But whilst the Engineer's chief concern is the preparation of the Drawings, Specifications and Quantities and in supervising the construction after the work is commenced, he is nevertheless interested in seeing that the clauses inserted in the Conditions of Contract are suitable and adequate to enable him to deal with any difficulties which may arise.

3.07 In some cases, particularly in Building Contracts, the Bill of Quantities is prepared by an independent Quantity Surveyor, who is usually chosen by the Architect and paid by the Employer. There is no reason why the same procedure should not be followed in Engineering Contracts if the Engineer does not desire to undertake the preparation of the Quantities.

3.08 The Bill of Quantities does not always form an essential part of the contract as do the Drawings and Specifications. Sometimes the Bill is deliberately excluded from the contract except in so far as it is used as a list of prices by which variations and extras can be valued. By basing the contract on the Drawings, Specifications and Conditions of Contract, and inviting Contractors to include in their tenders for everything necessary for the completion of the work as shown and described by those documents, the Employer knows exactly how much the work will cost apart from any additions which he may order during the progress of the work. Errors or omissions in the Bill of Quantities will not affect the contract price, as the Contractor will be required to satisfy himself as to their accuracy before signing the contract.

3.09 A more equitable arrangement from the point of view of the Contractor is to make the Bill of Quantities a part of the contract and to insert a clause in the conditions to the effect that any errors or omissions discovered in the Bill will be rectified and the corrections treated as a variation of the contract. This means that if serious omissions should be found the Employer may be called upon to pay a much higher sum than he anticipated. Such errors, however, are very unlikely to occur if the quantities are prepared by a competent person and the practice of making the Bill of Quantities a part of the contract is now common.

3.10 Schedule of Prices.—An alternative method very similar in effect to the use of the Bill of Quantities as part of the contract is the use of a Schedule of Prices, which is a list of all materials and labour necessary, or likely to be necessary, for the completion of the work, and accompanied in some cases by approximate quantities of each item for the guidance of the Contractor in his pricing. The Contractor puts his unit price to each item on the Schedule and these prices are used in the determination of the value of all completed work which is measured as it is completed. Another method is to invite contractors to quote a percentage on or off given rates.

3.11 An objection frequently raised to this method of pricing is that work invariably costs more than where a lump sum is agreed upon by the use of a Bill of Quantities. It is eminently suitable for work which cannot be accurately estimated before the contract commences, such as tunnelling or marine work.

3.12 Sureties.—Local Authorities and Statutory Bodies frequently require a Contractor to find at least two reliable persons who are prepared to be jointly and individually bound with the Contractor in a certain sum for the proper fulfilment of the contract. The contract with the Sureties is called a bond, and as it is a contract answering for the debt or default of another, it must be in writing and signed by the Sureties. It is not essential that the bond show any consideration for the guarantee given by the Sureties; as the consideration is not always clear, a Bond of this kind should without exception be under seal in England, and witnessed as a probative writ in Scotland.

3.13 The Bond provides that if the Contractor completes and maintains the Works in accordance with the Drawings, Specifications and Conditions of Contract and pays all damages, costs or expenses to which he may become liable, then in that event the covenant of the Sureties will become void and lapse.

3.14 Sureties are normally released from their covenant if any major alteration or variation is made in the contract which they guaranteed. For this reason the surety clause in the General Conditions should provide that no alteration or variation of the contract, or any arrangement for the modification of its conditions between the Employer and Contractor, whether made with the approval of the Sureties or not, shall discharge them from their liability. A fresh bond will not then be necessary.

3.15 The Contract of Sureties, not being one for personal service, is not affected by the death of any of the parties, nor by the bankruptcy of the Contractor.

3.16 It is well for an Employer requiring Sureties to make careful investigation as to the financial stability of the persons whose names are submitted by the Contractor, and if there is any doubt as to their ability to meet the liabilities of their guarantee, should they be called upon to do so, to require them to seek the approved backing of a Bank or Finance Company.

3.17 Payment of the Contractor.—An Engineering Contract usually provides that the Contractor will be paid by instalments during the progress of the work. It is necessary to lay down precisely the conditions under which these payments will be made by the Employer, firstly, because they are made on the authority of the Engineer who is not a party to the contract, and secondly, because unless agreed otherwise, payment for work complete and entire for a lump sum becomes due only when the work is completed.

3.18 The Engineer's authority for payment is given in the form of certificates in writing issued to the Contractor from time to time when the value of work executed and materials delivered has reached the amount specified in the Conditions of Contract (see Form "D", p. 210). Payment is then due on a fixed proportion of the value, usually 90 per cent., the balance of 10 per cent. being paid in two instalments, one when the Works are complete and handed over to the Employer, the second at the end of the maintenance period—which is usually six months—when the Engineer has given his final certificate that the whole of the Works have been carried out and maintained to his satisfaction.

3.19 It is seen that the granting of a certificate by the Engineer is usually made a condition precedent to payment. The Conditions of Contract should provide that no certificate of the Engineer, other than the last, is to be taken as an admission on the part of the Engineer or the Employer that the work to which the certificate applies has been satisfactorily carried out, and that the Engineer's power to require alterations or the removal of unsound work is not thereby prejudiced. The Engineer should be given the power to withhold a certificate if any part of the work has not been carried out in a satisfactory manner.

3.20 The Employer is liable for payment on the production by the Contractor of the Engineer's certificate. The only grounds upon which the Employer could resist payment would be fraud of the Engineer.

3.21 On the other hand, a Contractor refused a certificate by an Engineer, has no cause of action against an Employer unless he can show that the Engineer's refusal to certify is due to fraud.

3.22 Omissions, Extras and Variations.—In the absence of special provisions to the contrary, a contract cannot be altered in its terms, and no omissions, additions or variations may be made without the consent of the parties.

Although such care should be taken in the preparation of the Drawings and Specifications that "extras" will be avoided, few engineering works can be carried out without some variation from the original design. The necessity for a clause in the Conditions of Contract permitting the Employer to make alterations is therefore apparent.

3.23 In order that the Engineer may have complete control of alterations, it should be definitely stated that no omissions, additions or variations must be made without the written authority of the Engineer (See Form "A", p. 207). This is particularly important in the case of alterations which may give rise to a claim for extra payment. There is no implied warranty on the part of the Engineer that the work can be carried out in the manner shown on the drawings or described in the specifications and for that reason most contracts provide that the Contractor must include everything necessary for the due performance of the work. A Contractor will be tempted to construe all alterations as "extras" calling for extra payment, unless the contract stipulates that no extra payment will be made unless an order is given in writing by the Engineer prior to the execution of the work and that such order specifically states that extra payment will be made.

3.24 In cases of emergency where it may be necessary to proceed without such order, the Contractor should be required to give written notice to the Engineer immediately the work is commenced. (see Form "B", p. 208).

3.25 The amount to be paid for extra work is determined by the Engineer, who applies the prices in the Bill of Quantities so far as they are applicable for work of a similar character. If no prices in the Bill are applicable the contract should provide for the settlement of the prices to be paid before the commencement of the work.

3.26 In some cases the Contractor is required to make a weekly or monthly return giving the dates and references of the orders, and the quantity, description and price of all such extra work carried out during the preceding week or month.

3.27 Arbitration.—A method of settling disputes frequently used in engineering contracts is arbitration. It is a method which is favoured in disputes involving technical questions for several reasons.

(1) The arbitrator can be a person who has expert knowledge of the matter in dispute.

(2) He may make an inspection of the subject matter and so save time in hearing explanatory evidence.

(3) The time and place of hearing can be fixed to suit the convenience of the parties.

(4) The arbitration may be held in private and the expense is usually less than an action at Law.

3.28 Arbitrations in England and Wales are governed by the Arbitration Act,

1950; those in Scotland by the Arbitration (Scotland) Act, 1894, and the Administration of Justice (Scotland) Act, 1972.

3.29 An arbitration agreement is defined as "a written agreement to submit present or future differences to arbitration whether an arbitrator is named therein or not." As the provision of the Acts does not apply to oral agreements, it follows that the agreement should always be in writing.

3.30 Local Authorities submitting matters to arbitration must do so under the common seal of the authority.

3.31 Normally the arbitration clause in the Conditions provides for the appointment of one arbitrator only. This is important, as in the event of each party appointing a person, the two arbitrators are required by Section 8, Arbitration Act, 1950, to proceed to appoint an umpire who shall act in the event of disagreement between the arbitrators. If three arbitrators are appointed a majority decision prevails. The equivalent provision in Scotland is section 5, Arbitration (Scotland) Act, 1894.

3.32 Unless the agreement calls for particular qualifications, any suitable person may be an arbitrator provided he is impartial and unbiased. He must have no interest in the subject matter and he must not misconduct himself in any way, as for example by the acceptance of bribes.

3.33 The rule that an arbitrator must have no interest in the subject matter of the arbitration is not always strictly adhered to in engineering contracts where the Engineer is sometimes appointed sole arbitrator in all or certain matters of dispute that may arise. The contractor will be fully aware when he signs the contract that any dispute arising is more than likely to be due to some requirement of the Engineer and that the Engineer is the agent of the Employer.

3.34 Section 24, Arbitration Act, 1950, provides that where any party applies to a Court for leave to revoke the authority of the arbitrator or for an injunction to restrain any other party or the arbitrator from proceeding with the arbitration on the ground that the arbitrator is not, or may not be, impartial, it is not to be a ground for refusing the application that the party at the time he made the agreement knew, or ought to have known, that the arbitrator by reason of his relation toward any other party to the agreement, might not be capable of impartiality.

3.35 This Section shows the necessity for an Engineer, when acting as sole arbitrator, to hold the balance fairly between the Employer and the Contractor and not to use his position to make unreasonable demands.

3.36 After hearing all relevant evidence, the arbitrator makes his award, which must be in writing.

3.37 The award must be directed to all the matters referred to for settlement and its findings must be clear, definite and final.

3.38 Types of Contract between the Employer and Contractor.—A brief description of the types of contract which may be made between an Employer and a Contractor is now given, with some indication in each case of the circumstances for which each is suitable.

3.39 Lump Sum Contract.—This contract is suitable for work costing not more than about £5000 and is an offer by a Contractor to carry out the whole of the work shown on the drawings and described in the specifications for a fixed sum. Under such a contract it is essential that the work be accurately and completely shown on the drawings and described in the specifications and that full information as to site conditions should be available, otherwise disputes can easily arise. Although often used in conjunction with a schedule of prices it is not a suitable form of contract where considerable additions or variations are expected or contemplated. It has the advantage, however, that the employer knows beforehand exactly what the work will cost.

3.40 Prime Cost or Cost-plus or Percentage Contracts.—In this form of contract the Contractor supplies all labour and materials at cost price to which he is permitted to add a stated percentage for establishment charges and profit. This is a form of contract which has been frequently used by Government Departments for emergency work, but the close supervision and checking of delivery notes and invoices which it involves, makes it unsuitable for works where the necessary staff is not available. Another objection is that it is to the contractor's advantage to make the cost as high as possible by wasting material and employing inefficient workmen, but on the other hand, as the contractor takes little risk and his profit is assured, there is no need for him to make large allowances in his prices for the usual constructional risks.

3.41 Target Contract.—Some of the disadvantages of the prime cost contract may be overcome by a "target" contract. Here the contractor is paid on a prime cost basis for work performed under the contract, and in addition he receives a percentage on savings effected against either a prior agreed estimate of total cost or a target value arrived at by measuring the work on completion and valuing it at prior agreed rates. The Contractor is therefore encouraged to use his skill and experience in keeping the cost as low as possible.

3.42 Rates of Payment Contract.—Occasionally, owing to the uncertainty in the amount of work to be done, or the conditions under which it is to be carried out, it is impossible to make an accurate Bill of Quantities and inequitable to expect a Contractor to give a lump sum estimate. In such cases an approximate Bill of Quantities may be prepared and contractors asked to price the items with the stipulation that the work will be subject to measurement and payment made at the unit prices quoted. The quantities are therefore not part of the contract, but the totals of the tenders enable the Engineer to determine which is the lowest. As the quantities may be increased or decreased, a contract of this nature requires careful consideration by the Engineer and the Employer before it is entered into, as by wise anticipation or perhaps outside information a Contractor may quote high prices for items that are likely to be required in increased quantities and low prices for items likely to be decreased or required in small quantities. In that case the Employer would stand to lose heavily.

3.43 Schedule of Prices.—As stated in 3.10 a schedule of prices is a list of all items of labour and materials likely to be required in a contract, to which the contractors put their unit prices. All work is measured as executed and the total cost computed from the schedule of prices. It is useful for work of an uncertain character, but it has the disadvantage that it does not enable the Engineer to compare the tenders received except by taking out quantities and working up the totals by the use of the schedule of prices.

3.44 Labour Contract.—This is a contract where all labour and workmanship is supplied by the Contractor, but all materials are supplied by the Employer. It is suitable for those cases where an Employer, such as the Railway Executive, is in a position to buy large quantities of materials at favourable prices.

CHAPTER IV

CONDITIONS OF CONTRACT. CONTENTS OF CLAUSES

40.1 The clauses to be inserted in the Conditions of Contract will be governed by the character of the work to be carried out. Clauses which are suitable for one contract may not always be appropriate for another. If the Engineer is in any doubt as to whether certain clauses should, or should not, be inserted he should not hesitate to obtain the advice of a lawyer who would at the same time assist him in the phrasing of unusual clauses.

4.02 It is well for the Engineer to bear in mind when drawing up the Conditions of Contract without legal guidance that there are two parties to the contract and that the Contractor has rights as well as the Employer. Engineers naturally like to see the clauses drawn wide enough in scope to meet every possible contingency and to enable any sharp practices of a Contractor to be effectively checked. Nevertheless, the Contractor has the right to expect that the clauses will be fairly drawn and that they will protect him from unreasonable treatment at the hands of either the Engineer or the Employer.

4.03 It is, of course, possible for an Engineer to interpret a fair set of conditions in a harsh manner, but such conduct on his part is usually dearly paid for by the Employer. Contractors soon learn to increase their prices to allow for the exacting demands of an unreasonable Engineer.

4.04 The clauses discussed in this Chapter include those most frequently found in ordinary engineering contracts. Not all the clauses will be required in every contract and those inapplicable will be omitted. On the other hand special circumstances may occasionally demand the drafting of special clauses, but such cases are not frequent and it is as well for the Engineer to leave the drafting of suitable clauses to a lawyer.

4.05 The clauses are classified into nine groups as follows:—

Clauses relating to:—

1. Documents.
2. The general obligations of the Contractor.
3. Labout and personnel.
4. Assignment and subletting.
5. The execution of the work.
6. Default, delay and non-completion.
7. Measurement and payment.
8. Settlement of disputes; and
9. Special clauses.

The clauses in each of the above groups will be explained in detail.

1. Clauses relating to Documents.

4.06 DRAWINGS.—The clauses dealing with drawings should give a list of the drawings forming part of the contract and refer to them by number or title. Further drawings may be issued from time to time at the discretion of the Engineer as the need arises. If such further drawings show work which in the opinion of the Contractor is extra, the Contractor should be required first to give notice to that effect in writing to the Engineer. In the event of the Engineer and Contractor failing to agree as to whether such work is extra, the matter can be referred to arbitration.

4.07 The contract drawings are usually signed by the parties and are kept by the Engineer who provides a copy for the Contractor's use. The drawings, specifications and quantities are frequently stated to be the property of the Engineer and must be returned to him on completion of the contract.

4.08 Written dimensions are to be followed in preference to scaled dimensions and if doubts or discrepancies arise, these are to be referred to the Engineer whose decision is final and no extra payment of any kind will be made unless the Engineer gives a written order.

4.09 Frequently a clause requires the Contractor when tendering to examine carefully the drawings and specifications and to visit the site and satisfy himself as to the nature of the ground in which the work is to be carried out. The information supplied by the Engineer is not always complete and the Contractor may be requested to obtain his own information by independent enquiry, and to include everything necessary for completing the contract whether or not shown on the drawings or described in the specifications and quantities provided the same may reasonably be inferred therefrom.

4.10 BILL OF QUANTITIES AND SCHEDULE OF PRICES.—The Conditions should require that the Contractor submit with his tender, or within a given time after its acceptance, a fully priced out Bill of Quantities or Schedule of Prices, such bill or schedule to form the basis for the valuation of all additions, deductions or variations. Practice differs in regard to the part which a bill of quantities plays in a contract. Sometimes it is provided that errors or omissions in the quantities other than errors or omissions in the calculations will be treated as variations and allowed for accordingly. In other cases the bill of quantities is treated merely as a schedule of prices for the purpose of pricing extras and variations, in which case the Contractor is required to satisfy himself as to the accuracy of the quantities before he signs the contract. The latter method relieves the Employer of possible claims due to errors in the quantities, but it is only fair to the Contractor, if this method is adopted, that his attention is drawn specially to such a clause.

4.11 In cases where the method of payment is on a cost-plus basis, that is where the Contractor is paid the actual cost of the work plus a percentage for establishment charges and profit, the conditions should provide for all consignment notes and wages sheets to be submitted to the Resident Engineer and initialled by him when approved.

4.12 SURETIES.—The Contractor is usually required to find two approved Sureties who are jointly and severally bound with him for the due performance of the contract. Persons interested in the supply or manufacture of any of the plant or materials are usually barred as Sureties.

4.13 PROVISIONAL AND PRIME COST (P.C.) SUMS.—This clause should give the Engineer power to deduct, in whole or in part, provisional sums in the contract, which are not required. P.C. prices in the specifications or bill of quantities should be regarded as absolutely net after deduction of all trade and cash discount in excess of 2½ per cent. The Engineer should have the right to call for the receipted accounts from the manufacturers in respect of these items.

4.14 NOTICES.—It should be made quite clear in the contract document how legal notices to be given to the Contractor are to be delivered. This is usually by delivering the notice to the Contractor personally (or in the case of a company to the secretary), or sending it by post addressed to the Contractor either at his office on the site or at his last known place of business or abode. A notice to a Company should be addressed to the Registered Office and the clause should provide that in the case of partners, service of a notice on one of the partners will be deemed to be service on all.

4.15 BRITISH STANDARDS.—Various British Standards are frequently referred to in contracts and as these specifications are liable to change during the period of the contract the Conditions should provide that all references to British Standards are to specifications in force at the date of the Contractor's tender.

2. Clauses relating to General Obligations of the Contractor.

4.16 SITE.—A clause is usually inserted stating the position of the site and the date on which possession will be given to the Contractor. He should be required to sink at his own expense all trial holes and trenches as may be considered necessary by the Engineer, either for ascertaining the nature of the ground or for determining the position and levels of gas, water and electricity mains, drains, culverts or other likely obstructions.

4.17 HOARDINGS.—The Contractor should be required to provide to the satisfaction of the Engineer, all hoardings, fencing, gangways, handrails, etc., necessary for the protection both of the public and all persons employed on the works. In default of the Contractor the Engineer should be given power to provide the necessary protection and charge the cost to the Contractor.

4.18 LIGHTING AND WATCHING.—The works should be kept properly lighted and watched during the period of construction and the Contractor should be required to provide all necessary labour, plant, materials and fuel.

4.19 CANTEENS, ETC.—A clause of the contract should require the Contractor to provide all canteens, first aid equipment, latrines and conveniences necessary for the workmen employed. They must be kept in proper order and removed when directed by the Engineer.

4.20 MATERIALS, LABOUR, PLANT, ETC.—A general clause should be inserted requiring the Contractor to provide all materials, labour, plant and machinery for the safe and expeditious execution of the contract, and for the maintenance of the work during the period specified in the contract.

4.21 LIEN.—The Employer is usually given a lien on all plant and materials brought on to the site by the Contractor as a further security against the proper performance of the contract. The clause should provide that the Employer will not be responsible for damage to the property which is the subject of the lien. If it should be necessary for the Employer to exercise this right, the Employer or the Engineer should be empowered to use or sell any of the plant and materials as they may think fit, the money arising from such sale being placed to the credit of the Contractor.

4.22 ACTS, BYE-LAWS AND REGULATIONS.—The Conditions should require the Contractor to comply with any Acts of Parliament, Bye-laws or Regulations affecting the works and to give all notices and pay all fees. Should such compliance necessitate any alteration or variation of the contract the Contractor must give notice immediately to the Engineer and ask for his instructions. If such instructions are not given within a specified time, the clause usually permits the Contractor to proceed and comply with the Act or Regulation.

4.23 SETTING-OUT.—The works should be set out by the Contractor who should be made responsible for the accuracy of the setting-out. He should be required to correct any inaccuracies and to supply all labour, pegs, boning rods and sight rails necessary, and from time to time to check and maintain their accuracy.

4.24 ACCESS TO WORKS.—The Engineer or his authorised representative should have access to the Works at all times for the purpose of inspection, testing, sampling, weighing or any other purpose. He should also have access at all reasonable times to the workshops of the Contractor or any other place where work is being prepared for the contract works.

4.25 ENGINEER'S INSTRUCTIONS.—More often, perhaps, than is desirable it is taken for granted that an Engineer or his representative has the right to give instructions to the Contractor during the period of the contract. It is as well to give legal effect to such instructions by inserting a clause requiring the Contractor during the progress of the works to attend to any orders or instructions that may be given either by the Engineer or his representative. Such orders are to be deemed supplementary to the drawings and specifications and to entitle the Contractor to no extra payment unless the order involves an "extra" coming within the terms of the appropriate clause.

4.26 PATENTS AND ROYALTIES.—The Contractor should be made responsible for all royalties payable under Letters Patent applying to any portion of the work and to hold the Employer indemnified against all claims for infringement of patent rights.

4.27 INSURANCE.—Damage by fire or other causes may be the cause of heavy loss to the Employer and for this reason the Contractor should be required to keep the whole of the works insured against loss or damage by fire until the expiration of the maintenance period. All boilers used in the works should be insured and certified by a Boiler Insurance Company. The clause should direct that the policies are to be in the joint names of the Employer and the Contractor in offices approved by the Engineer.

4.28 In cases where the work or plant is liable to be damaged by storm or tempest the Contractor is usually required to insure against such loss, including all marine risks. Insurance Companies do not undertake this business; the policy is therefore taken out with an approved underwriter in the joint names as before.

4.29 If any claim arises under the policies the money obtained is paid to the Employer who, in turn, pays it to the Contractor in such instalments as the Engineer deems proper, as and when the damage is made good. Should there be a surplus of money after all the damage has been made good the balance is usually paid to the Contractor, but if the money is insufficient to make good the damage the Contractor is made responsible for the deficiency

4.30 The Contractor is required to notify the Engineer about any usable materials including Treasure Trove found on the site and to dispose of them on the Employer's behalf in accordance with his instructions.

3. Clauses relating to Labour and Personnel.

4.31 RESIDENT ENGINEER.—A clause in the conditions usually provides that a Resident Engineer will be employed and that the Contractor must provide a proper office with lighting and firing. The status of the Resident Engineer varies in different contracts. Sometimes it is provided that he is the representative of the Engineer and any instructions given by him are deemed to be given by the Engineer. At other times the contract stipulates that the Resident Engineer is merely an inspector for reporting to the Engineer, with no authority to bind either the Engineer or the Employer unless such authority is specially delegated to him.

4.32 AGENT OR REPRESENTATIVE.—The Contractor should always be required to have an agent or other competent representative in attendance on the works, and instructions or explanations given to him, or delivered at his office on the works, are to be deemed as given to the Contractor.

4.33 DISMISSAL OF WORKMEN.—The Engineer should be given the right to dismiss any foreman, superintendent or workman whom he considers incompetent or who, in the opinion of the Engineer, misconducts himself or is negligent in the performance of his duties. Clauses have been known to make a Contractor liable to pay a daily sum as liquidated damages for every day that any person coming within the terms of the clause is employed after the Engineer has given notice of dismissal. The Engineer's decision on the competency of a workman is usually made final, and in that case no appeal can be made by the Contractor to the Arbitrator.

4.34 ACCIDENTS TO WORKMEN AND EMPLOYEES.—It is important that the Contractor be required to keep the Employer indemnified at all times during the progress of the works against claims arising under the Employers' Liability Acts or any other Acts amending or extending these Acts in respect of accidents to workmen or other employees. The policy should again be in the joint names of the Employer and the Contractor and in the event of the Contractor failing to insure, the Employer should be empowered to do so.

4.35 RATES OF WAGES.—It is now usual to insert a clause requiring the Contractor to pay the standard rates of wages prescribed by the Civil Engineering Construction Conciliation Board and to produce when required by the Engineer for inspection the time sheets and wages books used on the works.

4. Clauses relating to Assignment and Subletting.

4.36 ASSIGNMENT AND SUBLETTING.—The Contractor should not, without the written consent of the Engineer, be allowed to assign or sublet the whole or part of the contract. A clause frequently specifies that should the Contractor assign or sublet without consent, the Employer shall not be liable for any further payment under the contract.

4.37 SUB-CONTRACTORS.—Where subletting of part of the contract is carried out with the Engineer's consent the conditions should ensure that the Contractor is entirely responsible to the Employer for the proper performance of the work by the sub-contractors.

4.38 SPECIALIST CONTRACTORS.—It is usual to provide that the Contractor will allow the execution of work by specialist tradesmen engaged by the Employer. Such work is usually the subject of a separate tender by the Specialist firm, the amount being included in the contract as a prime cost sum. The principal Contractor will be responsible for the attendance of one trade on another.

4.39 ASSIGNMENT OF CONTRACTS TO EMPLOYER.—In the case of the Contractor failing to complete the contract in a satisfactory manner, it may be desirable for the Employer to take over contracts which the Contractor may have with third parties for the supply of goods or materials. A clause should, therefore, be inserted providing that the Contractor shall, if called upon, assign any such contract to the Employer.

CHAPTER V

CONTENTS OF CLAUSES—(*continued*)

5. Clauses relating to the Execution of the Work.

5.01 MATERIALS AND WORKMANSHIP.—A general clause is commonly found stating that materials and workmanship are to be the best of their respective kinds. Materials which the Engineer considers defective or not complying with samples submitted and approved should be removed from the site immediately and if the Contractor defaults the Engineer should have the power to carry out the removal. The Engineer should be given the right to order any test or weighing he considers necessary, such tests or weighings normally being made at the Contractor's expense. Where the amount of testing is likely to be considerable a prime cost sum should be included in the quantities to cover the cost.

5.02 WATER.—The source of the water supply for the works should, whenever possible, be stated, and the Contractor should be required to pay all charges and lay all distribution pipes required.

5.03 DEFECTIVE WORK.—This clause should provide that if, during the progress of the work, or during the period of maintenance the Engineer is of opinion that any of the work is defective or unsound, the Contractor shall, at his own expense, alter, reconstruct or carry out whatever work is necessary to remove such defects to the satisfaction of the Engineer and in default the Engineer may employ other contractors to repair the defects. In cases where, from surface effects, it is apparent that work which is covered up is defective, the Engineer should have power to order the Contractor to make good such defective work without being under any obligation to the Contractor to specify the cause of the defects. If defects should appear during the maintenance period the clause usually provides that the maintenance period will be extended for such time as is necessary to make good the defects.

5.04 The power of the Engineer under this clause is not usually permitted to be the subject of a reference to arbitration. It is desirable, therefore, that the Engineer act in a reasonable manner, holding the scales fairly between the Employer and the Contractor, and for that reason the Engineer should never take action without first serving on the Contractor a written notice calling upon him to remedy the defects and giving him a reasonable time in which to do the work.

5.05 Opening-up of Work.—The opening-up of work will be provided for by a clause stipulating that if the Engineer, either during the progress of the work or during the maintenance period, requires for his satisfaction that any work be opened-up or laid bare for his inspection, the Contractor shall forthwith open up the work as directed. If as a result of such opening-up the work is found to be defective, such defects, including the cost of opening-up shall be made good and paid for by the Contractor. In any other case the cost should be borne by the Employer as an "extra."

5.06 Alterations, Additions and Omissions.—It is seldom that engineering work of any magnitude can be carried out without some departure from the drawings and specifications. For this reason the Conditions should always contain a clause giving the Engineer power to make alterations, additions, omissions and variations without in any way vitiating the contract. Such changes must be effected only on the written instructions of the Engineer and in cases where the changes involve extra payment to the Contractor, it should be a condition of payment that the Contractor produce such written authorisation.

5.07 The value of extra work, when authorised, is determined by the prices in the Bill of Quantities or the Schedule of Prices, and if such prices are inapplicable then at rates to be agreed between the Engineer and the Contractor before the extra work is commenced. This clause may also be used when an Engineer feels that the work done is inferior in quality to that required by the contract, but not so bad as to warrant an order for its destruction and re-execution.

5.08 Damage.—The Contractor should be made responsible for all damage arising to or through the works. He should be required to provide protection against inclement weather and to do all pumping required to keep the works clear of water. Water pumped from the works should be discharged only at points approved by the Engineer and the Contractor must keep all channels, grips, pipes and sumps clean and in good order.

5.09 Shoring.—In cases where the works adjoin a street or other building which may be damaged through lack of support during the progress of the work, the Contractor should be required to provide suitable shoring, to maintain it during construction and to clear it away when no longer necessary.

5.10 Blasting.—If blasting is to be carried out the Contractor should be required to indemnify the Employer against all claims arising from this cause in respect of persons, animals or things.

5.11 Extraordinary Traffic.—The Contractor must be warned to avoid damaging the public highways, and he must route his construction traffic according to the capacity of the bridges, etc. of the locality. He will be responsible for strengthening any bridges as necessary for moving his plant, and will be required to indemnify the Employer against any claims in this respect.

If hauliers cause damage, normally the Employer will negotiate the settlement of claims.

5.12 Making Good Damage.—The Contractor should be required to make good all surfaces damaged or disturbed whether of streets or private lands, and to keep the Employer indemnified in respect of claims for injury, including damage to crops. In the case of roads and streets the clause usually provides that the Contractor must maintain the surface during the whole of the maintenance period.

5.13 Obstruction of Streets and Interruption of Traffic.—This clause requires the Contractor to avoid obstruction of streets and footpaths and to leave proper access to premises. He should also be held responsible for interruption of traffic including the interruption of water, gas, electricity, telephone and hydraulic power services and for all accidents and damage arising from any such interruption.

5.14 Emergencies.—Accidents and failures occasionally occur on works and require immediate attention. In the event of such emergency arising and if, in the opinion of the Engineer, the Contractor is unable to deal with it the Engineer should be empowered by the contract to employ others to do whatever work he may consider necessary and charge the cost to the Contractor.

5.15 Sunday and Night Work.—Without the consent of the Engineer the Contractor is usually forbidden to carry out any work on Sunday or at night.

5.16 Clearing Site.—The Contractor should be required to leave the site clean and tidy and to remove all surplus rubbish on completion of the contract.

5.17 Defects Subsequent to Completion.—Any defects appearing in the work within a specified period after completion are required by this clause to be made good to the satisfaction of the Engineer. The decision of the Engineer as to what constitutes defective work under the clause is usually made final and binding on the Contractor.

6. Clauses relating to Default, Delay and Non-completion.

5.18 Engineer's Power to Delay Works.—In case of frost or exceptionally inclement weather the Engineer should have power to suspend operations for such time as he thinks fit. A clause should be inserted in the Conditions giving him power to do this without in any way vitiating the contract or leading to claims on the part of the Contractor for loss arising from such delay. To compensate for the loss of time the Engineer should be able to extend the period for the completion of the contract by such time as he thinks proper. For the purpose of giving effect to this clause the Resident Engineer should keep accurate records of all stoppages due to inclement weather.

5.19 Contractor's Delay or Default.—In cases where the Engineer is of the opinion that the Contractor, by reason of insufficient labour, plant and materials or through any other cause, is not proceeding with the contract with proper expedition, or if the Contractor fails to comply with any of the Conditions of Contract whether as to labour, materials, workmanship or conduct, the Engineer should have power to give the Contractor notice in writing requiring him to remedy his default. Should the Contractor not comply with the Engineer's notice the Engineer should be empowered to employ such other contractor or contractors as he thinks fit to remedy the default, and to deduct any costs incurred by the Employer from monies due or to become due to the Contractor.

5.20 Time for Completion.—This clause should state the time allowed for the completion of the whole of the work after the receipt by the Contractor of the Engineer's notice to commence. If the time for completion is to be strictly enforced the clause should stipulate that time is of the essence of the contract and that it is the intention of the Employer to enforce this provision.

5.21 Engineer may Extend Time for Completion.—The progress of the work may be delayed by causes outside the control of the Contractor other than bad weather. If any such delay should arise the Engineer is usually given power to fix another date for the completion of the work. Such extension of time will not give rise to any claim for extra payment by the Contractor and no extension of time should be recognised unless given by the Engineer in writing.

5.22 Damages for Non-Completion.—In the event of the Contractor failing to complete the works in the time fixed by the contract or such extended time as the Engineer may allow, the conditions usually provide that the Contractor shall pay to the Employer a specified sum per day for each day beyond the date or extended time, as the case may be, during which the works remain incomplete. Such sum is specified as ascertained and liquidated damages, and not as a penalty, which the Courts would not enforce, and the Employer is empowered to deduct the money from payments which may fall due to the Contractor.

5.23 Bankruptcy or Liquidation of Contractor.—A long clause is usually found in all engineering contracts providing for the bankruptcy or liquidation (if a Company) of the Contractor. Should the Contractor, during the progress of the works, commit any act of bankruptcy or enter into liquidation, whether voluntary or otherwise, or do any act similar to acts of bankruptcy, the Employer is given power, without affecting the Contractor's liabilities, to employ any other contractor or contractors to complete the work, with complete liberty to use the plant and materials of the Contractor. Any costs or expenses incurred by the Employer may be recovered from the Contractor.

7. Clauses relating to Measurement and Payment.

5.24 METHOD OF MEASUREMENT.—An important clause is that dealing with the method of measurement of completed work. It is usually stated that all measurements are to be the net dimensions of the work. The Contractor or his representative should be requested to be present when measurements are taken and in the event of the Contractor not being present the Engineer's measurements are to be accepted as final.

5.25 MEASUREMENT OF SPECIAL WORK.—Should the Contractor be required to execute special work which is to be covered up and for which no price in the Bill of Quantities is applicable, the Contractor is usually given the right to ask for full notes and measurements of the work to be taken with a view to fixing the price at a subsequent date.

5.26 METHOD OF PAYMENT.—Payments to a Contractor are made on the Engineer's certificates issued from time to time. The payment is usually stated as not exceeding 90 per cent. of the value of work executed and materials properly delivered on the site. Of the surplus 10 per cent., 5 per cent. is paid on the completion of the whole of the work, and the remaining 5 per cent. at the expiry of the maintenance period. The clause usually stipulates that no certificate of payment, other than the last, is to be deemed an admission of the proper performance of the part of the contract to which it relates, and that only the final certificate of the Engineer is to be evidence of the satisfactory completion of the whole of the work.

The Engineer should be given power under the clause to withhold a certificate if the works are not to his satisfaction, and where a certificate includes a sum for materials on the site, such materials are to become the property of the Employer and must not be removed by the Contractor.

5.27 PAYMENT TO SUB-CONTRACTORS.—Sub-contractors are paid by the principal Contractor and the certificates issued by the Engineer include sums for work executed or materials supplied by the sub-contractors. A clause should be inserted in the Conditions requiring the Contractor to pay such sums promptly to the Sub-contractor, and in the event of this condition not being complied with, the Engineer should have the power, at his discretion, to order payment to the Sub-contractor direct and to deduct such payments from the next payment to the Contractor. It should be made clear that any such payment will not relieve the Contractor of any responsibility for the proper completion of the whole of the works.

8. Clauses relating to Settlement of Disputes.

5.28 WHEN ENGINEER'S DECISION IS FINAL.—Provision for the settlement of disputes is necessary in all contracts. In certain matters, most of which have already been mentioned, the Engineer's decision is, as a rule, made final and binding on the Contractor and no appeal is allowed to an arbitrator.

It is permissible for the Employer to make any matter the subject for a final decision by the Engineer, but this power is usually restricted to the following:—

(*a*) The interpretation of the drawings and specifications.

(*b*) The power of the Engineer to order the removal of improper or defective work.

(*c*) The power of the Engineer to require the opening up of work.

(*d*) The dismissal of incompetent workmen.

(*e*) The granting of permission to assign or sublet.

5.29 ARBITRATION.—The contract may provide that, except in the matters mentioned above which are left to the discretion of the Engineer, any dispute or difference arising between the Employer and the Contractor, either during the progress of the work or after the determination, breach or abandonment of the contract, shall be referred to a specified person as arbitrator whose decision shall be final and binding on the parties. The clause should provide that in the event of a dispute coming within this category, either party may give to the other notice in writing of the dispute and such notice will be deemed a submission to arbitration under the Arbitration Act, 1950, or the Arbitration (Scotland) Act, 1894.

5.30 The giving of this notice within a specified time of the happening of the event should be rigidly insisted on, otherwise there is nothing to prevent a Contractor from bringing up matters which may have been settled verbally between him and the Engineer during the progress of the work and which, owing to the time elapsed since the completion of that part of the work, might place both the Engineer and the Arbitrator at a disadvantage in assessing the value of the work.

5.31 In some contracts it is provided that except with the consent of the parties in writing no matter, except the withholding of the amount of a certificate, may be referred to the Arbitrator until after the completion or alleged completion of the contract. This is to prevent delay due to the time usually required to determine a matter by arbitration.

5.32 The Arbitrator should be given power to determine all matters in dispute referred to in the notice and to alter or amend decisions, requisitions or notices as he may think fit. He should also have power to award costs, to direct by whom they shall be paid and to appoint, if necessary, a legal assessor to sit with him to determine points of law, and to fix the remuneration to be paid to such assessor.

9. Special Clauses.

5.33 NAMES OF FIRMS SUPPLYING MATERIALS.—Contracts prepared by Local Authorities frequently contain a clause forbidding the Contractor from purchasing materials from any member of the Authority, and the Contractor is required to submit for the approval of the Engineer the names of firms from whom he proposes to purchase materials or equipment. This clause, if inserted, should provide that no materials or equipment shall be purchased other than from firms whose names have previously been submitted to the Engineer for approval.

5.34 Bribery and Corruption.—A clause of this kind will provide that the Employer shall be at liberty to cancel the contract and to recover any loss sustained as the result of such cancellation, if the Contractor or any person employed by him be found to have offered, or given, or agreed to give any money or reward for the purpose of gaining favour or advantage in the matter of a contract. The Employer will have like powers in respect of any offence under the Prevention of Corruption Acts, 1889-1916, and for officers of a Local Authority it is a serious offence to accept any fee or reward contrary to Section 117, Local Government Act, 1972, or Section 68 of the Local Government (Scotland) Act, 1973.

CHAPTER VI

CONDITIONS OF CONTRACT FOR WORKS OF CIVIL ENGINEERING CONSTRUCTION. SUB-CONTRACTS

EXPLANATION OF CLAUSES

6.01 A form of Conditions of Contract recommended for general use has been drawn up by a joint committee of the Institition of Civil Engineers, the Association of Consulting Engineers and the Federation of Civil Engineering Contractors. The form is intended to meet all ordinary questions arising, or likely to arise, in contracts for the construction of civil engineering works, but clauses to meet special circumstances may be added. By the courtesy of these bodies, from whom copies may be purchased, a form is given in facsimile in appendix A to this book.

6.02 Notes on Clauses.—The notes on clauses given in the preceding chapter explain many of the clauses included in the Conditions, but certain clauses call for special comment and these will now be dealt with. The student should study carefully the whole of the clauses and endeavour to become familiar with the phraseology.

6.03 Definitions.—Clause 1 gives the meanings to be attached to certain terms frequently occurring in the contract documents. Such definitions are necessary if disputes as to the meaning of important words, which might otherwise be ambiguous, are to be avoided.

6.04 Authority of Engineer's Representative.—Clause 2 lays down the duties of the Resident Engineer. He cannot relieve the Contractor of any of his obligations, nor can he order extra work or make variations except in so far as he may be specially authorised by the Engineer.

6.05 Assignment and Subletting.—Clauses 3 and 4 provide against assignment of the contract without the consent of the Employer or subletting in whole or in part without the consent of the Engineer. Clause 4, however, provides that the provision of labour on a piece-work basis is not to be deemed subletting under this clause. This proviso is intended to apply both to workmen who are in the direct employment of the Contractor, and are subject to all the deductions usual in the case of workmen employed on a time basis, and to those in itinerant gangs of casual labourers.

6.06 Quantities Part of Contract.—Clause 5 provides that the several documents, including the Bill of Quantities, are to be read together. The Bill is therefore part of the description of the contract work and should the Contractor be required, in order to complete the work, to execute more work than is included in the quantities, he is entitled to be paid for the additional work as an extra.

6.07 Contract Agreement.—Clause 9 provides that the Contractor shall, when called upon, enter into and execute a Contract Agreement. It is usually assumed that the Contractor will execute such an agreement, but it is as well to have a clause of this description whereby he can be compelled to do so if necessary.

6.08 Inspection of Site.—The Contractor is required by Clause 11 to inspect the site and satisfy himself as to the nature of the ground as far as practicable. This apparently means that he is to take such action as a prudent person would take without involving a large scale investigation. If more than a superficial examination is necessary it is only fair that the Contractor's attention should be specially drawn to it.

6.09 Sufficiency of Tender.—Clause 11 (2) requires the Contractor to satisfy himself as to the sufficiency of his tender for all the labour and materials necessary to complete the contract. This obviously means sufficient, having regard to the information supplied to him by the contract documents, particularly the Bill of Quantities, since Clause 51 (3) provides that any increase or decrease in the quantity of work as the result of the quantities exceeding or being less than those stated in the Bill of Quantities does not require an order in writing from the Engineer.

6.10 Adverse Physical Conditions and Artificial Obstructions.—Unusual physical conditions and obstructions in respect of which the Contractor may wish to claim for additional payment are provided for by Clauses 12 (1) to 12 (4). Conditions for which such payment may be claimed are such as could not be reasonably foreseen by an experienced contractor. There may be some difference of opinion as to what constitutes an experienced contractor, but in the event of dispute the matter will be settled by the Arbitrator under Clause 66 (2), who at the same time will determine the sum, if any, to be paid for the additional work if the amount has not already been agreed by the Engineer and the Contractor.

6.11 Programme of Works.—The Contractor is required by Clause 14 to provide the Engineer with a programme showing the order of procedure in carrying out the work. This is necessary in large contracts, where much temporary work may have to be done, in order that the Engineer may satisfy himself that the Contractor is making satisfactory provision for carrying on the work.

6.12 Removal of Contractor's Employees.—The Engineer is given power by

Clause 16 to require the Contractor to remove from the works incompetent employees and to prevent their re-employment without the Engineer's consent.

6.13 Setting-out.—Clause 17 contains the usual provisions as to setting-out. It is customary for the Engineer's staff to assist in such work, but the clause holds the Contractor wholly responsible for its accuracy.

6.14 Limitation of Contractor's Liability in Certain Cases.—By Clause 20 the Contractor is made responsible for loss and damage to the works, whether temporary or permanent, except in the case of risks coming within the scope of "excepted risks." The "excepted risks" are war, invasion, civil war, riot, insurrection, military or usurped power, occupation by the Employer of any portion of the works or faulty design on the part of the Engineer. Damage due to "excepted risks" is made good by the Contractor at the Employer's expense.

6.15 Insurances.—Clauses 21, 23, 24 and 25 provide for the various policies of insurance which the Contractor is required to take out and keep in force during the period of the contract. In the event of the Contractor failing to effect the necessary insurances the Employer is empowered to provide for these and charge the cost to the Contractor.

6.16 Responsibility for Extraordinary Traffic.—Extraordinary traffic is traffic which by reason of its special character, such as weight, volume or speed, is likely to cause damage to road surfaces in excess of ordinary wear and tear. The Contractor is required by Clause 30 to use every reasonable means to prevent damage to roads and bridges by extraordinary traffic, but claims arising under the Highways Act, 1959, or the Road Traffic Act, 1930, are to be settled and paid by the Employer unless the Engineer certifies that the whole or part of the claim is due to the Contractor's default. But the Contractor will be responsible for any route improvement for moving his plant to site.

6.17 Returns of Men Employed and other Particulars.—Clause 35 requires the Contractor to make returns to the Engineer of the number of men employed on the works and other particulars of constructional plant in use. Such a provision is necessary so that the Engineer may satisfy himself that the necessary labour and plant is being provided to complete the contract in time.

6.18 Work, Materials and Plant.—Clauses 36 to 39 require the materials and workmanship to be the best of their respective kinds and power is given to the Engineer to order in writing the removal from the site of improper or defective materials or the re-execution of work in respect of which the materials or workmanship are not in his opinion in accordance with the specification. Should the Contractor fail to give effect to such order, the Employer may engage other persons to carry out the work and charge the cost to the Contractor.

6.19 Suspension of Work.—The Engineer is given power by Clause 40 to suspend the whole or part of the works for such time as he considers necessary, and the Contractor is debarred from demanding extra payment unless the delay is due to some cause other than weather conditions, the nature of the work, the default of the Contractor, or necessity for the safety of the works. The Contractor shall not be able to claim in any case unless he gives notice in writing to the Engineer within twenty-eight days of the latter's order delaying the works.

Should the suspension be for more than three months the Contractor may ask for permission to proceed and if such permission is not granted, he may at his option treat the suspension as an omission if it applies to only a part of the works, or as an abandonment of the contract if the suspension is in respect of the whole of the works.

6.20 Time of Completion.—The Contractor is required by Clause 41 to commence the works as soon as reasonably possible after the Engineer's order to commence and by Clause 43 to complete the works within the time stated in the tender and as extended by the Engineer if appropriate. The Engineer has power under Clause 44 to extend the time for completion by such amount as he may deem reasonable. It is open to the Contractor if he thinks the time for completion will be exceeded to ask permission to work both night and day. No additional payment is due if such permission is granted, but if it is refused, the Engineer is required to extend the time for completion if he is satisfied that there is no other practicable method of expediting the work.

6.21 Damages for Delay.—In the event of the time for completion stated in the tender being exceeded Clause 47 provides for payment by the Contractor of a fixed sum per week as liquidated damages and the Employer is empowered to deduct such damages from money due to the Contractor. Parts of the works may be assessed separately and the details inserted in the Appendix to the tender.

6.22 Certificate of Completion.—The Engineer is required by Clause 48 to grant a Certificate of Completion as soon as the works are completed and passed any test laid down by the contract. Such certificate may be given in respect of a part of the works, and the period of maintenance for the whole or the part, as the case may be, commences from the date of the certificate.

6.23 Maintenance of Works. Clause 49.—The period of maintenance is usually six months but any other suitable period may be inserted in the tender. The clause requires the Contractor to make good all defects and faults arising during the period of maintenance through defective materials and workmanship and in default the Employer may recover the cost from the Contractor.

6.24 Power to Vary Works.—The Engineer is given power by Clause 51 to vary the works on issuing a written order to that effect to the Contractor. This is a necessary provision in every contract. Apparently the only variations which a Contractor can make without a written order are variations due to the quantities being greater or less than those stated in the Bill of Quantities. No variation is to vitiate the contract and the value of such variations is to be taken into account and the contract price adjusted, provided the Contractor complies with Clause 51 (2), regarding the giving of notice of his intention to claim extra payment. A suitable form of Variation Order is given in Appendix "C". The Contractor is also required to give the Engineer a monthly statement of all extra and additional work ordered and executed during the preceding month.

6.25 Ownership of Constructional Plant and Materials.—By Clause 53 the Employer is given a lien on all plant and materials brought on to the works by the Contractor. Such plant and materials cannot be removed without the Engineer's consent, but the clause provides that the Engineer is not to withhold that consent unreasonably. This allows the Contractor to make the best use of plant on other jobs provided that the progress of the works will not thereby suffer.

6.26 Measurement of Works.—The Engineer is given power by Clauses 55 to 57 to measure any part of the works and to alter both the quantities and the rates in the Bill of Quantities accordingly. Notice is to be given to the Contractor before measurements are taken so that he may have an opportunity of being represented. Should the Contractor or his agent fail to attend, the Engineer's measurements are to be taken as correct.

6.27 Nominated Sub-Contractors.—Clauses 59A, 59B and 59C regulate the arrangements necessary for the employment of nominated sub-contractors. They provide for objections to their nomination by the Main Contractor, breaches and forfeiture of these sub-contracts, delays, extra costs, and payments.

6.28 Payment.—Clause 60 providing for the method of payment is important. Payment is made by the Employer on the monthly certificate of the Engineer, and the withholding of such certificate by the Engineer is one of the few matters which may be referred to arbitration before the completion of the works. A form of certificate is given in the Appendix.

6.29 Power to take Work out of the Contractor's Hands.—Clause 63 is the usual bankruptcy clause. The various circumstances in which the Employer may take the work out of the hands of the Contractor should be carefully noted.

6.30 Outbreak of War.—Clause 65 provides that in the event of an outbreak of war during the period of the contract, the Contractor is to carry on the work as far as possible for a period of twenty-eight days from the date of mobilisation. If the works are not completed within this period of twenty-eight days, the Employer is at liberty to determine the contract.

6.31 Settlement of Disputes.—The settlement of disputes arising out of the contract is provided for by Clause 66. All disputes and differences are determined in the first case by the Engineer who notifies his decision in writing to the Employer and the Contractor. Such decision is final and binding until the termination of the contract. It will be noted that notice must be given within three months if either the Employer or the Contractor wishes to dispute the Engineer's decision, on any matter referred to him. Another point worthy of note is that except with the written consent of the Employer and the Contractor, no question can be referred to arbitration before the completion or alleged completion of the works unless it refers to a dispute under Clause 12, to the granting of a certificate under Clauses 60 and 63 (1), or to the withholding of any portion of the retention money. This ensures that before disputes are brought up by either party they will have received full consideration, and after the contract is completed the Arbitrator will be better able to review such matters in relation to the whole contract. It is not necessary, however, that a Certificate of Completion must have been issued before a matter can be referred to the Arbitrator.

6.32 Maintenance Certificate.—The Contractor is not relieved of his responsibility under the contract until the Engineer has given a Maintenance Certificate under Clause 61. The clause further provides that neither the Employer nor the Contractor will be relieved of their contract obligations by the granting of this certificate.

6.33 Contract Price Fluctuations.—For at contracts likely to last least a year, it is usual to provide for variations in the prices of raw materials, labour, plant hire and other costs. In such cases, the unnumbered clause reproduced on pages 186 and 187 can be used.

CONDITIONS OF SUB-CONTRACTS

6.34 It is usual for practical reasons to permit the Contractor to sub-let specific portions of the work either to specialists in that particular form of construction or, if he is going to be extended to the full limit of his resources, to other contractors in the area. In addition he is usually made the channel of communication with any specialist tradesmen brought onto the site by the Employer. On some occasions he may be required to employ a named sub-contractor in accordance with the terms of the main contract. A Form of Sub-Contract has been drafted by the Federation of Civil Engineering Contractors for use in conjunction with the I.C.E. Conditions of Contract. This is intended to meet the ordinary questions which may be expected to arise in the course of a normal sub-contract, but this does not preclude the addition of extra clauses in special circumstances. By courtesy of the Federation, from whom copies may be purchased, a form is given in facsimile in appendix B.

6.35 Definitions.—The first clause relates the Sub-Contract to the Main Contract and defines the additional terms required. It should be noted that "Sub-Contract" means the specific document and any other writings named in the Second Schedule, but excludes "any standard printed conditions" in such other documents; and the "Price" is limited to the sum specified in the Third Schedule with any addition payable as a result of variations.

6.36 General.—The Sub-Contractor is required to do the work involved "to the reasonable satisfaction of the Contractor and the Engineer"; he is also forbidden to sub-let further without permission, but he may assign his financial benefits.

6.37 Main Contract.—The Sub-Contractor is assumed to have full knowledge of the Main Contract with the sole exception of the pricings of the Bill of Quantities and the Schedule of Rates: he may have a copy of the Main Contract documents on payment if he so wishes. In consequence he will neither do nor omit anything which would cause the Main Contractor to breach any condition in the Main Contract. The Sub-Contractor undertakes to indemnify the Main Contractor against any claims made by anyone in consequence of his breaches of the Sub-Contract.

6.38 Contractor's Facilities.—The Main Contractor usually allows the Sub-Contractor to use such facilities as are available on the site subject to the conditions that the Main Contractor suffers no inconvenience and that he incurs no liability for providing or failing to provide either plant or material.

6.39 Site Working.—The Sub-Contractor is required to conform to the site discipline of the Main Contractor in return for the necessary access and space to do the sub-contracted work.

6.40 Commencement and Completion.—The Sub-Contractor undertakes to start work within ten days of a written order to do so. If he is delayed by any cause entitling the Main Contractor to an extension of time, by any variation order, or by a breach of the Sub-Contract by the Main Contractor, he becomes entitled to a fair and reasonable extension of time, but he must give written notice of his claim within 14 days of the first occurrence of the cause. If different periods for completion are specified in the Third Schedule for different parts of the work, each portion is to be treated as a separate whole.

6.41 Instructions and Decisions.—The Engineer and his Representative retain under the Sub-Contract the overall supervisory authority that they have under the Main Contract, but they must pass their orders through the Main Contractor, who also has full supervisory powers under the Sub-Contract.

6.42 Variations.—The Sub-Contractor is required to vary the works as ordered by the Engineer under the main contract, as agreed by the Employer and the Main Contractor, or as ordered by the Main Contractor; but all orders must come from the Main Contractor, even if they are only confirmatory.

6.43 Valuation of Variations.—Variations are valued by reference to the rates and prices specified in the Sub-Contract for like or analogous work, or if this is not appropriate it will be "fair and reasonable". Unless there are definite provisions to the contrary, all the work actually done is measured and paid for at the rate quoted.

6.44 Notices and Claims.—The Sub-Contractor is required to provide the Main Contractor with all the necessary information, accounts and notices for inclusion in his returns of progress. At the same time the Main Contractor undertakes to secure any financial benefit claimable from the Employer under the Main Contract, and to pass on a fair and reasonable proportion to the Sub-Contractor.

6.45 Property in Materials and Plant.—Whenever under the terms of the Main Contract the property in materials and plant brought on to site vests in the Employer, then the Sub-Contractor's plant is affected in the same way as the Main Contractor's equipment. It may not be removed without permission.

6.46 Indemnities.—The Sub-Contractor agrees to indemnify the Main Contractor in respect of extraneous liabilities arising out of the sub-contracted works, except in so far as the Employer accepts responsibility or the claim is due to the wrongful acts of the Main Contractor.

6.47 Insurances.—Both parties agree to effect and maintain in force throughout the Sub-Contract period the necessary insurances specified in the Fifth Schedule.

6.48 Maintenance and Defects.—The maintenance period is defined as coincident with that for the relevant portion of the main contract.

6.49 Payment.—The Sub-Contractor undertakes to make the necessary financial returns to enable the Main Contractor to claim the appropriate payment from the Employer. The Main Contractor undertakes to pass on these monies within seven days of receipt.

6.50 Determination of the Main Contract.—If the Main Contract is ended for any cause outside the Sub-Contractor's control, he becomes immediately entitled to full payment for all the work he has done calculated by reference to the Bill of Quantities or the Schedule of Rates. If, however, the Sub-Contractor caused the failure to the Main Contract, the Main Contractor may treat him as being in breach of the Sub-Contract.

6.51 Sub-Contractor's Default.—The Sub-Contractor will be held to be in default if he fails to do the work with due diligence or, in accordance with the contractual terms, neglects or refuses to rectify bad work, becomes bankrupt or if a company goes into liquidation. If he is in default, the Main Contractor may end the Sub-Contract, retake possession of the site, with materials and plant, finish off the works and recover any additional cost thus incurred from the Sub-Contractor: he may, if he so wishes, elect to treat only part of the works in this fashion.

6.52 Disputes.—As in the case of disputes arising out of the Main Contract, the settlement of sub-contractual differences is a matter for arbitration. But there are two qualifications to this. Where the dispute also affects the Employer the Main Contractor may call for a joint arbitration subject to the approval of the arbitrator. If court proceedings arise between the Main Contractor and the Employer, the Main Contractor may abrogate the arbitration agreement and join the Sub-Contractor as a party.

6.53 Schedules.—The First Schedule gives the necessary particulars of the Main Contract, the Second defines the limits of the Sub-Contract, and the Third specifies the financial conditions and the period for completion. The Fourth Schedule enumerates the constructional plant and other facilities the Main Contractor is prepared to place at the Sub-Contractor's disposal, and the Fifth Schedule notes the insurances of the two parties.

CHAPTER VII

SPECIFICATIONS

SUBJECT MATTER OF CIVIL ENGINEERING SPECIFICATIONS. GENERAL PRINCIPLES

7.01 A specification is a specific description of a particular subject. An engineering specification is a detailed description of all workmanship and materials necessary in carrying out an engineering project in accordance with the drawings and details which it supplements.

7.02 Form of Specification.—The Conditions of Contract which have already been described are, in effect, the preliminary clauses of a specification, and although it is customary to look upon these as two separate documents, they are essentially one, and should be read together.

7.03 The method adopted by the Engineer in inviting tenders will affect the contents of the specification. The safest, and undoubtedly the best method, is to issue to each contractor tendering a complete set of documents comprising the conditions of contract, the specification and the bill of quantities. The Contractor is then left in no doubt as to what his obligations will be should his estimate be accepted.

7.04 A second method is to provide each contractor with a copy of the specification and of the bill of quantities with the information that the conditions of contract may be inspected at the office of the Engineer. If this method be adopted it is necessary to include in the specification the more important clauses of the conditions of contract, such as those dealing with setting-out, insurances, payment, time of completion and the like, indeed any clause which may influence materially the Contractor's prices.

7.05 A third method, which is not to be recommended except for unimportant jobs, is to issue only a bill of quantities to the contractors with extracts from the specification at the head of each trade, the conditions of contract and the specification being available for inspection at the Engineer's office. It is obvious, that the third method will call for much more detailed descriptions in the bill of quantities than either of the other methods, and for that reason alone, it is not suitable for large contracts.

7.06 Essential Features of a Specification.—The writer of a specification should endeavour to express his requirements with clearness and brevity, avoiding repetition and unusual words. He should be conversant with all the technical terms used in the various trades, and these must be used in preference to general and non-technical terms which might lead to ambiguity. As far as possible, the clauses are arranged in the order in which the work will be carried out. This does not restrict the Contractor to the order observed in the specification, but it facilitates reference. Each item in the specification should be numbered and an index inserted at the front of the specification following the title page.

7.07 BRITISH STANDARD SPECIFICATIONS AND CODES OF PRACTICE.—For some time there has been a growing tendency to standardise specifications for certain materials and classes of work. The British Standards Institution has done invaluable work in this direction by publishing Standards and Codes of Practice. A list of some of the more important of these is included in the text and the reader is advised to make himself familiar with those relating to his work, consulting the current British Standards Year Book for information upon additions to and revisions of the series.

7.08 In specifying materials coming within the terms of one of these specifications it is now common practice merely to refer to the number of the specification in a clause similar to the following example:—

> "The ( ) shall be from an approved manufacturer and shall comply in every respect with the current British Standard No. ( )."

This avoids lengthy descriptions and tends to uniformity in the quality of materials. Most manufacturers offer a guarantee that their goods are in conformity with British Standards requirements.

7.09 SPECIFYING RESULTS.—As a general rule it is more satisfactory to specify results required rather than the methods by which those results are to be obtained. In the first place, if methods are specified and the Contractor faithfully follows these methods he cannot be blamed if the results do not come up to the expectations of the Engineer, and in the second place the Contractor may prefer to use an alternative method at least as good as that specified. He may have special plant and equipment, if he is allowed to use it, by which he can produce the desired result quicker and cheaper than by any other method, and so long as he retains complete responsibility for the finished work, it is just as well to give him a free hand to choose his own method.

7.10 NOTES ON CLAUSES.—The following notes on clauses will assist the writer of a specification in forming the more usual clauses in a brief and concise manner. It is not possible within the limits available to discuss every clause which an Engineer may conceivably be called upon to write and it must not be assumed that every heading likely to occur has been given. The student should practise drawing up clauses for imaginary work, introducing as many new clauses as possible in his specification. It is only by such practice that he will ever acquire the necessary skill to write well-phrased clauses.

EXCAVATOR

7.11 Levels.—The datum from which all levels will be measured should be stated, or, if the datum is to be determined at the commencement of the work, the method by which it is to be recorded and used should be clearly set out.

7.12 Excavation Generally.—The excavation should be carried out to the lengths, widths and depths shown on the drawings or to such other dimensions as the Engineer may supply. The Contractor may be allowed to carry out the excavation in any manner he considers suitable subject to the approval of the Engineer. Measurements are taken net with no allowance for working space unless specially mentioned.

7.13 Unsound Ground.—Patches of bad ground are frequently found at the bottom of excavations. If such is found the Contractor should be required to call the attention of the Engineer to it, to excavate to such further depth as the Engineer may direct, and to fill up such extra depth with concrete. In bad cases it may be necessary to provide a foundation of timber or steel under the concrete. Any additional excavation and foundation so required should be treated as extra work.

7.14 Blasting.—Blasting is not usually permitted unless authorised by the Engineer. The necessity for blasting implies that the excavation is in rock, but it is important to define clearly what material will be regarded as coming within the term "rock". Geologists make no distinction between earth and rock, and the terms "soft" and "hard" are too loose for inclusion in a specification. Some engineers define as rock excavation anything, including boulders of one-half a cubic metre or more, requiring blasting. If this definition is adopted, it should be made clear that material such as shale or objects like tree trunks, which may be more economically removed by blasting will not be measured as rock. Another method is to class as "rock" any material having a hardness of three or more on "Mohr's" scale of hardness. Perhaps the most satisfactory method is for the Engineer to take sample borings in cases where it is suspected that blasting will be necessary, and to make such borings available for inspection by contractors at the time they are framing their estimates. Where rock is to be taken out close to existing buildings the system known as "wedging" should be used.

7.15 Timbering.—The Contractor should be required to provide all timbering and other supports necessary for securing the sides of trenches and excavations and be responsible for their safety. The length and depth of trench allowed to be open at one time should be specified or left to the discretion of the Engineer.

7.16 Sheet Piling.—In soft and treacherous soils sheet piling may be necessary to keep the excavations open. This may be of timber or steel units driven side by side to form a continuous partition against the side of the excavation. The type of piling should be specified and the Contractor required to provide all planking and strutting necessary for its support.

7.17 Timber and Supports Left In.—Timbering is normally removed as the work proceeds. If, in the Engineer's opinion, any timber should be left in the excavations for safety or other reasons, the specification should provide that such timber will be measured and paid for, but the Contractor must bear the cost of any timber or supports left in without the Engineer's instructions in writing.

7.18 Trimming and Levelling.—The bottoms of all excavations should be trimmed and levelled in accordance with the drawings and to the satisfaction of the Engineer. Bottoms of trenches should be rammed before concrete is deposited.

7.19 Water in Excavations.—The Contractor should be required to provide good and sufficient pumps and appliances to keep the excavations clear of water, and to pump out all water that may gain admission to the works without regard to the source from whence it comes, so that the excavations will be kept dry. The sump holes should be only in positions approved by the Engineer and arranged so that water can be pumped clear of sand, the operations generally being so conducted as not to endanger the foundations or stability of any adjoining structures.

7.20 Refilling Trenches.—The refilling of trenches should be carried out by filling to a height of 250mm above the crown of the pipe, and level across the trench from side to side, with selected hard dry material free from large stones or lumps. The remainder of the trench should be filled in layers not exceeding 300mm in depth, each layer being properly rammed before the next layer is placed. In large pipes and sewers if any displacement of the sides of the trench takes place below the level of the horizontal diameter and causing a space between the pipe and the earth such space should be filled solid with concrete at the expense of the Contractor.

7.21 Excavation in Tunnel.—Tunnels should be driven so that the work can be built everywhere to the dimensions shown on the drawings. The Contractor should be required to supply all timbering necessary and to leave in only such timbers or other supports as may be authorised by the Engineer to secure the safety of the works and other property. The space between the permanent work and the earth or timbering forming the sides and roof of the tunnel should be filled solid with brickwork in cement mortar or with concrete.

7.22 Additional Shafts in Tunnel.—If the Contractor thinks it advantageous to sink more shafts than are required for manholes or other means of access to a tunnel, he may be permitted to do so subject to the approval of the Engineer and the sanction of the owners and occupiers of land on which the shafts will be constructed. Such additional shafts would not be paid for as such, the cost being included by the Contractor in his price for the tunnelling.

7.23 Tunnels to be Kept Free from Gas.—If there should be any danger of noxious gases gaining access to a tunnel the Contractor should be required to provide proper apparatus to keep the tunnel free of such gases, whether they rise from blasting or any other cause.

7.24 Compressed Air.—Should running sand, silt, waterlogged subsoil or other unsound ground be met with to such an extent as to warrant the execution of the work under air pressure higher than atmospheric, the Engineer should have power to call upon the Contractor to provide the necessary plant and labour to maintain a uniform pressure night and day whether excavation is proceeding or not. The air pressure should be taken off when the Engineer wishes to test the watertightness of any part of the work. The specification usually stipulates that the Contractor must allow in his overall price for the possibility of compressed air being required.

7.25 Underpinning.—In carrying out excavation near the foundations of existing structures it may be necessary for those foundations to be under-pinned. The excavation, in this case, should be carried out in short lengths not exceeding 1 metre and the underpinning constructed in alternate sections. In excavating each length the foundations of the existing structure and all sides of the trench or heading should be boxed with close boarding all round and properly strutted.

7.26 Topsoil.—At the commencement of all contracts the topsoil should be removed and stacked in a convenient bank for reuse on completion. This is measured as an extra over excavation and is computed in square metres, the depth, usually of the order of 250mm, being quoted in the bill of quantities. At the conclusion of the contract, any surplus topsoil should be spread and levelled in some place specified by the Engineer or, exceptionally, removed from the site altogether.

7.27 Enbankments.—In the formation of embankments it is important that the work be carried forward uniformly, as nearly at the finished height and width as the due allowance for subsidence of the materials will admit of, and this allowance should not fall short of the quantity considered necessary from time to time by the Engineer. This should be strictly attended to in order to avoid the necessity of making subsequent additions either to the height or width of the embankment to bring them to the proper level and dimensions. No more material should be deposited at any one place than can be compacted there with the plant available at the time. The surface should be kept as dry as possible during the progress of formation and it should not be permitted to make the top temporarily wider and the bottom temporarily narrower than the contract width for the purpose of trimming down from the top of the slope to the bottom. The Contractor should be held responsible for all risks of subsidence, payment being made only on the dimensions of the embankment shown on the drawings.

7.28 Soiling Slopes.—Sides of embankments and slopes should be covered with at least 150mm of soil which will normally be removed from the ground occupied by the base of the embankment.

7.29 Surplus Excavation.—All surplus excavation arising on the works should be carted to an approved tip. In all works connected with alternate excavation and embankment, the Contractor is obliged to move excavated material a fixed distance, known as the freehaul distance. Any additional distance which the material must be moved is called the overhaul, and is paid for as an extra. To reduce such haulage expenses, Contractors are often tempted to deposit surplus material on land adjacent to the works. This should be prohibited without the written permission of both the owner and the occupier of the the land; if this is given, the rate for overhaul should be adjusted.

7.30 Reinstatement of Surfaces.—All materials forming the surfaces of roads, footpaths, lands or premises affected by the works should be carefully taken up and set aside for reuse, sufficient new material being added by the Contractor, if necessary, to ensure the new surface being equal in thickness to the old. Trenches should be left slightly proud, and if in roadways, rolled with a 10 tonne roller to bring the surface flush with the general road level, such rolling being performed not earlier than two months after the trenches are filled in. Surfaces of fields disturbed by the work should have the soil carefully replaced and rolled and afterwards sown with meadow grass seeds at a time to be determined by the Engineer.

7.31 Surface Damage.—Temporary fences should be erected and maintained during the progress of the work and on completion all walls or fences disturbed should be re-erected. The Contractor should be made responsible for all charges arising from surface damage, trespass, erection of temporary buildings, haulage of materials or other damage arising from the execution of the contract.

7.32 Debris and Materials.—All surplus materials of every description, rubbish, litter, etc., collected on the works during the period of construction and maintenance should be removed and the whole of the works left clean, tidy and to the satisfaction of the Engineer.

7.33 British Standard Codes of Practice applicable:—

CP 2001. Site investigations.
2003. Earthworks.

CHAPTER VIII

SPECIFICATIONS—(*continued*)

CONCRETOR

8.01 Cement.—Cement should be from works approved by the Engineer and complying in every respect with the appropriate British Standard specification. The consignments of cement should be delivered in sealed bags, steel drums or by pressurized bulk vehicles and be accompanied by the manufacturer's test certificate showing that a representative sample of the consignment has been tested and complies with the above specification. The test certificates should also show the quantity consigned, the date consigned, and the number of the delivery note accompanying the cement when delivered. The Contractor should be required to deliver promptly to the Engineer all manufacturer's certificates and delivery notes as they are received. It is usual for the Engineer to reserve the right to have samples of the cement taken either at the manufacturer's works or from consignments on the works, and to submit such samples to an independent authority for test. He should be at liberty to reject any cement as a result of such test, notwithstanding that the manufacturer's certificate may have shown the cement to be satisfactory. The Contractor should be required to provide proper sheds with a raised wooden floor on the works in which to store the cement under dry conditions, and if different brands of cement are in use, these should be kept in separate stores. The cement should be delivered in sufficient quantity to ensure that there is no suspension or interruption of the work of concreting. Each consignment should be kept separate and distinct.

8.02 Sand.—Sand should be specified as clean and sharp river or pit sand, free from loam and organic matter, and washed if so required by the Engineer. It should be well graded and if used for concrete, should all pass a 10mm BS sieve. For mortar the sand should all pass a 2·36mm BS sieve and in neither case should more than 10 per cent. pass a 150μm BS mesh. The Contractor should be required to submit, as often as called upon by the Engineer, 10kg samples of the sand for sieve analysis in accordance with BS 812, the test certificates in respect of such analyses being sent direct to the Engineer.

8.03 Aggregate.—The aggregate used should be the hardest available, such as granite, shingle, gravel or broken stone, free from dust, soft material, or any organic matter, and where possible, the source should be specified. For general purposes all the material should pass a 37·5mm BS mesh and be retained on a 5mm BS mesh. Fine aggregate for special work should all pass a 20mm BS mesh and be retained on the 5mm mesh. Samples of 75kg should be submitted for sieve analysis when required, as in the case of the sand.

8.04 Water.—Only clean fresh water should be used in the mixing of concrete and mortar.

8.05 Proportions.—The proportions of the ingredients of concrete will depend upon the purpose for which it is to be used. Some Engineers specify the mass of cement as a function of the mass of sand and aggregate, but it is more usual to express this as a function of the volume, particularly where special aggregates, either of high or low density, are to be employed. The proportions recommended are those published in Tables 1 and 5 of BSCP 114 Part 2, The Structural Use of Reinforced Concrete in Buildings, reprinted below. In the method of proportioning by sieve analysis results, the ratio of fine to coarse material is fixed from time to time during the progress of the work so as to give a dense workable concrete with a minimum water/cement ratio. Mixtures of cement, sand and aggregate agreeing with the following figures will give workable mixes approaching maximum density.

BS Sieve size	150 µm	300 µm	600 µm	1·18 mm	2·36 mm	5 mm	10 mm	20 mm	25 mm	37·5 mm
Percentage Passing. Max. size 37·5mm	4	10	15	22	29	35	45	63	75	100
Percentage Passing. Max. size 20mm	2	6	18	25	30	40	63	100	—	—

Owing to the variations in the grading of aggregates it may not be possible to make a mix on the works complying exactly with the above figures, but the proportions should be arranged to give as close an approximation as possible. The Contractor should be required to provide boxes for measuring the proper proportions of materials as determined by the Engineer from time to time.

8.06 Water/Cement Ratio.—The amount of water to be used in concrete should be stated and the Contractor required to provide proper measuring apparatus so that the correct amount for each batch can be determined. The quantity used will depend upon the workability required and the method of consolidation, and the water/cement ratio by weight will vary from 0·40 to 0·65. Maximum strength is usually obtained with a ratio of about 0·40 provided mechanical consolidation is used. For the convenience of the Contractor this ratio should be expressed in litres per 100kg of cement.

8.07 Slump Test.—Some Engineers prefer to measure consistency by the slump test. The apparatus used consists of a hollow truncated cone, open at both ends and made of sheet iron or brass. The height is 300mm and the internal diameter 200mm at the bottom and 100mm at the top. Handles are provided on the side for lifting the cone. The mould is filled with concrete in 100mm layers and each layer is punned 25 times with a 15mm diameter pointed iron rod 600mm long. The mould is then removed by a steady vertical lift leaving the concrete free to spread. The slump, or reduction in vertical height, is then measured. Slumps usually specified for different grades of concrete are:—

		Max. Slump (mm)
Mass concrete		25 to 75
Reinforced concrete—	Heavy sections	100 to 150
	Thin, vertical and horizontal sections	75 to 100
Roads and Pavements—	Hand finished	25 to 75
	Vibrated	0 to 25

8.08 Mixing.—The concrete should be mixed in batch mixing machines of approved type. Hand mixing should not be allowed except on small, unimportant work.

8.09 Test Cubes.—The Contractor should be required to make 150mm specimen cubes with concrete taken from the various batches as they come from the mixer, at least six cubes being made for each consignment of cement. The specimens should be made in steel or cast-iron moulds and kept in moist air of at least 90 per cent. relative humidity for 24 hours. They should then be taken from the moulds and immersed in water (15-20°C) until tested, which is usually at the end of 7, 14 or 28 days as the Engineer may direct. Cubes made from concrete consisting of 80kg cement, 0·1m^3 of fine sand and 0·2m^3 of coarse aggregate should show a crushing strength not less than the following:—

7 days	14·5N/mm^2
28 days	20·5N/mm^2

For rapid hardening Portland cement the figure at 7 days should not be less than 20·5N/mm^2, and for high alumina cement 41N/mm^2.

8.10 Method of Laying Concrete.—Concrete should be used as soon as mixed, and deposited directly in the work from barrows, trucks or any other method approved by the Engineer. It should not be thrown into its final position from a height, nor should it be deposited in water. Each layer of about 300mm in thickness should be spread out and rammed until the concrete is thoroughly consolidated and the cement begins to appear on the surface. The surface of each layer should be left rough for the succeeding layer which should be deposited before the previous one has set.

8.11 Consolidation of Concrete.—Concrete should be thoroughly rammed with approved tools to ensure that it is homogeneous and free from honeycomb. Ramming should not be confined to the upper surface of the layer deposited, but the whole should be rammed to uniform consistency. Cement which has partially set must not be reworked or used. Various forms of mechanical vibrator are now used to bring about consolidation. It is important that vibration shall not be applied by way of the reinforcement, and suitable precautions should be taken to ensure that internal vibrators do not contact either the reinforcement or any inserts. The advantages of vibrated concrete are that drier mixes may be used with resulting higher strength, and formwork may be removed earlier.

8.12 Stops in Concrete.—Where it is found necessary to leave off concreting, the concrete should be finished off vertically. The concrete should not be allowed to slope away to a thin edge. If directed the Contractor should form vertical grooves of approved dimensions at the end of each vertical section of concrete. Before starting to deposit new concrete against that which has set, the surfaces of the latter should be cleaned and loose or porous concrete removed and cut back until a solid face is exposed. The surface of the concrete should then be well hosed down and the new concrete thoroughly rammed against the face.

8.13 Shuttering and Moulds.—All the shuttering and moulds should be in every respect adapted to the structure and to the required surface finish of the concrete. The timber falsework for walings, braces, panels, girders, beams and all other parts should be of a kind and thickness that will avoid deflection and warping and remain rigid and true to line and level. All joints whether flush, mitred or bevelled should be carefully and accurately made and timber in boxes for girders, beams, walings and the like should be of a width that will form the required bottom or sides in one piece. Any timber that shows any tendency to warp, shrink or twist should be readjusted and kept damp by means of fresh water spread by a hose and rose. Strips should be placed in all boxes so as to form chamfered edges to all beams, piles, columns, etc., where required. Faces of shuttering in contact with the concrete should be treated to prevent the concrete adhering to them.

8.14 Centering.—The centering necessary for the support of girders, decking, beams and other parts should be of a size satisfactory to the Engineer, and should be capable of adjustment by wedging or otherwise to prevent any sag or settlement.

8.15 Traffic over Concrete.—No traffic should be allowed over any part of the finished concrete or other work until it has set and been properly protected to the satisfaction of the Engineer.

8.16 Removal of Shuttering.—No shuttering should be removed until the concrete has set and the Engineer has given his permission. The minimum period that should elapse before shuttering is removed will depend upon the nature of the part supported and the quality of the concrete used. For ordinary Portland cement the time varies from three to four days for the sides of beams to four weeks for timbers taking the full weight of beams and girders. For rapid hardening cement the latter period may be reduced to seven to ten days. Any weak places found on inspection after the shuttering is removed should be cut out and repaired with material in a manner to be approved by the Engineer.

8.17 Surface Finish.—The surface finish on concrete should be specified. No rendering or surface patching should be allowed and all shuttering for fair face should be coated with oil, whitewash or other approved composition to prevent adhesion.

REINFORCED CONCRETE

8.18 In addition to such of the foregoing clauses on concrete as are applicable, all or some of the following clauses may be required for reinforced concrete work.

8.19 Steel.—The mild steel for reinforcement should be from an approved manufacturer and comply with BS 4449 or BS 4482. At least one bending test and one tensile test should be made from each cast, and the Engineer should reserve the right to test any steel after arrival on the site. The test certificates should be marked to correspond with the marks on the batches of steel to which they refer so that easy identification will be possible.

8.20 Cleaning Steelwork.—All steelwork should be thoroughly cleaned of rust, dust, scale, oil and dirt before being assembled. If trusses are made and left to stand before being fixed in position in the boxes they should be kept under cover and washed over with a thin wash of neat cement and water, so that all parts are thoroughly covered. This should apply to all exposed ends of bars that must be left for continuation work or junctions with other parts.

8.21 Bending of Steel.—All steel work should, as far as possible, be bent cold to templates of exact dimensions, by the gradual and uniform application of force. The ends of all bars in trusses must be so fixed or treated as to secure adequate anchorage without overstressing the concrete. Tension bars should be provided with hooked or bent ends where necessary.

8.22 Links.—Links should be made of mild steel and, if circular, bent around a pipe of the same diameter as the bars they have to embrace, the ends being twisted together cold to form a link of true gauge.

8.23 Spacing and Securing of Steel Bars.—Every care should be taken in spacing bars correctly and in securing them in position. Shear bars should all be wired tightly to truss bars and any slackness or misplacement of bars should be rectified before the truss is concreted in. Diagonal wiring of sufficient strength and quantity must be adopted in all trusses to ensure the absolute rigidity of every truss frame.

8.24 Spacers.—Spacers of wrought iron or steel, made to template, should be used to ensure the correct positioning of bars.

8.25 Lacing.—All lacing should be of clean soft black 1·6mm steel wire in the positions shown on the drawings. Lacing and wiring should be drawn up tight round the bars they connect.

8.26 Cleaning of Shuttering.—No steel trusses should be put into any timber framing until the framing has been thoroughly cleared of all shavings, sawdust, chips, spikes, nails and other things by sweeping out and washing down with clean water under pressure from a hose, and no steel trusses should be put into position in their boxes until the concreting is ready to proceed. All timber should be washed down with fresh water under pressure in order to moisten it before any concreting is commenced.

8.27 Joints in Work.—Concreting in beams, girders, floors or decking which has to be temporarily stopped should be finished with a vertical face. Breaks should not be made where either shear or bending stresses are likely to be high. Thus for beams the breaks will be in general at from one-quarter to one third of the span from the ends, if it is not possible to form joints over intermediate supports. The location of all joints should be fixed by the Engineer.

8.28 Reinforced Concrete Piling.—All piles should be placed axially with or centrally under the loads to be borne. The sizes of piles and their reinforcement, the shoes and all methods of fixing, wiring, lacing and tying together should be in accordance with the drawings, and where not specially shown should be in accordance with the best practice. They should be moulded straight, true on each face, and the concreting done in one operation. Corners should have bevelled edges and the minimum thickness of concrete cover over the bars should be specified, a usual figure being about 40mm. The length from shoe to head and date of manufacture are frequently required to be scribed on the pile near the head before the cement sets. Piles should not be slung from the middle or ends only, but at points which divide it approximately into thirds.

8.29 Pile Driving.—No pile is to be driven until at least 28 days have elapsed since casting. All piles should be driven vertically unless otherwise required and particular attention should be paid to the accuracy of pitching and driving as no drawing up or wedging into line should be permitted. The weight of ram should be stated and an approved dolly cap and cushion used. The piles should be driven to a specified set depending upon the load to be carried and the ram used.

8.30 Lengthening Piles.—Where it is necessary to increase the length of any pile after it has been driven, the head of the pile should be cut off to expose the reinforcement for a length of not less than 500mm below the top of the steel reinforcement. The joint is made by butting the lengthening bars to the pile bars with the addition of a supplementary bar to every pile bar and of equal area. These supplementary bars extend at least 500mm on each side of the joint and should be secured to both pile and lengthening bars by 1·6mm wire wound in figure of eight so as to keep the bars from contact. The extension should be carried up vertically so as to form a true continuation of the pile. Any holes cut through piles should be cleaned out and filled up with cement mortar after the removal of all timbers and bolts. Driving must not be resumed until the cube strength of the concrete in extension is equal to that in the pile.

8.31 Treatment of Surface of Concrete Work.—The surface of all work should be kept moist by being continually sprayed with clean water from a hose for a specified period, usually about one month, from completion. Exposed horizontal surfaces such as decking should be covered with sacks 48 hours after concreting and these should be kept continuously wet.

8.32 Finishing and Pointing of Concrete Surfaces.—After the removal of the shuttering the exposed faces of the concrete should be inspected by the Engineer and any rough or projecting surfaces left by the joints of the false-work should be smoothed down to the face of the surrounding surface. All signs of timber work should be removed from the concrete surfaces and all holes used for temporary work should be filled up, pointed and made good. All signs of rust arising from embedded nails, ironwork or other causes should be investigated and cut out and made good. Areas where it appears that the matrix has not sufficiently filled the aggregate should be cut out and pointed. Exposed surfaces of concrete in structures such as jetties and the like should then be brushed down and washed over with a mixture of cement and water.

8.33 Testing Finished Work.—Any loading tests which it is proposed to apply to the finished structure should be carefully specified. Piling, decking and and floors are usually tested by loading the structure with a stated uniformly distributed load. Structures that have to carry rolling loads are usually tested by using vehicles with specified wheel loads. Deflections, if measured, should be determined when the load is on the structure.

8.34 British Standards applicable:—

BS 12 Portland cement (ordinary and rapid hardening).
146 Portland blast furnace cement.
405 Expanded metal (steel) for general purposes.
410 Test sieves.
882, 1201 Concrete aggregates from natural sources for concrete (including granolithic).

BS 915 High alumina cement.
1047 Air-cooled blast furnace slag coarse aggregate for concrete.
1370 Low-heat Portland cement.
1926 Ready-mixed concrete.
2028 Precast concrete blocks.
2691 Steel wire for prestressed concrete.
4027 Sulphate-resisting Portland cement.
4246 Low-heat Portland blast furnace cement.
4248 Super-sulphated cement.
4449 Hot rolled steel bars for the reinforcement of concrete.
4461 Cold worked steel bars for the reinforcement of concrete.
4482 Hard drawn mild steel wire for the reinforcement of concrete.
4483 Steel fabric for the reinforcement of concrete.

British Standard Codes of Practice applicable:—

CP 110 The structrual use of concrete.
114 Structural use of reinforced concrete in buildings.
115 The structural use of prestressed concrete in buildings.
116 The structural use of precast concrete.
2007 Design and construction of reinforced and prestressed concrete structures for the storage of water and other aqueous liquids.

CHAPTER IX

SPECIFICATIONS—(*continued*)

BRICKWORK

9.01 Common Bricks.—The term common bricks includes all those intended for structural purposes in which no special care is taken in their manufacture. They are generally unsuitable for facing or ornamental work. Common bricks should be specified as from an approved manufacturer, hard burnt, well shaped and free from lime, fire cracks or other imperfections. The absorption after drying should not exceed 12 per cent. in 24 hours.

9.02 Engineering Bricks.—Engineering bricks should be of uniform colour, machine pressed, true to gauge and unless otherwise agreed shall conform to the dimensions and tolerances laid down in BS 3921. They should be carefully stacked by hand on the site and not tipped from a vehicle. Bricks chipped, cracked or with broken arrises should be rejected.

9.03 Blue Bricks.—Staffordshire blue bricks are of a deep blue colour and are specially suited for all situations where great strength is needed. They should be hard, true to gauge, and not absorb more than 2 per cent. by weight of water in 24 hours.

9.04 Glazed Bricks.—Glazed bricks are made in many varieties and the name of the manufacturer should be stated. Chipped or imperfect bricks should be prohibited.

9.05 Special Bricks.—Radiating and special bricks should be provided for all circular work under 2·5m internal diameter.

9.06 Mortar.—Proportions of ingredients for mortar vary somewhat, but good practice calls for cement mortar composed of 1 part of cement to 2 parts of sand mixed as required for use. Lime mortar should be composed of 1 part of slaked lime with 3 parts of sand freshly mixed in an approved type of mixer.

9.07 Laying Brickwork.—Brickwork should be executed with cement or lime mortar in English bond unless otherwise specified. In dry weather the bricks should be immersed in water for ten minutes immediately before use. The brickwork should be true to line, plumb, radiated or curved as required, built solid throughout with joints not exceeding 5mm in thickness. Each course should be completely flushed up with mortar, but no grouting of the joints of brickwork should be allowed. Walls should be carried up together so as to maintain, as far as possible, uniform height. Pipes passing through brickwork should have not less than a two half-brick ring relieving arch built over the pipe to take the weight off it. Centering should not be struck until brickwork is properly set and the Engineer has given his consent.

9.08 Pointing of Brickwork.—Joints exposed to view should be neatly pointed with a struck joint as the work proceeds. The interior joints of arches built on centering should be cleaned and smoothed off with mortar immediately the centering is struck.

9.09 Rendering.—Rendering of brickwork for tanks, manholes and similar work should be of cement mortar, 20mm thick, applied in two coats, the final coat being trowelled to a smooth, hard finish.

9.10 Frost.—No bricklaying should be allowed to proceed in the open during frosty weather without the consent of the Engineer and all brickwork liable to be damaged by frost should be properly covered at night. An air temperature below 3°C should be considered as frosty.

MASONRY

9.11 Stone.—The kind of stone to be used for any engineering work should be carefully specified, giving where possible the name of the quarry from which it is to be obtained. Samples are frequently required to be deposited at the Engineer's office. Except where otherwise specified stone should be tooled on exposed faces, with joints truly horizontal, vertical or radial as the case may be, and bonding properly with adjoining work. Copings and cills should be in lengths of not less than 1 metre and have cement keys at transverse joints.

9.12 Ashlar Facing.—Ashlar facing should be well bonded with the backing either by alternating courses of different thicknes or by the use of galvanised iron anchors dowelled into the facing and built into the backing. The stone should be laid on the natural quarry bed with bed joints square to the face and not less than 150mm wide. Joints in masonry which is to carry heavy loading should be left open for a short distance from the face to prevent spalling. The joint is pointed up after the mortar is set. Rough masonry should be laid in courses as level as possible with the joints left open for pointing.

9.13 Joggles, Cramps and Dowels.—All joggles, cramps and dowels for giving additional strength to masonry should be provided in accordance with the drawings and the directions of the Engineers. Special forms of joint such as for raking coping stones should be carefully specified.

9.14 Centres for Arches.—Arches should be formed on strong centering capable of sustaining the imposed weight without flexure. Centering should not be struck without the Engineer's permission, which permission should in no case relieve the Contractor from responsibility for the safety and stability of the work.

9.15 Rubble Masonry.—This should consist of large, flat-bedded stones not less than 100mm in thickness and 300mm wide on the bed. They should be laid horizontally, well bonded together with at least one through stone to every superficial metre of face, such through stones being not less than 450 × 300mm on the face and of the full thickness of the wall where such thickness is less than 750mm. All stones to be firmly bedded in mortar, levelled up every 300mm in height and the face pointed in cement mortar.

9.16 British Standards applicable:—

BS	187	Calcium silicate (sandlime and flintlime) bricks.
	648	Schedule of weights of building materials.
	890	Building limes.
	1180	Concrete bricks and fixing bricks.
	1198–1200	Building sands from natural sources.
	3921 Part 2	Bricks and blocks of fired brickearth clay or shale.

British Standard Codes of Practice applicable:—

CP	111	Structural recommendations for load-bearing walls.
	121.101	Brickwork.
	121.201–2	Masonry.
	122	Walls and partitions of blocks and slabs.

TIMBERWORK

9.17 Timber.—The Engineer should carefully specify the kind of timber to be used on the works. It should be of good quality, reasonably free from sap, shakes, dead and loose knots, worm-holes and all signs of decay, sawn true, out of wind, and of the full specified dimensions.

9.18 Framing.—Should be assembled in a workmanlike manner to a close fit without any blocking or shimming. Before fitting together, all joints and surfaces which will be inaccessible after erection should be treated with hot creosote oil or white lead and pure linseed oil according to whether the timber is to be creosoted or painted. Bolt and other holes bored for the purpose of framing should be saturated with hot creosote oil or paint as the case may be, and all bolts coated with a similar preparation before being fitted. All holes for bolts should be bored 1·5mm smaller than the bolt diameter and the bolts tightly driven into place.

9.19 Timber for Piles.—Piles should be of heartwood, square or round in section of the full size shown on the drawings, pointed and shod with W.I. shoes in accordance with details furnished. The head should be banded with 75 × 20mm W.I. bands to prevent splitting. Piles should be driven into hard strata until the set under the last four blows of the hammer is not greater than a specified amount and any piles damaged in driving or driven out of place should either be withdrawn or cut as the Engineer may direct and others driven in their place.

9.20 Creosoted Timber.—All timber to be creosoted should be cut and framed before treatment, so that no cutting or trimming of any kind will be necessary after creosoting except the drilling of holes and the cutting of pile heads. Tops of piles, where cut off, should first be thoroughly treated with hot creosote oil before the cap is fixed in position. The timber should be creosoted by being impregnated with hot creosote oil in a closed cylinder at a temperature of 75°C under a pressure of $1 N/mm^2$ until the oil absorbed is not less than 200–250 kg/m^3 of timber. The BS 913 should be consulted for more detailed information. Accurate records of the weights of the various pieces before and after creosoting should be delivered to the Engineer and no timber should be used until he has signified his approval.

9.21 Painting Timber.—All uncreosoted timber which is to be fixed against masonry or concrete should have two coats of approved red lead in oil before fixing. Exposed surfaces should, after completion, receive two coats of white lead in oil followed by such other finishing coat as may be specified.

9.22 British Standards applicable:—

BS 144 Coal tar creosote for the preservation of timber.
373 Testing small clear specimens of timber
565 Glossary of terms applicable to timber, plywood and joinery.
881, 589 Nomenclature of commercial timbers including sources of supply.
913 Pressure creosoting of timber.
1282 Classification of wood preservatives and their method of application.
1860 Structural timber. Measurement of characteristics affecting strength.

British Standard Code of Practice applicable:—

CP 112 The structural use of timber in buildings

STEEL AND IRONWORK

9.23 Quality of Steel.—All steel should be graded in accordance with BS 4360 and from an approved manufacturer. The cost of all tests and analyses should be borne by the Contractor even if specified otherwise in the British Standard.

9.24 Workmanship.—Ends of beams, channels and other parts abutting against or upon other parts should be cut to exact lengths and true and square so as to provide a good bed or joint as the case may be. Proper cover plates should be provided where necessary and covers to angles should be of diminished leg dimensions while maintaining at least the same sectional area. Edges of web plates should be flush with the faces of the flange angles, and stiffeners should fit closely against the flanges. Bolt heads and ends of eye rods should not be welded on but formed out of the solid metal. Workmanship generally should be in accordance with best modern practice to the Engineer's approval.

9.25 Holes.—All holes should be accurately marked off from template or corresponding plate, and drilled, except in plates 8mm thick or under, when they may be punched. Holes should be cleaned of burrs or rough edges and countersunk where required. No drifting should be allowed. The diameter of all holes should not exceed the diameter of the bolt or rivet by more than 1·5mm, except where machined bolts or pins are specified, when they may be a push fit.

9.26 Rivets.—Rivets should be of best quality mild steel in accordance with BS 4360. The rivets, except those to be put in at the site, should be set up by hydraulic power, pneumatic riveting being allowed only for light work. If hand riveting is necessary, service bolts should be inserted in at least 20 per cent. of the rivet holes for a length of at least 1·5m beyond the rivet which is being driven, such service bolts being distrubuted so that the parts to be riveted may be properly closed while the riveting is in progress.

9.27 Bolts, Nuts and Washers.—Bolts and nuts should be of best quality with ISO metric threads unless otherwise specified and approved by the Engineer. Wherever a bolt is subjected to a tensile stress, as in the case of tie bolts, the ends should be of larger section so that the full sectional area of the bolt is maintained at the bottom of the threads. Bolts and nuts should have hexagonal heads and nuts with round shanks unless otherwise specified, and furnished with circular washers of an outside diameter equal to two and a half times the diameter of the bolt. For flanges of joists and similar positions tapered washers should be supplied. Bolts should be of such a length as to project not less than 3mm nor more than 15mm beyond the nut when tightened up. Except for replacement purposes, the use of Whitworth and Unified screw threads, both coarse and fine, should be discouraged.

9.28 Marking Steelwork.—All steelwork should be marked in accordance with a marking diagram supplied by the Contractor.

9.29 Cast Iron.—Castings should be of tough grey iron, free from blowholes, true to pattern and with a smooth workmanlike finish. Sample pieces 25mm square cast from the same heat of metal in sand moulds should be capable of sustaining on a clear span of 1·5m a central load of 250kg when tested in the rough bar.

9.30 Painting Steelwork.—All cast and wrought ironwork and steelwork, including all contact surfaces, should, except when used in reinforced concrete work, be coated with one coat of red oxide paint before erection. After erection the whole of the steel and ironwork should receive three coats of lead paint finished in an approved colour. The work should be thoroughly cleaned before painting, and paint should be from an approved manufacturer and delivered on to the site in the maker's original tins or drums. Steel or ironwork which, after erection, is in contact with earthwork or masonry should have three coats of approved bitumastic paint of approved manufacture.

9.31 Corrugated Iron Sheeting.—Galvanised corrugated iron sheets can be obtained in thicknesses from 2mm to 400μm, the usual width being 762mm, or ten 76·2mm corrugations. The sheets should be laid with a side lap of at least one-half corrugation with a minimum of 150mm end lap. Fixing to steel angle purlins is by 8mm diameter galvanised hook bolts, and to steel channel or R.S.J. purlins by square bend hook bolts. Curved diamond washers should be provided with all hook bolts. They should be fixed to wood purlins by 75 × 8mm diameter galvanised drive screws. On the sheets the fixing bolts must be driven through the ridges; if any sheets are fixed in the valleys, these should be removed, replaced and the hole made good.

9.32 Welding.—Welding should be carried out only by welders who have passed the tests laid down in BS 2645, and under the direction of experienced supervisors. Where electric welding is used, the plant should be capable of maintaining the voltage and current specified by the electrode manufacturer. After each welding run, the surface of the weld should be cleaned of all slag, etc. before any further welding takes place. Where inspection reveals slag inclusions, porosity, blow-holes, etc., the whole of the defective work should be removed and replaced. Inspection costs should be borne in the first instance by the Employer, except where re-inspection is necessary after cutting out faulty work.

9.33 British Standards applicable:—

BS	4	Structural steel sections: Part 1 Hot rolled sections. Part 2 Hot rolled hollow sections.
	18	Methods for tensile testing of metals.
	131	Methods for notched bar tests.
	153	Steel girder bridges.
	275	Dimensions of rivets.
	449	The use of structural steel in building.
	970	Wrought steels in the form of blooms, billets, bars and forgings.
	1856	General requirements for the metal arc welding of mild steel.
	2645	Tests for use in the approval of welders.
	2994	Cold rolled steel sections.
	3083	Hot dipped galvanised corrugated steel sheets for general purposes.
	4360	Weldable structural steels.
	4848	Hot rolled structural steel sections: Part 4 Equal and unequal angles.

British Standard Code of Practice applicable:—

CP 143: Part 2: Sheet roof and wall coverings. Galvanised corrugated steel.

CHAPTER X

SPECIFICATIONS—(*continued*)

ROADS AND PAVINGS

10.01 Forming Carriageway.—After any necessary filling or excavation has been carried out the whole width of the road formation should be formed to the levels shown on the drawings and coated with hard clinker ashes well consolidated with a 10 tonne roller to a thickness of 100mm after consolidation.

10.02 Pitching.—If the foundation is to be of pitching or penning, this should consist of slag or approved stone broken to not less than 150mm and not more than 300mm gauge, hand-packed across the roadway with each course as far as possible breaking joint. The pitching should then be ragged over with a knapping hammer, racked with small stone and rolled with a 10 tonne roller to the required thickness.

10.03 Strengthening Coat.—Pitching is usually covered with a strengthening coat of stone or slag broken to a 40–80mm gauge and laid to the finished contour of the road with a final consolidated thickness of 80mm. Interstices should be filled with slag or stone screenings, watered and consolidated with a 10 tonne roller.

10.04 Concrete Foundation.—Where a concrete foundation is to be provided, the formation, after being ashed and rolled as described above, should be well watered or covered with a layer of waterproof paper spread over the whole area to be concreted. The concrete, the proportions of which should be specified, should be laid to correct camber by the use of camber boards and tamping boards. Concreting should be done in bays of specified length and whenever possible a bay the full thickness of the slab and the full width of the road should be concreted in one operation. Where work is to be stopped it should finish at a face parallel or perpendicular to the direction of the road. At joints in the concrete, other than expansion joints, an approved key should be formed in the face of each joint which should be cleaned and damped before concreting is recommenced. Concrete surfaces which are to receive a wearing carpet of asphalt are sometimes covered with 35mm gauge chippings lightly tamped into the concrete before it has set to form a key for the asphalt carpet.

10.05 Concrete Reinforcement.—The type and weight of reinforcement to be used should be stated together with the amount of lap and concrete cover. Reinforcement should comply with BS 4449, 4461, 4482 or 4483.

10.06 Expansion Joints.—Vertical expansion joints should be formed across the foundation for its full depth in the positions indicated on the drawings, the joints being filled with plastic fibrous bitumen or other approved jointing material.

10.07 Tarmacadam.—Specifications for tarmacadam vary considerably, but a typical specification calls for a bottom coat of 60mm gauge material to a minimum thickness of 70mm after consolidation and a second or top coat of 20mm material to a minimum thickness of 40mm after consolidation. The aggregate should be slag or stone of approved quality, thoroughly dried in a rotary drying machine and coated with an approved binder in the proportion of not less than 40 litres and not more than 50 litres of binder to one tonne of aggregate. The binder should be refined tar complying with BS 76 for tars for road purposes, and brought to a temperature of 105°C before mixing is carried out. The coats should be laid in separate layers and each thoroughly consolidated with a 10 tonne roller after laying. The surface coat should be rolled to a smooth surface and covered with 12mm dry chippings at the rate of about 42 square metres per tonne, well rolled into the surface which should be left free from corrugations. The Contractor should be required to supply samples of the aggregate and the binder for testing whenever required by the Engineer.

10.08 Asphalt Surfacing.—Asphalt surfacings to carriageways is usually carried out in a single coat having a consolidated thickness of from 50mm to 75mm or in two-coat work consisting of a binder or base-course about 50 to 60mm thick, with a wearing surface having a thickness after consolidation of 30 to 40mm. The cross fall of the finished surface from the crown to the channel will not be greater than 1 in 35 and not flatter than 1 in 60.

10.09 Bitumen.—The bitumen used should be either petroleum or native bitumen as defined by the British Standards for asphaltic bitumen. It should be at least 99 per cent. soluble in carbon bisulphide in the case of petroleum bitumen, and 66 per cent. soluble in the case of native or lake asphalt. When tested under water at 25°C with a standard needle weighted to 100 grams the downward penetration of the needle in 5 seconds should be between 4 and 6 millimetres. The softening point by the ring-and-ball method should be between 50°C and 60°C and the ductility at 25°C not less than 500mm.

10.10 Aggregate.—The aggregate should consist of clean granite or other approved material, sand containing not more than 2 per cent. of clay or loam, and filler of either Portland cement or limestone ground to pass a 75mm mesh.

10.11 Proportions.—The proportions of aggregate and bitumen in asphalt mixtures vary considerably and the reader is referred to BS 594 for suggested mixtures. For two-coat work the base-course usually contains about 65 per cent. of coarse material from 20mm to 5mm gauge, 29 per cent. of sand passing a 5mm BS mesh and 6 per cent. of asphaltic bitumen. The wearing course will consist of about 25 per cent. of 20mm to 5mm material, 55 per cent. material passing 2·36mm BS mesh and retained 75μm BS mesh, 11·5 per cent. passing 75μm mesh and 9 per cent. of soluble bitumen.

10.12 Mixing and Laying.—The aggregate should be thoroughly dried at a temperature of 150°C and mixed in a mechanical mixer with the specified percentage of bitumen. After mixing, the respective layers should be spread while hot and rolled with a 10 tonne quick reverse roller until the two coats are firmly united. To provide a roughened surface, the asphalt, after rolling and whilst still warm may be covered with a layer of 12mm chippings pre-coated with 3 per cent. of bitumen. The chippings are spread at the rate of about 1 tonne to every 100 square metres and then well rolled and pressed into the surface.

10.13 Joints.—Care is necessary in making joints between successive days' work. The exposed edge of asphalt already laid should be cut back and painted with hot bitumen before laying is resumed. Manhole covers, kerbs and other surfaces against which asphalt is to be laid should first be coated with hot bitumen and the surfacing then carefully and firmly tamped into position.

10.14 Concrete Kerbs.—These should be splayed and hydraulically pressed, obtained from an approved manufacturer, and complying in all respects with BS 340. The kerb should be in 1m lengths and have a smooth surface on the top and face and for at least 25mm down the back and ends. It should be laid on a bed of concrete 150mm thick and 450mm wide haunched up to a height of 200mm at the back. Joints should be run for the full depth of the joint with 3:1 cement grout.

10.15 Channels.—Channels may be formed by hand-beating the tarmacadam for a width of 300mm from the face of the kerb, the longitudinal gradient being not less than 1 in 200 and free from depressions. Alternatively channels may be formed by one or two courses of channel bricks set on the concrete foundation with the kerb, or by using one of the standard concrete channel blocks now manufactured.

10.16 Flagged Footpaths.—Footpaths should be paved with granite concrete flags 50 or 60mm thick complying with BS 368. The flags should be solidly laid on a prepared bed of ashes and jointed with lime mortar and pointed in cement and they should be laid to break joint uniformly and regularly. Flagging at corners and around lamp columns, poles, boxes or projections should be cut to radii or shape.

10.17 Tar-paved Footpaths.—Tar-paved footpaths should be laid with tar-macadam of the same quality as for roads. The bottom layer should be of 25mm gauge material to a thickness of 50mm and the top coat should be 25mm in thickness of 10mm gauge material. The tarmacadam should be well rolled and consolidated to correct levels and cross falls with a 2 tonne roller and the surface finished with blinding of 5mm gauge slag or stone dust well rolled in. Edges of footpaths where they do not abut against walls or stonework should be supported by 150 × 25mm creosoted deal edging secured by 35 × 35 × 600mm hardwood stakes fixed at 1·5m centres.

10.18 Gullies.—Road gullies should be of an approved pattern in earthenware, concrete, or cast iron with 150mm diameter outlets. The cast iron grates and frames, in the case of earthenware and concrete gullies, should be bedded on two courses of engineering bricks set in cement mortar, the gullies themselves being bedded on and surrounded with 150mm of concrete.

10.19 British Standards applicable:—

BS 63 Single-sized roadstone and chippings.
76 Tars for road purposes.
340 Precast concrete kerbs, channels, edgings and quadrants.
368 Precast concrete flags.
434 Bitumen road emulsions (anionic).
435 Granite and whinstone kerbs, channels, quadrants and setts.
505 Road traffic signals.
556 Concrete cylindrical pipes and fittings, including manholes, inspection chambers and street gullies.
594 Rolled asphalt (hot process).
598 Sampling and examination of bituminous mixtures for roads and buildings.
706 Sandstone kerbs, channels, quadrants and setts.
802 Tarmacadam with crushed rock or slag aggregate.
812 Methods of sampling and testing of mineral aggregates, sands and fillers.
873 The construction of road traffic signs and internally illuminated bollards.
892 Glossary of highway engineering terms.
1241 Tarmacadam and tar carpets (gravel aggregate).
1242 Tarmacadam 'tarpaving' for footpaths playgrounds and similar works.
1446 Mastic asphalt (natural rock asphalt aggregate) for roads and footways.
1447 Mastic asphalt (limestone aggregate) for roads and footways.
1621 Bitumen macadam with crushed rock or slag aggregate.
1690 Cold asphalt.
2040 Bitumen macadam with gravel aggregate.
2542 Recommendations for the use of bitumen emulsion (anionic) for roads.
3416 Black bitumen coating solutions for cold applications.
3690 Bitumens for road purposes.
4690 Method for determination of solubility of bitumen.

BS 4691 Method for determination of penetration of bitumen.
4692 Method for determination of softening point of bitumen (ring and ball).
4693 Method for determination of viscosity of outback bitumen and road oil.
4707 Method for determination of loss on heating of bitumen and flux oil.
4710 Method for determination of ductility of bitumen.

British Standard Code of Practice applicable:—

CP 2006 Traffic bearing structures. Pavings.

SEWERS AND DRAINS

10.20 Glazed Earthenware Pipes.—Earthenware pipe, bends and fittings should be salt glazed and comply with BS 65.

10.21 Concrete Pipes.—Concrete pipes and specials should conform with BS 556 with spigot and socket ends. They should be supplied in lengths of not less than 2·5 metres unless specially ordered or approved by the Engineer.

10.22 Cast Iron Pipes.—Cast iron pipes, bends, junctions and fittings should conform with BS 78 for Class "A" spigot and socketed pipes or BS 437 for cast iron drain pipes and be coated with tar composition or other not less suitable modern equivalent.

10.23 Laying and Jointing Pipes.—The Contractor should be required to provide and fix, at such points as may be directed, properly painted substantial sight rails set to correct levels. At least three sight rails should be in position for each length of sewer. Pipes should be accurately boned and laid to even gradients, concentric and in straight lines between manholes. The earthenware and concrete pipes should be jointed with 1:1 cement mortar and tarred yarn and finished with a neat fillet forming an angle of 45° with the barrel of the pipe. The spigots and sockets of concrete pipes should be thoroughly wet before the joint is made.

Cast iron pipes should be packed with yarn to a depth of about three-eighths of the socket, run with lead and well caulked so that the lead is left flush with the socket of the pipe.

10.24 Manholes.—Manholes should be built of the size, form and dimensions shown on the drawings. The foundations should be of 300mm of concrete with walls of engineering bricks of approved quality in cement mortar. Glazed earthenware half pipes should be firmly bedded in the foundation concrete to form the channels through the manholes. An approved wrought iron step should be built into every fourth course of brickwork. Covers should be of an approved pattern, the weight being specified, with double-seated solid tops and firmly bedded on the brickwork.

10.25 Testing Sewers and Drains.—It is usual before any haunching or filling is done to test sewers and drains by means of water pressure, or, if water is not available or the sewer is large, by compressed air. The water test should be carried out by plugging the lower end of the pipe and filling with water to a head of 1·5m above the highest point of the section under test. Loss due to absorption should be allowed for by adding water until the water level becomes stationary, when the test proper will commence. In the air test, after plugging as above, air is pumped into the pipe until the pressure as shown on a U-tube is about 100mm of water. The drop of pressure should not exceed 25mm of water in five minutes.

For the purpose of discovering the presence of obstructions in small diameter sewers and drains a smooth ball of diameter 12mm less than the pipe may be passed through. Manholes should be tested separately. The Contractor should be required to provide all apparatus required for testing and to make good any defects shown by the pressure test.

10.26 Flushing Tanks.—If flushing tanks are provided they may be built of brickwork or concrete. If of brickwork the walls should be built with engineering bricks in cement mortar on a firm bed of concrete. The floor of the tanks should fall with a slope of not less than 1 in 12 to the cast iron flushing syphon of approved make. A 20mm coat of cement rendering in two coats should be applied to the interior of the tanks and worked to a smooth watertight surface. Covering arches, if of brickwork, should have a layer of 75mm of concrete over their outer surface, and the outer walls of tanks should be backed with a similar thickness of concrete.

10.27 British Standards applicable:—

BS 65 and 540 Clay drain and sewer pipes including surface water pipes and fittings.

78 Cast iron spigot and socket pipes (vertically cast) and spigot and socket fittings.

437 Cast iron spigot and socket drain pipes and fittings.

497 Cast manhole covers, road gully gratings and frames for drainage purposes.

539 Dimensions of fittings for use with clay drain and sewer pipes.

1130 Schedule of cast iron drain fittings.

1194 Concrete porous pipes for underdrainage.

1196 Clay ware field drain pipes.

1247 Manhole step irons (malleable cast iron).

2760 Pitch impregnated fibre pipes and fittings for drainage below and above ground.

3656 Asbestos cement pipes and fittings for sewerage and drainage.

4101 Concrete unreinforced tubes and fittings with ogee joints for surface water drainage.

British Standard Codes of Practice applicable:—

CP 3 Chapter VII. Engineering and utility services.
301 Building drainage.

SEWAGE DISPOSAL WORKS

10.28 In addition to the items of construction dealt with in previous sections, some or all of the following special clauses will be required in a specification for Sewage Disposal Works.

10.29 Sluice Valves.—The sluice valves should be from an approved maker of light or standard pattern for sewage with four faces, nut and spindle of gunmetal. If extended spindles are required the length should be stated and the type of bracket or pillar at the tip of the spindle clearly specified.

10.30 Penstocks.—Manufacturers make a variety of penstocks and the type required should be specified together with the length of spindle. Where penstocks have to be fitted against a wall, it is desirable to have a spigot piece bolted to the back of the penstock for building into the wall. Rectangular channel penstocks should have gunmetal faces and sides extended for building into the channel walls, the door being operated by a steel screwed rising spindle working through a gunmetal nut in the handwheel at the top of the frame.

10.31 Floating Arms.—The diameter of the arm and the depth of draw-off should be stated. A floating arm should have swivel bend at the base bushed with gunmetal and mounted on a cast iron sole plate. The float tube, out of not less than 1·25mm steel, should have flanged connection to the swivel bend, the other flange of the bend having a sluice valve and spigot piece. Float tube and float should be heavily galvanised after manufacture.

10.32 Dosing Syphon.—The type, diameter and number of syphons required should be stated together with the depth of draw-off and the maximum and minimum quantities each syphon must be capable of passing. All such ironwork should be coated with tar composition after assembly.

10.33 Distributors.—The type of distributor used will depend upon the site conditions and may be either of the rotary or the travelling type. The size of filter for which the distributor is required should be stated together with the maximum and minimum volume to be passed. The larger sized rotary distributors will usually have four arms, with cast iron supporting base having flanges for both feed and washout pipes. The arms should be 4·50mm thick, not less than 48mm in diameter and heavily galvanised. They should be drilled to give uniform distribution over the surface of the filter, the sprayholes being fitted with gunmetal bushes or nozzles. Ropes for supporting the arms should be of galvanised wire rope and provided with the necessary adjusting screws and clips.

10.34 Pumping Plant.—Machinery such as pumps will usually be provided for by including in the bill of quantities a p.c. sum for the complete installation to which the Contractor will add for profit and unskilled labour assisting the pump makers in the erection. If, however, the plant is thrown open to tender, the specification must state the type and size of pump, speed, and delivery against a stated head.

10.35 The type frequently adopted for sewage pumping is the full way centrifugal vertical direct coupled type with cast iron stool for building into the floor of the pump chamber. The pump should be specified as complete with suction and delivery pipework, sluice valves, non-return valves, bends and auxiliary suction for emptying the pump chamber.

10.36 The motor will usually be of the three-phase squirrel cage induction type, continuously rated, with flexible coupling between the motor and pump and provided with triple pole star-delta automatic control panel with three adjustable overload trips. The regulations of most electricity authorities prohibit the use of squirrel cage motors with star-delta starting if the power exceeds a stated figure, usually from 15 to 25kW. Motors larger than this should be of the slip ring type.

10.37 If float switch gear is used this should include galvanised steel float, gunmetal float rod and all the necessary guides, pulleys, brackets and counterweights. Electrical controls of the "No Flote" type are now frequently used.

10.38 False Floor Tiles.—False floor tiles for the bottom of filters should be from an approved manufacturer, the size and height being specified. For circular filters the outer edge should be finished with special radiating wall tiles.

10.39 Media for Biological Percolating Filters.—Clinker is the material usually specified for filtering media, although crushed stone, gravel, coke and slag have been used with success. It should be good, hard material, free from dust, and a washed and dried sample should not show a loss in weight exceeding 5 per cent. The first foot above the floor tiles should consist of material broken to pass a 50mm mesh and retained on a 38mm mesh. The remainder, which should pass a 25mm mesh and be retained on a 12mm mesh, should have an index of flakiness not exceeding 20 per cent. and an index of elongation not exceeding 40 per cent. The outer slopes of filters are often formed of rough clinker or stone built dry or of brickwork in mortar.

10.40 Activated Sludge Plant.—Machinery and equipment for activated sludge plants will usually be the subject of patents and the supply and installation of the plant is based on a separate contract with the manufacturers. The Contractor for the works should be required to attend upon, and supply unskilled labour to the erection engineers.

10.41 British Standards applicable:—

BS 587 Motor starters and controllers.
170 The electrical performance of fractional horsepower electric motors and generators
3979 Dimensions of electric motors (metric series).

British Standard Code of Practice applicable:—

CP 302.100 Small domestic sewage treatment works.

CHAPTER XI

SPECIFICATIONS—(*continued*)

PIPES AND PIPE LINES

11.01 The following additional clauses may be required in a specification for pipe lines.

11.02 Spun Iron Pipes.—Straight spun iron pipes should be in 5m lengths or such shorter lengths as may be required for closing. They should be of approved manufacture equal to pipes complying with the BS 1211 for centrifugally spun cast iron pipes. They should be tested to a head appropriate to the class of pipe and dipped in tar composition. Various types of screwed gland joint are now available incorporating a lead-tipped rubber joint ring which is compressed and held in position by an internal gland screwed into position in the socket.

11.03 Ordinary Cast Iron Pipes and Specials.—Bends, junctions and pipes other than spun pipes should comply with BS 78 having been tested to the standard pressure for the class of pipe and dipped in tar composition.

11.04 Steel Pipes.—Steel pipes should be from an approved maker of the spigot and socket type suitable for jointing with lead and supplied in 7·5m lengths or such shorter lengths as may be required for closing pieces. The pipes should be dipped in bituminous solution after testing and double wrapped with hessian impregnated with bituminous solution. After laying all joints should be double wrapped with hessian and thoroughly coated with hot bituminous solution.

11.05 Laying and Jointing Pipes.—The pipes should first be brushed through to remove stones or other matter on the interior of the pipe and then laid in the trench so that they bed evenly throughout the whole length. Each pipe should be driven home and the joints made by inserting in the sockets so much white hempen spun yarn as may be required to leave a space for lead of at least five-eighths of the depth of the socket. Sufficient pure soft virgin lead should then be poured in to fill up the remainder of the socket and leave ample projection for caulking down. The lead for each joint should be poured at one time and then set up at least three times all round with properly proportioned caulking irons and hammer of not less than 2kg mass, until the lead is neat and flush with the socket of the pipe.

11.06 Testing.—Pipe lines after laying should be submitted to a specified hydraulic test, at least equal to twice the working pressure of the pipe line, before the trenches are filled in, and if any leaks are discovered the joints should be re-caulked and the pressure re-applied until they are proved to be watertight. Defective pipes should be removed and replaced with sound pipes. The Contractor should be required to provide water and attend upon the Engineer whilst tests are being carried out. The apparatus for testing is usually provided by the Engineer.

11.07 British Standards applicable:—

BS 61 Copper tubes (heavy gauge) for general purposes.
486 Asbestos cement pressure pipes.
534 Steel spigot and socket pipes and specials for water, gas and sewage.
659 Light gauge copper tubes (light drawn).
1211 Centrifugally cast (spun) iron pressure pipes for water, gas and sewage.
1387 Steel tubes and tubulars for screwing to BS 21 pipe threads.
2494 Rubber joint rings for gas mains, water mains and drainage purposes.
3505 Unplasticised PVC pipe for cold water services.
3601—2 Steel pipes and tubes for pressure purposes.
4363 Distribution units for electricity supplies for construction and building sites.

British Standard Codes of Practice applicable:—

CP 310 Water supply.
331 Installation of pipes and meters for town gas.
413 Design and construction of ducts for services.

RAILWAY TRACKWORK

11.08 Rails.—Steel rails for trackwork will be either of the bull-head or flat bottom type. The former was most extensively used in this country for main line work but is now going out of fashion with the development of long welded rails. They should be of best quality open hearth, acid, Bessemer or other approved steel and comply with the appropriate British Standard. Variation from the standard length at 16°C should not exceed 4mm. The holes for fishplates should be clean cut, at right-angles to the web of the rails, and in accordance with the British Standard for steel fishplates. Deviation in the size or position of the holes should in no case exceed 0·75mm. The rails should be securely fixed into the chairs by means of oak or steel keys driven tightly into position to the required gauge of the rails. Rails on curves should be accurately crowed to the required radius and fitted in accordance with the Engineer's instructions as to adjustment of gauge on curves.

11.09 Bolts and Nuts.—Should be of steel having a tensile strength of not less than 550 N/mm ^{2} and an elongation of not less than 20 per cent in a gauge length of 250mm. Heads should be solid with the shanks which should be threaded to ISO metric dimensions.

11.10 Chairs.—Should be of tough grey cast iron, free from blowholes, true to pattern and smoothly finished. They should be secured to the sleepers with heavily galvanised steel screws or spikes as specified.

11.11 Wooden Sleepers.—Wooden sleepers are usually specified of Baltic red fir 250 × 125mm × 2·75m long creosoted as described for timberwork. Sleepers should be spaced at 750mm centres, their centre line coinciding with the centre line of the track.

11.12 Steel Sleepers.—Steel sleepers for flat-bottom rails should comply with British Standard 500.

11.13 Concrete Sleepers.—Should be in accordance with BS 986, Class A for lightly worked lines or Class B for heavily worked lines.

11.14 Oak Keys.—Oak keys should be of good quality English oak, chamfered and slightly tapered in accordance with the Engineer's instructions.

11.15 Ballast.—Should be of slag, broken stone or clinker to the approval of the Engineer, and laid in two layers. The lower layer should consist of 350mm of 75–40mm gauge material and the top layer of 150mm of 25–40mm gauge material. After the sleepers and rails have been laid the finer aggregate in the top layer should be well packed under and around the sleepers to bring them to the correct level.

11.16 British Standards applicable:—

BS	2	Tramway and dock rails and fishplates.
	9	Bull-head railway rails.
	11	Flat-bottom railway rails.
	47	Steel fish plates for bull-head and flat-bottom railway rails.
	64	Steel fishbolts and nuts for railway rails.
	105	Light and heavy bridge-type railway rails.
	500	Steel railway sleepers for flat-bottom rails.
	536	Light flat-bottom railway rails and fishplates.
	751	Steel bearing plates for flat-bottom railway rails.
	986	Concrete railway sleepers.

CHAPTER XII

THE BILL OF QUANTITIES

METHOD OF PREPARATION

12.01 Purpose of the Bill of Quantities.—The purpose of the Bill of Quantities is to provide a complete list of all materials and labour necessary for the completion of any engineering project and so to enable an estimate of the cost of the work to be made. The Bill is prepared from the Drawings and Specifications and its accuracy will therefore depend upon the accuracy of those documents. Moreover, the person entrusted with the preparation of a Bill of Quantities must have a thorough knowledge of engineering construction and be familiar with technical and trade terms used in civil engineering. Careful and accurate work should be the first consideration; accuracy should never be sacrificed for speed.

12.02 Steps in the preparation of the Bill.—There are four clearly defined steps in the preparation of a Bill of Quantities:—

(1) The making of a detailed list of all labour and materials necessary for the work and entering the items on dimension paper. This operation is called "taking-off."

(2) Squaring out the dimensions taken off under (1).

(3) Collecting all similar items together and arranging according to trades. This is called "abstracting."

(4) Writing the final Bill.

Each of these operations should be carefully checked by an independent person before the Bill is finally passed for copying.

	5·00		Excavate for founds	3/	7·50		Bk. work in	3·00
	2·00		depth n.e. 1·500 and		4·00		cement	2·75
	1·50	15·0	cart away.		1·50	135·0	mortar	1·75
								7·50
2/	5·00							
	2·00		ditto		10·00	10·0	Bk. on edge	
	1·25	25·0	1·500 to 3·000				coping.	

FIG. 1.

12.03 Taking Off.—The dimension paper used for taking-off is A4 size, double-ruled, as shown in Fig. 1. The first column is used for stating the number of times an item occurs and is called the timesing column. The dimensions of the item are entered in the second, or dimensions, column and the third, or squaring, column is used for the squared or cubed dimension. The description of the work is written in the fourth column.

Dimensions are always entered on the dimension paper in the same order, viz.: length, breadth, depth or thickness. The dimensions are written thus, 4·32 which means 4 metres 320 millimetres or 0·70 which means 700 millimetres. If an item occurs more than once, the number of times it occurs is indicated by the number in the timesing column followed by a sloping line as shown in the second and third items of Fig. 1. If, say, another one is to be added, the figure 1 is "dotted on," *i.e.* placed under the previous timesing figure thus $\begin{smallmatrix}3\\ \bullet\\ 1\end{smallmatrix}$ and if it should later be found that the whole is then to be doubled, this would be indicated thus, $2\Big/\begin{smallmatrix}3\\ \bullet\\ 1\end{smallmatrix}\Big/$ which means that the dimension is to be multiplied by 8.

Further examples are:—

$$5\Big/\begin{smallmatrix}2\\ \bullet\\ 1\end{smallmatrix}\Big/\begin{smallmatrix}3\\ \bullet\\ 2\end{smallmatrix} = 75 \qquad\qquad \tfrac{1}{3}\Big/10\Big/\begin{smallmatrix}5\\ \bullet\\ 1\end{smallmatrix} = 20$$

In taking-off a triangle of base 3m and height 10m the dimension should be entered as $\frac{1}{2}\Big/\begin{matrix}3.00\\ 10.00\end{matrix}$ not as $\begin{matrix}3.00\\ 5.00\end{matrix}$. The first method indicates at once to a person looking at the figures that the dimensions refer to a triangle. Other figures whose areas are shown in special ways are:—

Circle of radius 5·000	$\pi\Big/\begin{matrix}5.00\\ 5.00\end{matrix}$
Semi-circle of radius 4·000	$\frac{1}{2}\Big/\pi\Big/\begin{matrix}4.00\\ 4.00\end{matrix}$
Quadrant of radius 3·600	$\frac{1}{4}\Big/\pi\Big/\begin{matrix}3.60\\ 3.60\end{matrix}$
Segment of base 10·000 and height 3·000	$\frown$ 3.00 10.00

If any of these areas are to be multiplied by a third dimension, that dimension should be written underneath thus:—

$$\pi\Big/\begin{matrix}5.00\\ 5.00\\ 8.00\end{matrix}$$

which represents the volume of a cylinder of 5·000 radius and height 8·000

In the case of the segmental solid the dimensions might be entered thus:—

$$\begin{matrix}\frown\ 3.00\\ 10.00\\ 8.00\end{matrix}$$

In taking-off, no attempt is made to separate the items into the various trades. This separation is carried out at a later stage.

12.04 Wastes.—Whenever dimensions are obtained from a drawing by adding up a number of smaller dimensions, the latter should be set down in the fourth column and are called wastes. An example is given in the third item of Fig. 1 where the three dimensions added together to obtain the total of 7·50 shows how the latter dimension is obtained.

12.05 Units of Measurement.—The units of measurement are, for length, the linear metre or metre run, for area, the square metre or the metre super, and for volume the cubic metre or the metre cube.

These units are usually, but not necessarily, carried to two places of decimals. The coarser the type of work, the less necessary it becomes to carry the calculation refinements to even one decimal place. For major earthworks performed by large items of machinery such as scrapers and bulldozers, it is obviously absurd to attempt to measure dimensions to the nearest centimetre; but by the same token the hand excavation for a drain manhole requires just this sort of measurement. The student should remember that there is nothing inconsistent in dimensioning works executed by different methods in different ways.

12.06 Squaring.—The dimensions in the second column are squared or cubed, as the case may be, multiplied, if necessary, by the timesing number and the result entered in the third column. If the entry in the second column is only a linear measurement, that dimension, timesed if necessary, is entered in the third column. All squared dimensions should be carefully checked by another person before abstracting is proceeded with, and if correct, the items should be ticked in red.

12.07 Abstracting.—The dimensions in the third column of the dimension paper are transferred to abstract sheets and all the dimensions are cast up to obtain the total quantity of each item expressed in the units that are now accepted as standard.

12.08 Writing the Bill.—After the abstract sheets have been completed and checked the final Bill of Quantities is written. The dimensions and descriptions are copied from the abstracts and as each item is transferred to the Bill it should be deleted from the abstracts by a vertical line. In works of small magnitude with few items in the Bill the quantities are frequently transferred straight from the dimension sheet to the Bill and the items arranged in their correct order in the operation. In the case of large works however, the advantages of the abstract sheets are apparent. The items are there arranged in their correct order and the work of writing the Bill is very much simplified.

12.09 Abbreviations.—To save space and time in writing, abbreviations are frequently used in the description column of the dimension paper. The more common abbreviations are:—

a.b.	As before.	G.I.	Galvanised Iron.
A.C.	Asbestos Cement.	G.S.W.	Glazed Stoneware.
Bk.	Brick.	H.L.M.	Hydraulic Lime Mortar.
B.N. & W.	Bolt, nut and washer.	M.S.	Mild Steel.
c.a.	Cart away.	n.e.	Not exceeding.
C.I.	Cast Iron.	P.C.	Prime cost or Portland Cement.
Ddt.	Deduct.	P. & F.	Provide and fix.
D.P.C.	Damp-proof course.	R.C.	Reinforced Concrete.
E.O.	Extra only.	R.F.I.R.	Return fill-in and ram.
E.O.C.	Extra only in cement.	R.W.P.	Rain water pipe.
Ex.	Excavate.	Sup.	Superficial.
Foots.	Footings.	W.I.	Wrought Iron.

These abbreviations may also be used on the abstract sheets, but they should never be used on the final bill.

CHAPTER XIII

UNITS OF MEASUREMENT. EXAMPLES IN TAKING-OFF AND SQUARING

SITE INVESTIGATION, SITE CLEARING AND EXCAVATION

13.01 Site Investigation.—The units of measurement for site investigation are:—

Loan of plant, including erecting, dismantling and removing	Lump sum
Moving plant on site	Number
Sinking test pits, carrying out penetration tests or borings including the provision of "disturbed" samples ..	Lin. m of depth
Removal of obstructions, labour and plant	Hour
Undisturbed samples	Number

Test pits to be described by plan area and separate items to provide for each increment of depth of 1·5m. Timbering, pumping and penetration tests to be kept separate.

Separate items for borings in soil should be made for depths up to 10m, and then in increments of 5m. For borings in rock separate items should cover depths up to 10m, and thereafter in steps of 10m. The rates to include for extraction of cores.

13.02 Site Clearance.—

Clearing site of bushes, undergrowth, trees of less than 300mm girth, tree stumps of less than 100mm dia., hedges, fences and rubbish	Lump sum or per hectare
Trees, if over 300mm girth	Number
Tree stumps over 100mm dia.	Number
Demolition of buildings (overall cubic contents above ground level stated)	Lump sum
Demolition of steel work (approx. weight stated) ..	Lump sum
Demolition of pipelines, including supports	Lin. m

Hedges and fences may, if desired, be measured in linear metres.

Separate items should be included for trees over 600mm girth in steps of 300mm measured 1 metre above ground level and for tree stumps over 100mm dia. in steps of 100mm measured at ground level. The method of disposal of each item should be given. Credit given by the contractor for materials which become his property should form a separate item.

13.03 General Excavation.—The unit of measurement for general excavation is the cubic metre. Where it is considered necessary to include items for various depths of excavation, steps of 1·5m are taken. Stripping of turf, if a separate operation, and excavation of top soil, if it is to be re-used, are measured by the square metre extra over excavation.

13.04 Special Excavation.—Excavation which through depth, material or other difficulties of execution will warrant an increased price should be kept separate from the general excavation. Such items will include:—

Shallow surface excavation.
Excavation in bulk where machinery may be used.
Trenches (other than for drains and pipes), pits and pier-holes up to 3m in depth, and then in steps of 3m.
Excavation in underpinning.
Excavation in cuttings for roads and railways.
Excavation in tunnels and headings.
Excavation in hard materials and rock.
Excavation in compressed air.
Excavation above high water level, between high and low water levels and below low water.

Trenches for drains and pipes are measured in linear metres, stating the diameter of the pipe or the overall width of the concrete protection, if any, and the average depth in metres. For such trenches up to 6m in depth separate items will be taken for each 1·5m of depth. Deep trenches will have separate items for depths up to 6m, and then in steps of 3m. For removing and reinstating roads and other paved surfaces in connection with drains and pipes the unit of measurement is the linear metre and for other classes of excavation the square metre. In both cases the measurement is described as extra over excavation.

Other items which will require to be treated separately are:—

Breaking up of old structures of brickwork, etc., encountered in excavation, measured extra over excavation	Cu. m
Dredging	Cu. m
Filling (back filling to be covered by excavation rates unless of selected material)	Cu. m

13.05 Method of Measurement.—Excavation is normally measured net with no allowance for bulking of the material or for working space, but the specification should state clearly that this is the basis of measurement. In some cases it may be necessary to include a separate item to cover for additional excavation required to accommodate timbering or to provide for working space. When such allowance is made a measurement is included representing the area in square metres of the exposed sides of the excavation. Similarly in tunnel excavation a superficial measurement of the outer surface of the lining is included to cover the cost of additional excavation and of making good the voids between the lining and the earth, no thickness being stated.

13.06 Timbering.—The cost of timbering and temporary sheet piling for supporting the sides of trenches and excavations, and trimming the bottom of excavations for concrete are included in the price of the excavation and should not be measured.

13.07 Pumping.—The price also includes all ordinary pumping necessary to keep the excavations dry, but if pumping is likely to be a large item in the cost of construction, as for example, where trenches may have to be pumped dry after each tide, this work may be included as a separate item which will provide for supplying and dismantling pumps of a specified capacity, the cost being quoted on an hourly basis for the pumps both working and standing.

13.08 Reinstatement of Surface.—Trimming, soiling and sowing surfaces should be measured by the square metre, sloping surfaces being kept separate from surfaces on the level.

13.09 *Ex.* 1.—Take off the excavation for the site shown in Fig. 2. The material is to be removed to the depths shown and carted away.

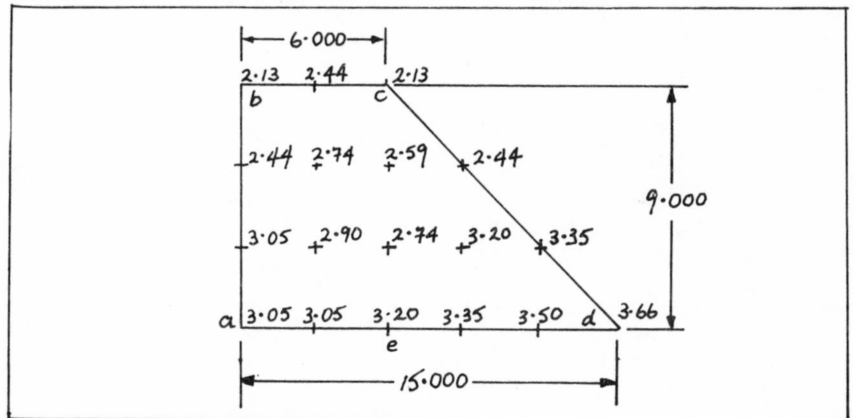

FIG. 2.

As the site is irregular it is divided into a rectangular portion *abce* and a triangular portion *cbe*. The depth to be taken is found by obtaining the average of the given depths for each part. The items are entered on the dimension paper as shown in Fig. 3.

	9·00 6·00 2·70	145·8	Ex & C.A. Area abce	2·13 2·44 3·05 3·05 2·44 2·74 2·90 3·05 2·13 2·59 2·74 3·20 12)32·46(2·70	½/	9·00 9·00 3·02	145·8 122·3 268·1	Ex & C.A. Area cde m³	2·13 2·59 2·74 3·20 2·44 3·20 3·35 3·35 3·50 3·66 10)30·16 3·02

FIG. 3.

13.10 In taking off excavation for cuttings, such as road and railway cuttings, the information is usually in the form of sections across the route at intervals of 10, 20, or 25m as shown in Fig. 4.

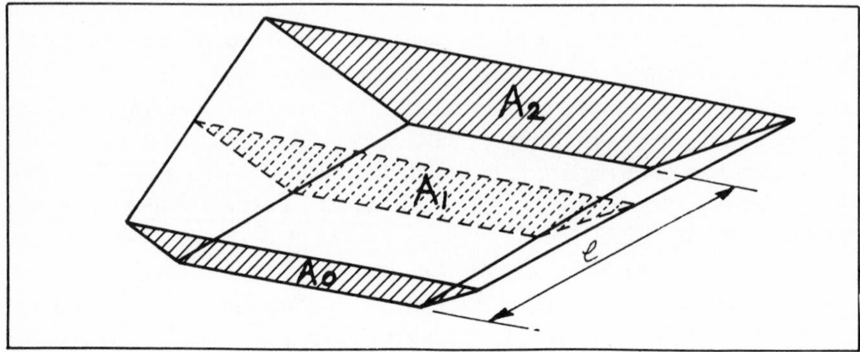

FIG. 4.

Separation for depth is not usually made and the volume is calculated by the prismoidal formula which is as follows:—

$$V = \frac{1}{6}\, l\,(A_0 + 4A_1 + A_2)$$

Where

V = Volume in cu. m.
A_0 & A_2 = Area of end sections in sq. m.
A_1 = Area of middle section in sq. m.
l = perpendicular distance between the end sections in m.

If the formula is to be applied to a number of sections other than three, provided the number of sections is odd the formula takes the form:

$$V = \frac{1}{6} l (A_0 + 4\Sigma A_1 + 2\Sigma A_2 + A_n)$$

Where

A_0 & A_n = Area of end sections.
ΣA_1 = Sum of areas of intermediate sections whose subscripts are odd.
ΣA_2 = Sum of areas of intermediate sections whose subscripts are even.
l = Twice the perpendicular distance between adjacent sections.

Should the number of sections be an even number the volume between the last two sections must be calculated separately by interpolating a middle section and applying the prismoidal formula.

Ex. 2.—Calculate the excavation in the cutting shown in Fig. 5. The intermediate sections are to be obtained by interpolation between the given sections which are 5·0m apart.
The taking-off sheet is shown in Fig. 6.

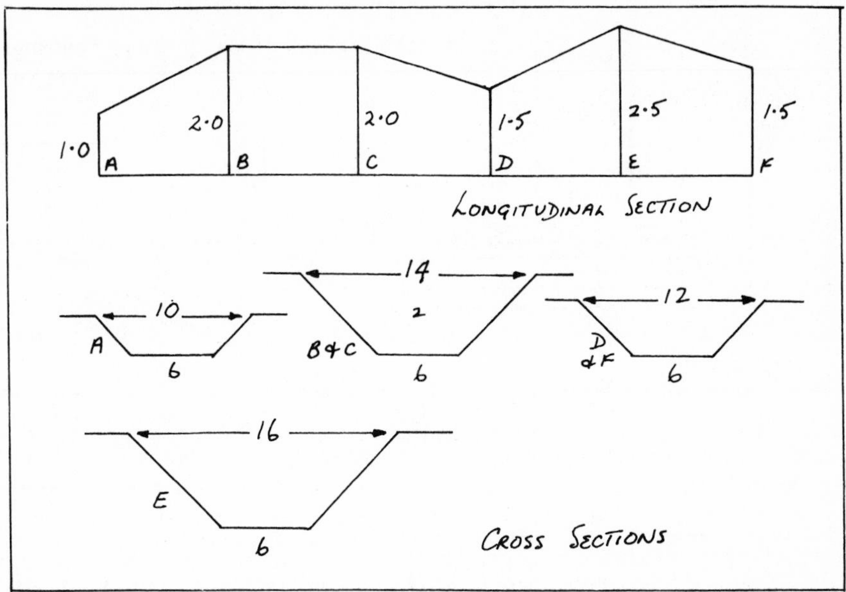

FIG. 5.

	8·00 1·00	8·0	Section A 10/6 2)16(8
2/2/	10·00 2·00	80·0	B & C 14/6 2)20(10
2/	9·00 1·50	27·0	D 12/6 2)18(9
2/	11·00 2·50	55·0	E 16/6 2)22(11
	9·00 1·50	13·5	F
4/	9·00 1·50	54·0	a 12/6 2)18(9
		237·5	

		237·5	Section b
4/	10·00 2·00	80·0	
4/	9·50 1·75	66·5	c
4/	10·00 2·00	80·0	d 13/6 2)19(9·5
4/	10·00 2·00	80·0	e
		544·0 1·67	
		948·5	m^3

FIG. 6.

13.11 *Ex*.3.—Take off the excavation for the building shown in plan in Fig. 7. The material is to be carted away, part being kept and returned, filled-in and rammed.

First take the excavation from ground level to the underside of the site concrete. The length of this excavation is the length of the building plus twice the projection of the foundation concrete beyond the face of the wall or, $4 \cdot 5 + 2 \times 0 \cdot 375 = 5 \cdot 250$. The width is $9 \cdot 0 + 2 \times 0 \cdot 375 = 9 \cdot 750$, and the depth $0 \cdot 750$. Hence the volume is $5 \cdot 250 \times 9 \cdot 750 \times 0 \cdot 750 = 38 \cdot 4$ cubic

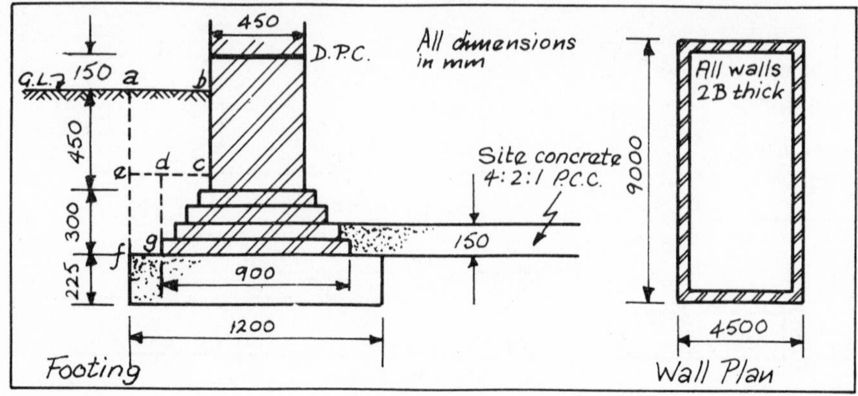

FIG. 7.

metres. For the foundation concrete, measuring between centre lines of walls, the total length is 2 × 9·0 + 2 × 4·5 −4 × 0·450 = 25·20 and the volume is 25·2 × 1·2 × 0·225 = 6·8 cubic metres. The total of these two items is 45·2 cubic metres.

A correction must now be made for the portion *abcgf* which is to be retained and returned, filled-in and rammed. Take first the portion *abce* down to a depth of 0·375. The length of the centre line is 2 × 4·500 + 2 × 9·000 + 4 × 0·375 = 28·500, and the volume is therefore 28·500 × 0·375 × 0·375 = 4·01 cu.m. The portion *dgfe* has a length of 2 × 9·450 + 2 × 4·950 + 4 × 0·150 = 29·400, and the calculated volume is 29·400 × 0·150 × 0·375 = 1·65 cu.m. The portion *dcg* has an average width of ½ × 0·225 = 0·112 and a length of 2 × 9·300 + 2 × 4·800 = 28·200. The volume is ½ × 28·200 × 0·225 × 0·375 = 1·19 cu.m., making a total volume of 4·01 + 1·65 + 1·19 = 6·85 cu.m.

These items are entered on the sheet as a deduction from cart away, and as the same volume is to be returned, filled-in and rammed, only one entry is necessary. The corrected volume of material to be carted away is therefore 45·2 − 6·9 = 38·3 cu.m.

	9·75 5·25 0·75	38·4	Ex. over site & C.A. 2/0·375 9·00 0·75 9·75 4·50 0·75 5·25		28·50 0·38 0·38	4·0	Ddt C.A. 9·00 Add R.F.I.R. 18·00 (abce) 4/0·38 1·50 28·50
	25·20 1·20 0·23	6·8	Ex. in trench & C.A. 2/9·00 18·00 2/4·50 9·00 27·00 ddt 4/0·45 1·80 25·20		29·40 0·15 0·38	1·7	ditto 2/9·45 18·90 (dgfe) 2/4·95 9·90 4/0·15 0·60 29·40
		45·2		½/	28·20 0·22 0·38	1·2	ditto 2/9·3 18·60 (dcg) 2/4·8 9·60 28·20
						6·9	

FIG. 8.

It will be noted that in the dimension column dimensions are taken to the nearest centimetre. The measurements are entered on the dimension sheet as shown in Fig. 8.

13.12 *Ex.* 4.—Take off the mass excavation for the filter and humus tanks shown in Fig. 9.

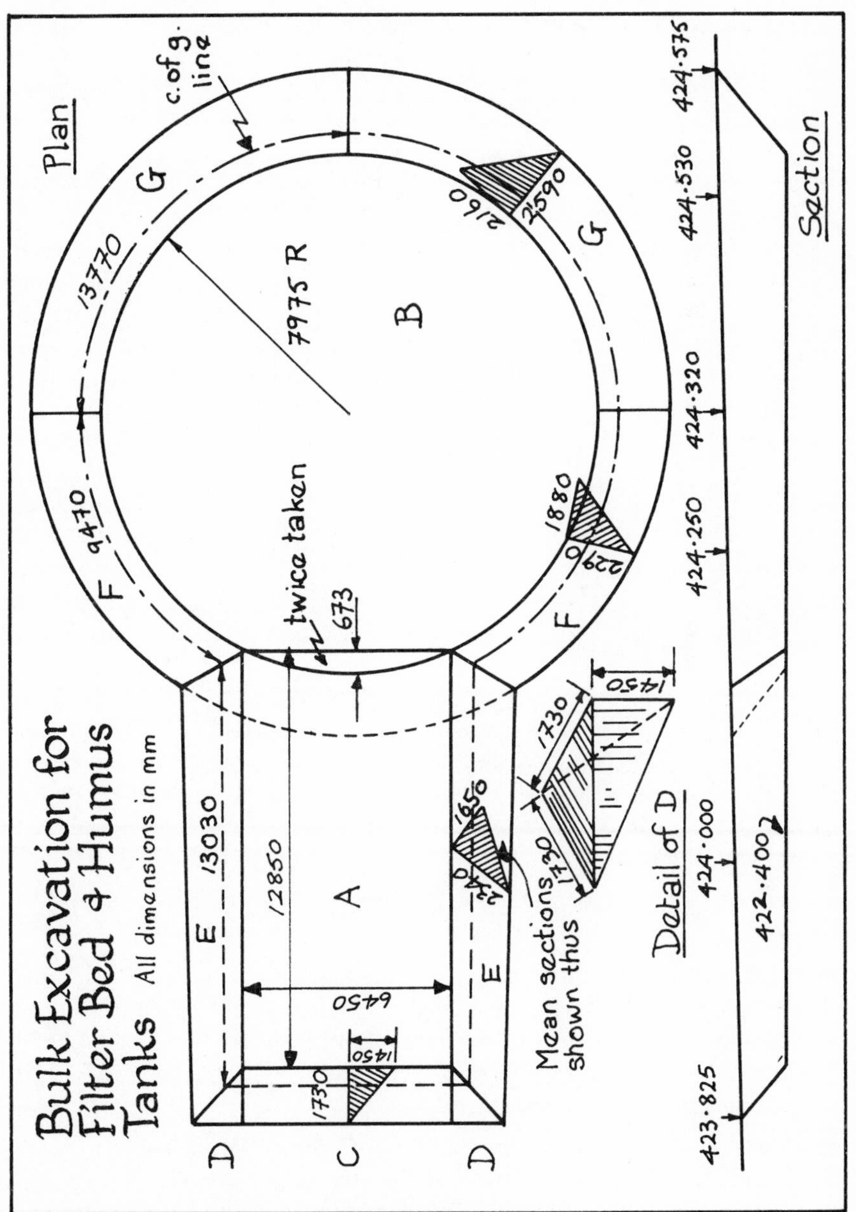

FIG. 9.

In Fig. 10 the taking-off sheet is shown. The method employed here is to divide the work up into a number of parts which can be estimated by the ordinary methods of mensuration, and deal with the more difficult shapes found at the boundary by determining the product of the mean cross sectional area of the solid and the length of the line joining the centre of gravity of all the cross sections of the solid. Note the method of dealing with overlapping portions as "Twice taken."

			Bulk Excavation for filter beds and humus tanks
	12·85 6·45 1·60	132·6	A
π/	7·98 7·98 1·92	384·1	B
1/2/	6·45 1·73 1·45	8·1	C
2/1/2/1/3/	1·73 1·73 1·45	1·4	D Pyramids
2/1/2/	13·03 2·34 1·65	50·3	E
2/1/2/	9·47 2·29 1·88	40·8	F
2/1/2/	13·77 2·59 2·16	77·0	G
		694·3	
			Values are taken to the nearest tenth of a cu. m 7·976 / 0·673 / 6·452

0·0115/ *	15·95 15·95 1·78	5·2	Ddt where twice taken, segment.
*	In this example, the ratio of the versed sine of the segmᵗ to the diameter is $\frac{0\cdot673}{15\cdot952} = 0\cdot0425 = 4\cdot25\%$ Tables of percentage area of unit diameter circle for segments of versed sine ratio varying from 0 to 50% are available (See Appx F) and show that the area of a segment whose ratio is 4·25% is 1·47% of the whole circle, i.e. 1·47% of $\frac{\pi}{4}$ Hence the corresponding segmᵗ of a circle having diameter 15·952 $= \frac{1\cdot47 \times \pi}{100 \times 4} \times (15\cdot952)^2 = 0\cdot0115 \times (15\cdot952)^2$ If tables are not to hand, the area of the segment may be found by calculating the difference between the sector and the triangle.		
	694·3 5·2 689·1		say 689 m^3

FIG. 10.

CONCRETE

13.13 Mass Concrete.—Mass concrete is measured by the cubic metre with no deductions for small cavities, chamfers, nosings, bolt holes and embedded rails and joists. Concrete of different qualities should be separately billed, and also concrete under 300mm thick, stating the thickness and whether vertical, sloping or horizontal.

13.14 Shuttering.—Shuttering for both mass and reinforced concrete work is measured by the square metre over the area of the surfaces of the finished structure requiring support during construction. Wrought shuttering and shuttering on curves and battered work should be kept separate. Shuttering

300mm in width or under and all fillets or splays over 50mm wide on the splay are measured by the linear metre. Holes for pipes and the like are measured by number.

13.15 Facework.—Special facework is measured by the square metre extra over mass concrete. Rails and joists embedded in mass concrete are given in tonnes.

13.16 Facings.—When mass concrete is faced with stonework or brickwork such facing is measured by the square metre, the average thickness being stated.

13.17 Concrete Blockwork.—For concrete blockwork the unit of measurement is the cubic metre, the size and weight of the blocks being given. Joggles and dowels are numbered extra over blockwork. Concreting on blockwork carried out under water or between tides should be kept separate.

13.18 Precast Concrete.—Precast concrete, such as beams, columns, steps and the like are measured in cubic metres, linear metres or number, slabs and pavings being in square metres, with the thickness stated.

The following units of measurement should be noted:—

Bedding and grouting of base plates	Sq. m
Mortices for bolts 300mm deep and under and grouting	Number
Ditto. over 300mm deep and grouting	Lin. m

Separate items to be given for mortices in steps of 100mm up to 300mm, then in steps of 300mm.

REINFORCED CONCRETE

13.19 For reinforced concrete placed *in situ* the units used are:—

Concrete, including prestressed concrete	Cu. m
Bar and rod reinforcement	kg or tonne
Fabric reinforcement	Sq. m
Steel wire or cable for prestressing on site	kg or tonne or lin. metre

No deduction is made for the volume of the reinforcement, and columns, beams, slabs and panels are kept separate. The weight of bar reinforcement is calculated on the basis of 0·785 kg/cm ^{2} per linear metre. Bending, hooking and binding wire are all included in the price of the reinforcement. Fabric reinforcement is measured net, the weight per square metre being stated. Allowance for laps, cutting, bending and waste is made in the rates. Bars or rods less than 25mm dia. or side should be kept separate for each size, and also for bars or rods 12m in length and upwards in steps of 1·5m.

13.20 Precast Prestressed Concrete.—Precast prestressed concrete is measured as follows:—

Factory made precast pre-tensioned members, including steel	Lin. m or cu. m
Erection of above	Number
Site-made members, pre-tensioned (steel measured separately)	Lin. m or cu. m
Pre-cast members to be post-tensioned	Lin. m or cu. m
Assembly and post-tensioning of above (steel measured separately)	Number of assemblies
Erection of above	Number

The rates to include for cost of jointing and for moulds. Differing cross sections and lengths to be kept separate and cross sections and lengths stated.

Forming holes, including ducts, casings, sheathing or chases	Lin. m
Anchorages	Number
Post-tensioning on site	Number of wires or cables
Grouting of cables	Lin. m
Loan of tensioning plant, and removal	Lump sum
Post-tensioning on site, including anchorages	Number of wires or cables

Pre-tensioning and post-tensioning are to be kept separate, also longitudinal and transverse tensioning.

13.21 *Ex.* 5.—Take off the concrete in the foundations of the building shown in Fig. 7.

The item for concrete in foundations is the same as the item for excavation in Fig. 8. The dimensions for the site concrete are the dimensions inside the concrete foundation with the addition of 180mm all round for the overlap on the foundation. The dimension sheet is shown in Fig. 11.

	25·20 1·20 0·23	7·0	Conc. in founds.		7·76 3·26 0·15	7·0 3·8	Site conc. 2/0·80 9·00 1·60 7·40 2/0·18 ·36 7·76 — 2/0·80 4·50 1·60 2·90 2/0·18 0·36 3·26
						10·8	

Fig. 11.

BRICKWORK

13.22 The units of measurement for brickwork are:—

General brickwork up to and including 700mm thickness, thickness stated	Sq. m
General brickwork exceeding 700mm thickness ..	Cu. m
Special facings measured extra over general brickwork	Sq. m
Plinths, corbels and bull noses measured extra over general brickwork	Lin. m
Brick copings	,, ,,

Brickwork is measured net and is described as "in lime mortar" or "in cement mortar" and the kind of pointing stated.

13.23 Special Work.—Battered or circular work is kept separate, as also are manholes, wells, pits, chimney shafts, arches and sewer and tunnel linings. Facings to arches are measured per square metre, the area given being the sum of the faces and exposed soffit of the arch.

13.24 Waterproofing.—Waterproofing is measured as follows:—

Ashpalt and waterproof sheeting	Sq. m
Angle fillets and strip less than 300mm wide and lining to culverts	Lin. m
Rendering in ordinary or waterproofed cement mortar	Sq. m
Waterproof painting	,, ,,
Lining to small sumps	Number

Measurements are net with no allowance, except in the rates, for joints, laps and falls. The thickness of the finished work and number of coats to be stated.

Separate items should be included for work on horizontal, vertical, inclined and curved surfaces.

13.25 *Ex.* 6.—In the example shown in Fig. 7 take off the brickwork to 150mm above ground level and including the damp-proof-course.

The items are shown in Fig. 12. In measuring footings the average width of the top and bottom courses is taken.

	25·20 0·72 0·30	5·4	Bkwk in ftgs 0·55 0·90 2)1·45 0·72		25·20 0·45	11·1	Horiz. D.P. Course
	25·20 0·60	15·1	Do. in 2 bk wall up to D.P.C.				

FIG. 12.

STEEL AND IRONWORK

13.26 Steel and ironwork are billed by weight, the tonne being the unit of measurement except in cases where the weight is less than 1 tonne when the unit is the kilogram, and calculations are based on the following weights per sq. metre, 100mm thick.

Steel (rolled or cast)	785 kg
Wrought iron	770 kg
Cast iron	725 kg

13.27 Tolerance.—Tolerances and rolling margin are ignored but an allowance is added for rivet heads either by calculating their actual weight or by adding a percentage to the total weight. In the latter case the percentage should be stated.

13.28 Painting.—The cost of painting at the factory is covered by the rates per tonne. Painting on the works is measured in square metres of steelwork painted except for bars 300mm in girth and under when the unit is the linear metre. Where the manufacture and erection of steel is by the same firm the rate per tonne to cover painting on site. Eaves, gutters and rain-water pipes should be measured in linear metres.

13.29 Corrugated Iron.—Corrugated iron is measured by the square metre of net area covered, the rate including for laps, cutting and fastenings.

13.30 *Ex.* 7.—Fig. 13 shows a grillage foundation. Take off the excavation concrete and steelwork and square the dimensions.

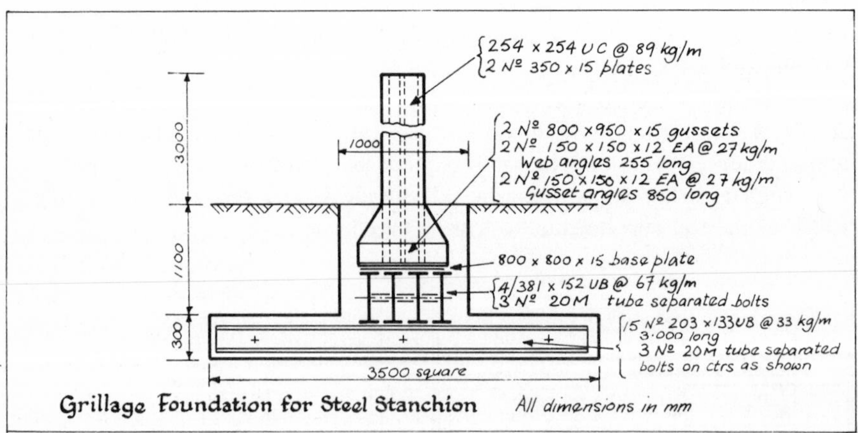

Grillage Foundation for Steel Stanchion

FIG. 13.

All the items are shown in Fig. 14.

	3·50 3·50 1·40	17·15	Ex. in soil n.e. 1·500 deep & R.F.I.R.
	3·50 3·50 0·30	3·68	Ddt R.F.I.R. Add C.A. & 3:2:1 conc
	1·00 1·00 1·10	1·10	
		4·78	
			Steelwork
15/	3·00	45·00	203 × 133 UB @ 30 kg/m
4/	3·00	12·00	381 × 152 UB @ 67 kg/m
3/	2·87	8·61	20M BN & W Wt 0·82 kg
3/	0·45	1·35	Ditto Wt 0·22 kg
9/	0·16	1·44	25 mm int. dia. tube separators Wt. 3 kg/m
42/	0·21	8·82	
		10·26	
	3·70	3·70	254 × 254 UC @ 89 kg/m

2/	0·26	0·52	150 × 150 × 12 E.A. @ 27 kg/m.
2/	0·85	1·70	Ditto
		2·22	
			15 mm plate
	0·80 0·80	0·64	Base plate
2/	0·35 0·95	0·71	Gusset
2/½/	0·45 0·95	0·43	Gusset
2/	0·35 3·70	2·59	Stanchion
		4·37	
2/2/4/		16 No	20 M fixing bolts @ 0·35 kg
2/2	9	36 No	Rivet Heads 24 mm Gusset Ls
2/	9	18 "	do.
2/3	4	24 "	Web Ls
2/4	33	264 "	Stanchion
		342	No. @ 9·55 kg/100

FIG. 14.

MASONRY

13.31 Units of measurement for masonry are:—

Ashlar masonry and dressed stone	Cu. m
Rubble masonry	Cu. m
Facework to concrete (average thickness stated) ..	Sq. m
Ditto to rubble or mass masonry measured extra over rubble masonry	Sq. m
Dowels and cramps	Number

The volumes for ashlar and dressed stone are obtained by taking the contents of the smallest rectangular figure which will enclose the finished stone. Masonry should be described as "in lime mortar" or "in cement mortar" and the rates include for grouting and pointing. Copings, voussoirs, steps and similar work are measured separately as well as any additional work incidental to the fixing of steel or ironwork.

13.32 *Ex.* 8.—Take off the ashlar masonry for the pier and cap shown in Fig. 15.

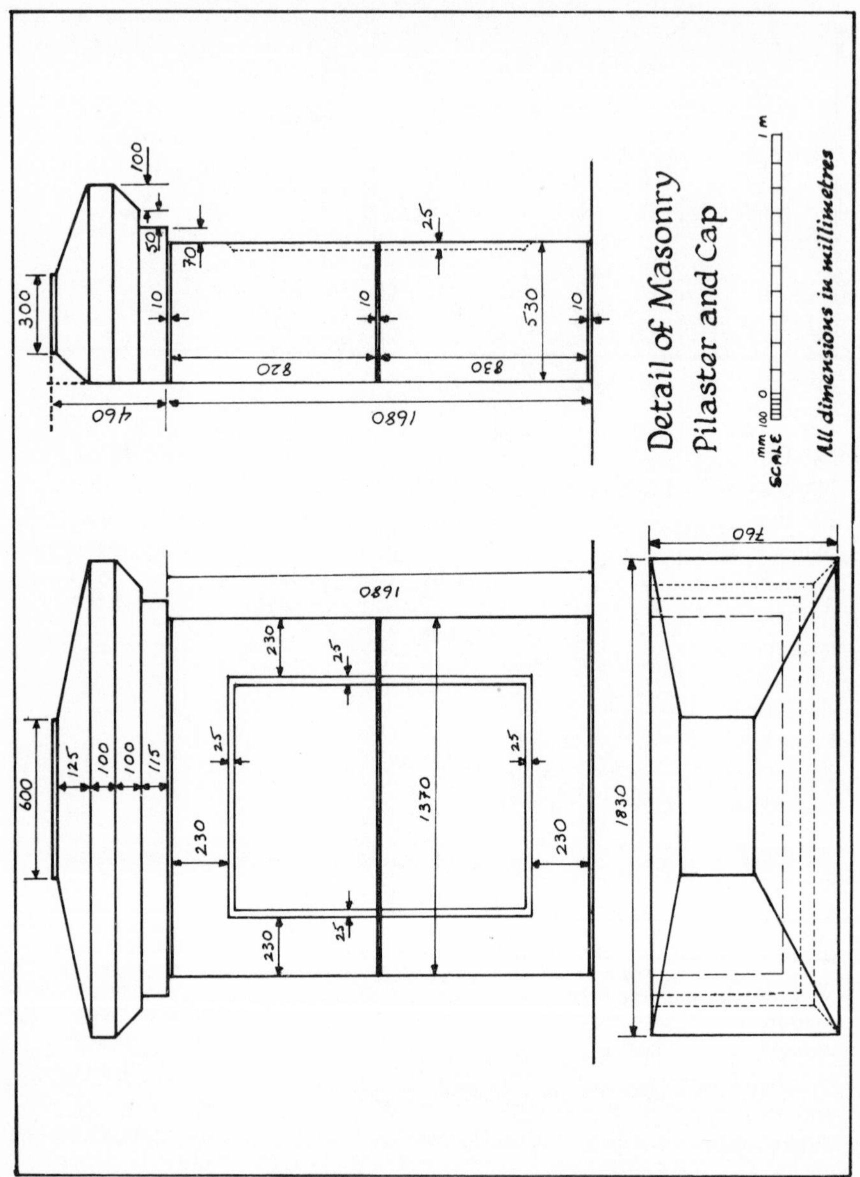

FIG. 15.

The dimensions are entered as shown in Fig. 16 and need no explanation.

			MASONRY PILASTER + CAP		1·22 0·91	1·11	25 mm sunk work 2/1·22 2·44 2/0·86 1·72 4·16
	1·37 0·53 1·68	1·22	Pier in Darley Dale Sandstone in cement mortar incl. plain beds & joints		4·16	4·16	25 mm chamfer
	1·83 0·76 0·46	0·64	Ditto in weathered & chamferred cap & ditto				The stone is measured net as set & no allowance has been made for waste.

FIG. 16.

TIMBER

13.33 Timber is measured per cubic metre, except for small scantlings such as handrails, guard rails, treads to steps and similar work which are measured per linear metre. Steel or wrought iron straps, spikes, coach screws, bolts, plates and similar work are measured and billed by number. No deductions are made from timber for nosings, splays, sinkings and the like, but additional timber required for scarfed joints is included in the measurements. All labour is described and the cost included in the price for the item. If tolerance is allowed on baulk timber above or below the specified sizes, such tolerance should be stipulated in the quantities. Flooring is measured per square metre. Plane square edged floor boards should be billed separately from tongued and grooved ones. Separate items are to be provided for beams in excess of 9m in length and thereafter in steps of 3m.

13.34 Painting.—Painting of timber is normally measured in square metres but painting on surfaces not exceeding 300mm in width or girth should be given in lineal metres and the nature of the work described. The description in all cases should state the number of coats in addition to the priming, as for example, "knot, stop, prime, and paint three coats in addition to priming." The symbol C^{3}_{s}, see Fig. 39 (*c*), is frequently used by quantity surveyors as an abbreviation for this.

Painting in casement and sash frames is measured by number of frames and multiplied by 2 for both sides. Frames are always taken as one-light unless otherwise described such as two-light or three-light as the case may be. Sash squares are taken by number and described as sash squares if not exceeding 0·25 sq. m, as large sash squares if not exceeding 0·5 sq. m and as extra large sash squares if between 0·5 and 1·0 sq. m. For larger squares the size should be stated.

Edges of doors and extra width of panels should be measured, but where the amount of painting is small, allowance for these may be made by adding 10%.

13.35 *Ex.* 9.—Take off the timber for the fencing shown in Fig. 17.

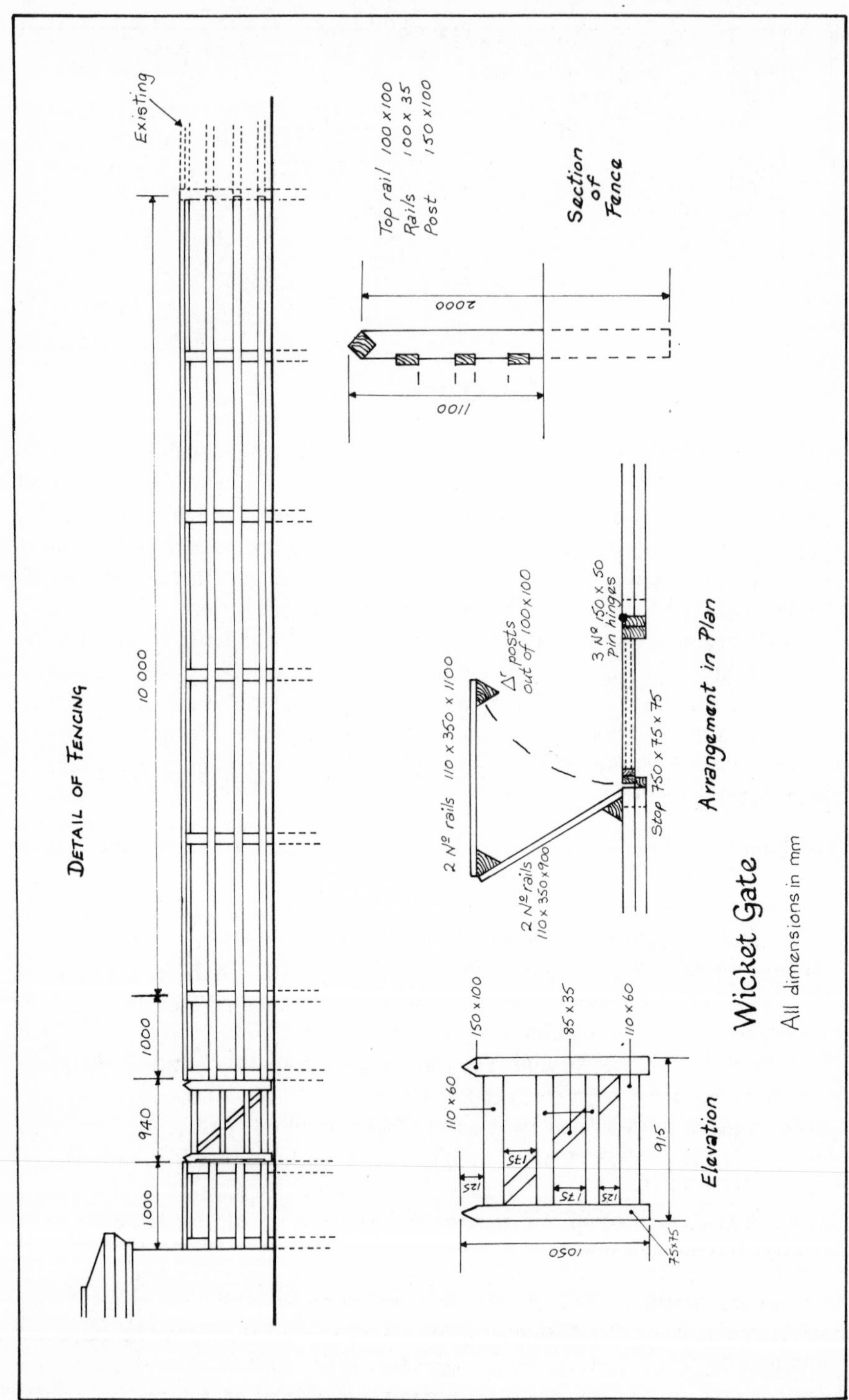

The dimension sheet is given in Fig. 18.

	1·05	1·05	0·075 × 0·075 creasoted fir framed in wicket gate
	1·05	1·05	0·150 × 0·100 do. hinge post
2/	0·83	1·66	0·110 × 0·060 do.
2/	0·83	1·66	0·085 × 0·035 do.
	1·22	1·22	do. do. diagonal
		2·88	
		3 No.	0·150 × 0·050 hinges

			Creasoted fir in fencing incl. spikes + fixing	
8/	2·00	16·00	0·150 × 0·100	
	12·00	12·00	0·100 × 0·100	10·00
3/	12·00	36·00	0·100 × 0·035	1·00
2/	0·90	1·80	do.	1·00
				12·00
2/	1·10	2·20	do.	
		39·00		
	0·75	0·75	0·075 × 0·075 gate stop	
3/	2·00	6·00	100 × 100 × 100 △ posts	

FIG. 18.

PILING

13.36 The units of measurement for concrete piles are:—

Concrete	Cu. m
Reinforcement	kilogram
Shoes (weight stated)	Number
Handling and pitching	,,
Driving piles to given level ..	Number or linear metre of penetration
Driving piles to given set	
Re-driving lengthened piles ..	
Dollying piles below ground level, the average depth being stated	
Cutting off or stripping heads of piles	Number
Stripping piles for junctions ..	,,
Travelling pile frame back to re-drive lengthened pile	Per hour or move

No deductions are made for chamfers, tapered points or the volume of the reinforcement. The rates cover the cost of moulds, but piles of differing cross section and differing lengths in steps of 3m should be billed separately.

For cast *in situ* piles the units are:—

Loan of plant, erecting and removing ..	Lump sum
Driving casings to a given level or set ..	Length of penetration
Providing pile shoes or enlarged bases ..	Number
Casting pile shafts, including reinforcement	Lin. m
Projecting reinforcement	Number of sets

In situ piles exceeding 10m in depth are kept separate in steps of 3m.

13.37 Timber piles are measured in cubic metres. Shoes, handling, pitching and driving are measured as for concrete piles. Fishplates and bolts for scarfed joints are billed by number. Timber piles exceeding 10m in length are kept separate in steps of 3m.

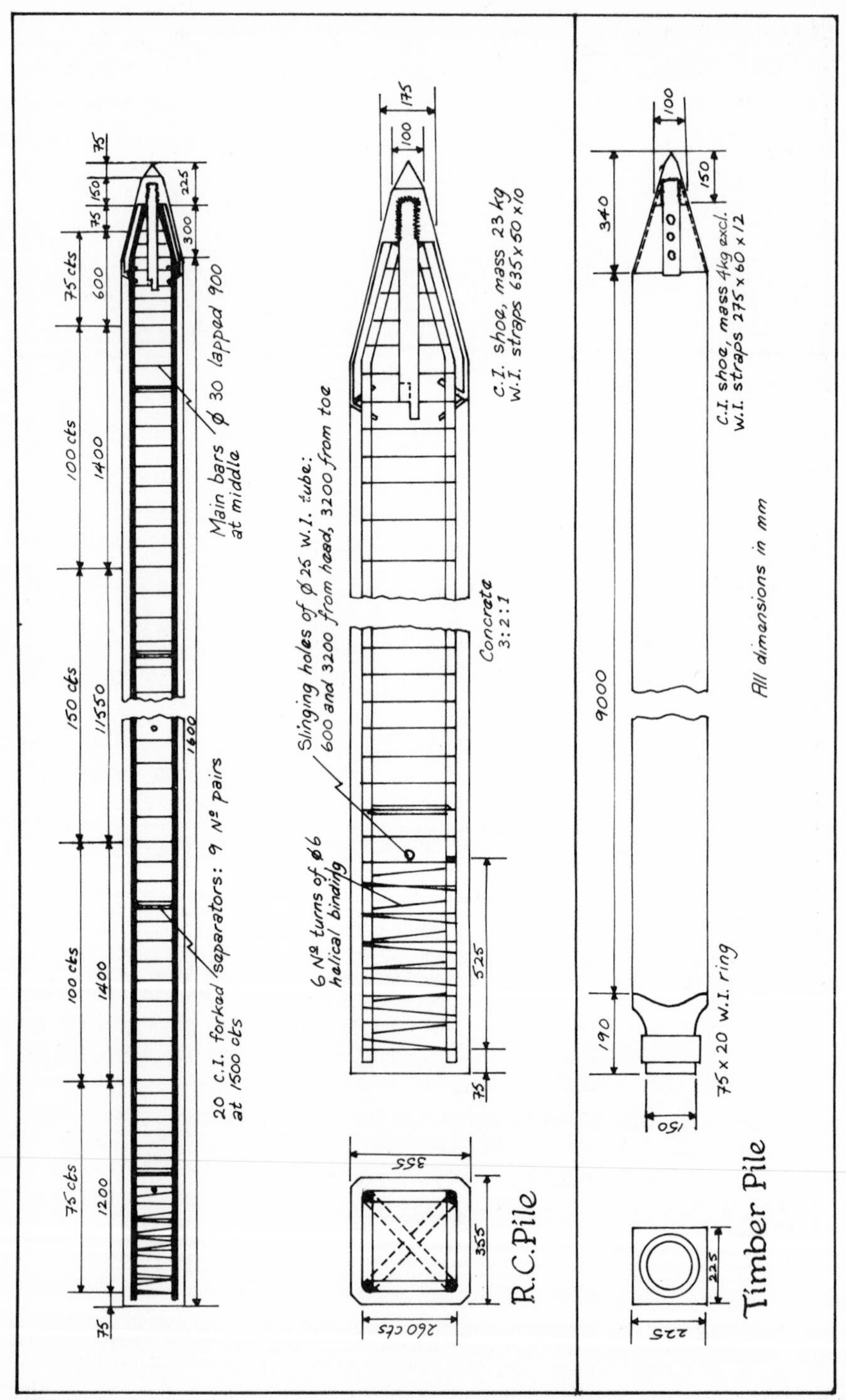
R.C. Pile
Timber Pile
Main bars at middle
ø 30 lapped 900
20 C.I. forked separators: 9 No pairs at 1500 cts
Slinging holes of ø 25 W.I. tube: 600 and 3200 from head, 3200 from toe
6 No turns of ø 6 helical binding
C.I. shoe, mass 23 kg
W.I. straps 635 x 50 x 10
Concrete 3:2:1
C.I. shoe, mass 4 kg excl.
W.I. straps 275 x 60 x 12
All dimensions in mm
75 x 20 W.I. ring

FIG. 19.

13.38 Sheet piling is measured in square metres and later reduced to tonnes. Corner piles and junction piles are measured per metre run as extra over sheet piling. Sheet piling 12m and upwards is kept separate in steps of 3m.

13.39 *Ex*. 10.—Take off the quantities for the piles shown in Fig. 19.
The dimension sheet is given in Fig. 20.

	R.C. Pile			3/	0.36	1.08	25 mm dia. W.I. tube @ 0.5 kg/m
	16.30 0.36 0.36	2.12	3:2:1 conc in pile 15 to 18 m long				
4/	17.20	68.4	30 mm dia. bar @ 0.7 kg/m	4/117/	0.65	305	6 mm dia. binding general
4/	0.64	2.56	50 x 10 flats welded to shoe	4/3/	0.30	4	do: toe
		1 No	23 kg shoe	4/6/	0.28	7	do: helical
		18 No	C.I. Separators @ 1 kg			316	@ 0.03 kg/m
	Timber Pile						
	9.38 0.23 0.23	0.50	Pine in pile 9 to 12 m long			1 No.	C.I. shoe, wt 4 kg
				4/	0.28	1.12	60 x 12 mm flats welded to shoe
		1 No	75 x 20 mm W.I. ring 150 mm dia. wt 6 kg			12 No	12 M x 75 av. Coach screws.

FIG. 20.

13.40 There follows in Figs. 21 to 46 a number of miscellaneous exercises in taking-off and squaring. The student is recommended to make his own attempt at the solution first, preparing such freehand sketches as he requires, and afterwards compare his results with the worked examples. The following points deserve special notice:—

Fig 35. (*a*) & (*b*).—The bending schedule for steel reinforcement has been prepared in accordance with BS 4466:1969, as amended, to which reference should be made for full details of measurement, designation and coding.

Appendix G provides a readily accessible table showing the method of bar measurement employed in this example.

Fig. 38 (*a*), (*b*) & (*c*).—The volume of a frustum of a cone is given by the prismoidal formula as:—

$$V=\frac{\pi h}{12}(D+D^2d+d^2).$$

where h = height of frustum,
D = diameter at the base,
d = diameter at the top.

This volume is entered on the dimension sheets as the sum of the three items,

$$\frac{\pi D^2h}{12}, \frac{\pi Ddh}{12} \text{ and } \frac{\pi d^2h}{12}.$$

Fig. 43.—For taking off the quantities for the concrete in the bottom of the Humus Tank, a separate drawing of the parts has been made. Such sketches are frequently necessary when taking off complicated details.

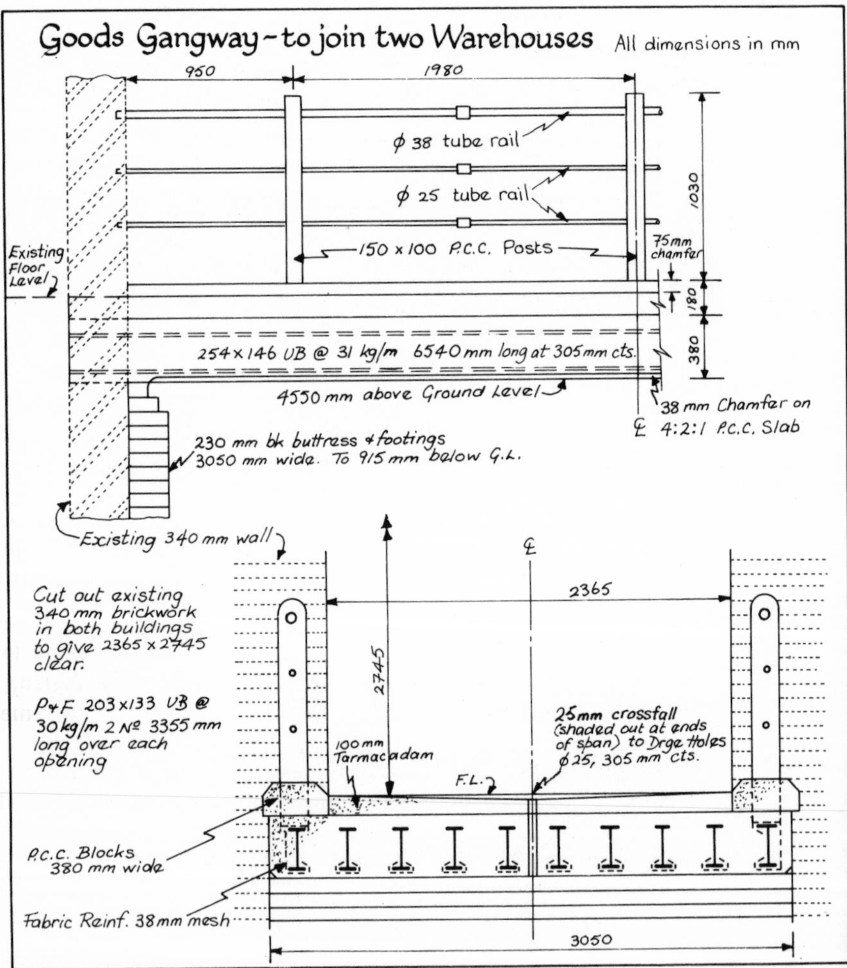

FIG. 21.

			Goods Gangway
2/	3·05 0·23 0·92	1·4	Ex & C.A.
2/	3·05 0·23 5·47	8·0	Bkwk in buttress
			Ddt Bkwk at top & add bkwk at foots & add Ex. & C.A.
2/	3·05 0·11 0·08	0·05	1st course
2/	3·05 0·06 0·08	0·03	2nd course
		0·1	
			Cut out existing bkwk making good reveals:
2/	2·37 0·34 2·85	4·7	Openings
2/	3·05 0·34 0·38	0·8	slab.
2/	3·36 0·34 0·15	0·5	Head beams
		6·0	

			The following in gangway 4·600 m above gd
	6·54 3·05 0·38	8·1	4:2:1 conc. incl. shuttering
2/	5·86 0·38 0·18	0·8	Pre-cast conc. coping chamfered 75 mm on upper edges
6/	0·15 0·10 1·25	0·1	Pre-cast conc. posts holed for tube rails & rad. 75 mm at head
10/	6·55	65·5	254 x 146 UB @ 31 kg/m
8/	6·55 0·20	10·5	Fabric No 5 in strips bent round U.B.
2/	6·55 0·50	6·6	do.
		17·1	
2/	3·36	6·7	203 x 133 U.B. @ 30 kg/m
2/	5·90	11·8	38 mm dia. W.I. tube rail @ 2·6 kg/m
2/2/	5·90	23·6	25 do. @ 1·9 kg/m
		4 No	38 screw joints
		8 No	25 do.
		12 No	Housing to ends: cut & fix in bkwk
	6·54 2·37	15·7	Tarmacadam 100 mm thick laid to falls
7/	0·50	3·0	Drainage holes formed by 25 dia. W.I. pipe @ 1·9 kg/m.

FIG. 22.

(*Fig. 23: See envelope inside back cover*)

Timesing	Dimensions	Squaring	Description
			DROP JUNCTION
	3·83 2·93 1·50	16·83	Ex. n.e. 1·500 deep + C.A. & Ex. 1·500-3·000 deep + C.A. & Ex. 3·000-4·500 deep + C.A. & Ex. 4·500-6·000 deep + C.A.
	1·47 2·25 1·50	4·96	Ex. n.e. 1·500 deep + C.A. & Ex. 1·500-3·000 deep + C.A.
	1·47 2·25 0·75	2·48	Ex. 3·000-4·500 deep + C.A.
	3·83 2·93 1·35	15·15	Ex. 6·000-7·500 deep + C.A.
	0·75 2·93 1·05	2·31	Ddt last at base.
			Ddt Ex. n.e. 1·500 deep + C.A. Add Ex. n.e. 1·500 deep + R.F.I.R.
	1·20 0·11 1·05	0·14	2/0·225 0·750 0·450 1·20
	1·16 0·11 1·05	0·13	2/0·225 0·600 0·450 0·112 1·162
	1·33 1·09 1·05	1·52	1·575 0·337 1·912 0·825 1·087
	2·06 2·25 1·05	4·86	2·700 0·337 3·037 ·975 2·062
	1·92 0·13 1·50	0·38	
	1·92 0·56 1·50	1·61	
	1·92 2·93 1·50	8·45	
		17·09	
			Ddt. Ex. 1·500-3·000 deep + C.A. Add Ex. 1·500-3·000 deep + R.F.I.R.
		0·38 1·61 8·45	
		10·44	

Timesing	Dimensions	Squaring	Description
			Ddt Ex. 3·000-4·500 deep + C.A. Add Ex. 3·000-4·500 deep + R.F.I.R.
	1·92 0·13 1·20	0·30	
	1·92 0·56 1·20	1·29	
	1·92 2·93 1·20	6·75	
		8·34	
			1 : 2 : 4 conc:
	3·83 2·92 1·35	15·15	Fdn. chls. + benching
	1·91 2·25 0·30	1·29	Upper chl.
	1·58 1·58 0·60	1·50	do.
		17·94	
			Ddt. last:
	0·75 2·93 1·05	2·31	at base
	0·90 2·93 0·60	1·58	where 900 chl.
½/π/	0·45 2·93 0·45	0·93	do.
¼/π/	0·45 0·45 0·83	0·13	where 450 branch chl.
	0·83 0·62 0·60	0·31	do.
¼/π/	0·23 0·23 0·60	0·02	where 450 branch chl.
2/π/	1·03 0·45 0·08	0·23	where ends of 900 pipe
	1·20 0·53 0·30	0·19	where upper chl.
½/π/	1·20 0·28 0·28	0·15	do.
π/	0·38 0·28 0·28	0·09	where C.I. pipe.
2/	1·20 0·23 0·13	0·07	where B.N. blue bk.
		6·01	

FIG. 24 (*a*).

			3:2:1 conc. incl. shuttering:
	3·83 2·93 0·30	3·37	Lower chamber roof
	4·20 2·25 0·30	2·83	Upper chamber roof
	1·20 1·05 0·15	0·19	Under M.H. cover
	0·13 1·05 0·15	0·02	Round R.S.J.
		6·41	
			Ddt. last:
	1·15 1·58 0·30	0·54	Lower chamber roof
	0·75 0·60 0·30	0·14	Upper chamber roof.
		0·68	
			Fabric No. 62:
		3·37 2·83	
		6·20	
			Ddt. last:
		0·54 0·14	
		0·68	
	2·48	2·48	203 × 102 R.S.J. @ 25·3 kg/m
	1·05	1·05	127 × 76 R.S.J. @ 13·4 kg/m
		18.No.	2·5 kg. step irons
		2 No.	Hooks
		1 No.	Chain 1·750 long
		1 No.	C.I. Manhole cover & seating, wt/325 kg
		6 No.	150 × 24M Rag bolts 1·1 kg each.

			Eng. Blue Bk. in walls in cement mortar:
	11·70 1·50	17·55	2 Bk 2/2·925 5·850 Lower 2/2·025 4·050 Chamber 4/0·450 1·800 11·700
2/	0·90 0·60	1·08	Arches
		18·63	
	6·65 0·45	2·99	1½ Bk 2/1·125 2·250 Shaft 2/1·575 3·150 4/0·312 1·248 6·648
	9·80 2·10	20·58	Upper 2/2·700 5·400 Chamber 2/1·575 3·150 4/0·312 1·248 9·798
	4·45 0·30	1·34	do 2/1·125 1·250 2/0·312 1·575 0·624 4·449
		24·91	
π/	0·35 0·35	0·38	Ddt last where inlet pipe
			Manhole shaft
	3·60 0·75	2·70	1 Bk. 2/0·750 1·500 2/0·600 1·200 4/0·225 0·900 3·600
π/	0·46 0·27	0·39	E.O. bkwk for gauged arch in two rings in 1½ bk walls 0·300 0·050 0·117 0·457
2/ ½/π/	0·68 0·35	0·75	do. but three rings in 2 Bk wall. 0·450 0·063 0·169 0·682
2/	1·20	2·40	Bullnosed Bk. on edge to chl.
	0·45	0·45	450 dia. C.I. flanged pipe
	2·25	2·25	
		2·70	
		1 No.	450 dia. C.I. flanged 90° bend.
		2 No.	Pipe brackets 510 int. dia. bolted in halves P. & F.

FIG. 24 (*b*). (*Fig.* 25: *See envelope inside back cover*)

	Ex. 13.		BRIDGE PIER:
	7.00 4.30 5.12	154.1	Ex. in caisson below water level
2/½/	2.15 4.30 5.12	47.1	do.
		201.2	
	7.00 4.30 5.50	165.8	Precast conc. blockwork in c.m.
2/½/	2.15 4.30 5.50	50.6	
	6.75 3.70 1.90	47.5	10.45 3.70 6.75
2/½/	1.85 3.70 1.90	13.0	
	6.50 3.10 1.90	38.3	9.60 3.10 6.50
2/½/	1.55 3.10 1.90	9.1	
	5.30 2.35 5.00	62.3	2.70 2.00 4.70 ½ 2.35 8.00 2.70 5.30
Area	4.44 5.00	22.2	2.70^2 7.29 2.00^2 4.00 2/½/π/¼/½/ 11.29 4.437 m² av.
	3.35 1.98 0.30	2.0	2.00 1.96 2)3.96(1.98
2/	0.76 1.52 0.30	0.7	
	5.25 1.93 0.38	3.9	
		415.4	

			E.O. conc. blockwork for fine-axed granite facing:
	21.79 1.90	41.4	300 mm av. thickness 2/6.500 13.00 4/√2/1.050 8.79 21.79
	19.05 1.50	28.6	225 mm av. thickness 2/5.42 10.94 2/½/π/2.58 8.11 19.05
	18.32 1.80	33.0	250 mm. av. thickness. 2/5.42 10.94 2/½/π/2.35 7.38 18.32
	17.64 1.50	26.4	275 mm av. thickness 2/5.42 10.94 2/½/π/2.13 6.70 17.64
2/	3.35 0.30	2.0	225 mm. av. thickness
	14.74 0.38	5.6	350 mm. av. thickness 2/5.42 10.94 2/1.90 3.80 14.74
4/	0.95 0.45 0.30	0.5	Fine-axed moulded & weathered capping
2/½/½/π	1.25 1.25 0.50	2.5	Circular do.
2/	2.20 1.25 0.38	2.1	Fine-axed chamfered padstones.
	3.05 1.90 0.28	1.6	Ditto coping
	4.60 1.20 0.75	4.1	Cement grout under part of last

FIG. 26.

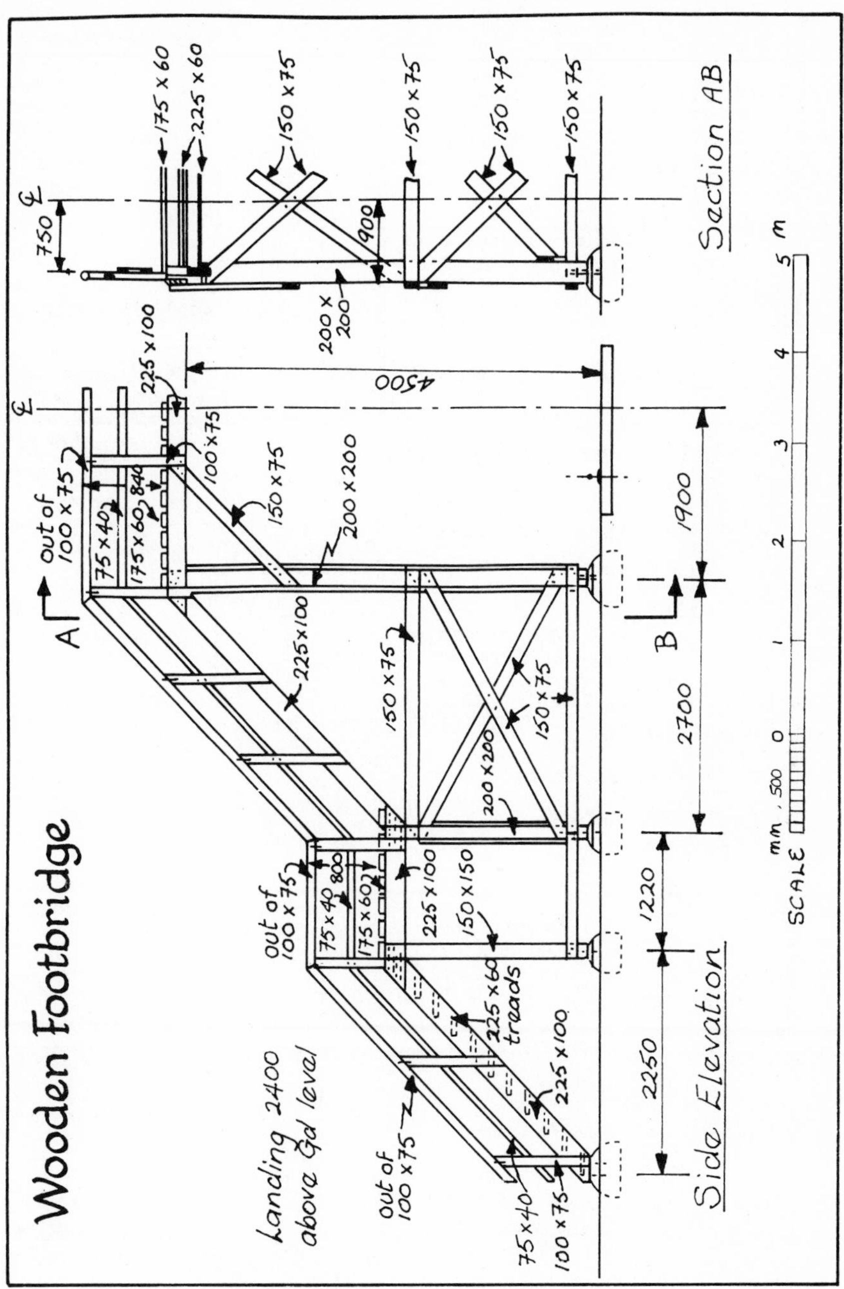
Wooden Footbridge
Landing 2400 above Gd level
Section AB
Side Elevation
175 x 60
225 x 60
150 x 75
150 x 75
150 x 75
150 x 75
750
900
200 x 200
225 x 100
4500
100 x 75
150 x 75
200 x 200
out of 100 x 75
75 x 40
175 x 60
840
225 x 100
150 x 75
150 x 75
200 x 200
out of 100 x 75
75 x 40
800
175 x 60
225 x 100
150 x 150
225 x 60 treads
225 x 100
out of 100 x 75
75 x 40
100 x 75
1900
2700
1220
2250
A
B
SCALE mm 500 0 1 2 3 4 5 m

FIG. 27.

			FIR FRAMED IN FOOTBRIDGE.
2/2/	2·26	9·0	150 x 150 posts
2/2/	2·26	9·0	200 x 200 posts
2/2/	4·60	18·4	do.
		27·4	
			150 x 75 bracing incl. cutting & fixing:
2/2/	1·29	5·2	horizontal - base
2/2/	2·80	11·2	do - do
2/2/	2·90	11·6	do - side upper
2/2/3/	1·80	21·6	do - abutment
2/2/2/	3·20	25·6	cross bracing - side
2/2/2/	2·44	19·5	do - lower abut^{t}
2/2/	2·90	11·6	do - upper abut^{t}
2/2/	1·98	7·9	do - haunch
		114·0	
			225 x 100 treadrails incl. mortises for hand rail posts, cutting & fitting:
2/2/	3·43	13·7	lower
2/2/	2·00	8·0	landing
2/2/	3·96	15·8	upper
2/	4·34	8·7	span
		46·2	
			100 x 75 moulded handrail incl. cutting & fitting:
2/2/	3·20	12·8	lower
2/2/	1·37	5·5	landing
2/2/	3·58	14·3	upper
2/	4·12	8·2	span
		40·8	
2/2/16/		64 No	M10 x 1·5 B.N. & W to handrail posts 180 mm long
2/2/4/		16 No	Conc. bases to posts each av. 0·2 m³ of P.C.C.

			75 x 40 second rail incl. cutting & fixing:
2/2/	3·18	12·7	lower
2/2/	1·35	5·4	landing
2/2/	3·65	14·6	upper
2/	3·90	7·8	span
		40·5	
2/11·12/	1·45	66·7	225 x 60 stair treads incl. housing, blocking & wedging
2/7/ ·17/	1·60	49·6	175 x 60 landing & bridge treads incl. double railing with 150 spikes
			100 x 75 handrail posts, cut & housed:
2/2/	1·07	4·3	lower
2/2/	1·15	4·6	do.
2/2/2/	1·00	8·0	landing
2/2/2/	1·22	9·8	upper
2/2/	1·15	4·6	span
2/2/	1·05	4·2	do.
		35·5	
2/2/11/		44 No	Trenails
2/2/5/		20 No	25 dia. coachscrews as dowels
			10 x 150 do. to posts:
2/2/11/		44	treadrails
2/2/22/		88	horizontal bracing
2/2/22/		88	diagonal bracing
		220	No
2/2/9/		36	M10 x 1·5 B.N. & W. to treadrails & 2nd rails 125 mm long
2/2/8/		32	
		68	No

The whole to be erected without interference with the traffic on the line.

FIG. 28. (*Fig. 29: See envelope inside back cover*)

			Steelwork in Dome
			In trusses Type AA
2/4/	5·29	42·4	70×70×8L @ 8·36 kg/m radiused 2·820
2/4/ 2/4/ 2/4/	1·35 1·53 1·56	35·3	do. horizontals do. verticals do. diagonals
2/4/ 2/4/	2·14 1·02	25·3	65×8 flats @ 4·0 kg/m diagonals
2/4/	0·30 0·20	0·5	8mm gusset out of 300 × 200
2/4/	0·28 0·15	0·4	do. out of 275×150
		0·9	@ 62·3 kg/m²
2/4/	0·23 0·20	0·1	Bent plate at joist out of 225×200×10 @ 74·7 kg/m²
2/4/	0·23 0·20	0·1	do. at ring out of 225×200×8 @ 62·3 kg/m²
2/4/20		160 No.	16mm dia rivets
2/4/6		48 No.	16 M bolts
2/4/14	0·15	16·8	Cleats to purlins 100×75×8L @ 10·6 kg/m forge bent to fit.
			In trusses Type BB + CC
2/2/	6·12	24·5	70×70×8L @ 8·36kg/m radiussed 4·300 & 3·175 from two ctrs as shown.
	3·54	3·6	do. horizontal BB
2/	1·72	3·5	do. horizontals CC
2/2/	1·76	7·0	do. verticals
	2·26	2·3	do. vertical to ring & base plate gussets
2/2/	2·00	8·0	do. diagonals
		24·4	
2/2/ 2/2/	2·49 1·48	31·8	65×8 flats @ 4·0kg/m diagonals
2/2/	0·38 0·23	0·4	8 mm gusset out of 375 × 225
	0·40 0·23	0·1	do. BB out of 400 × 225
2/	0·23 0·15	0·1	
		0·6	@ 62·3 kg/m²

2/2/	0·28 0·25	0·3	Bent plate at joist out of 275×250×10 @ 74·7 kg/m²
2/2/	0·25 0·20	0·2	do. at ring out of 250×200×8 @ 62·3 kg/m
π/	0·75	2·4	150×12 plate @ 15·2 kg/m in ring
	0·74 0·20	0·2	12 mm cross plate to do. @ 99·5 kg/m²
4/	0·15	0·6	100×100×12L @ 17·8 kg/m forge bent to fit
2/2/14	0·15	8·4	Cleats to purlins 100×75×8L @ 10·6 kg/m forge bent to fit
2/2/25		100 No.	16mm dia. rivets
2/2/4		16 No.	16M bolts
			70×70×6L @ 6·38 kg/m purlins:
4/	1·30		Top
4/	1·88		
4/	2·44		
4/	2·97		
4/	3·43		
4/	3·83		
4/	4·24		
4/	4·54		
4/	4·80		
4/	5·00		
4/	5·13		
4/	5·20		55·21
4/	5·20		4
4/	5·25		Base 220·84
		220·8	
4/14/3/		168 No.	16M bolts to cleats and purlins

The whole of the steelwork for the dome is to be erected on steel framed structure as indicated, the upper joists of which have a top level of approximately 23·465 above ground level

FIG. 30.

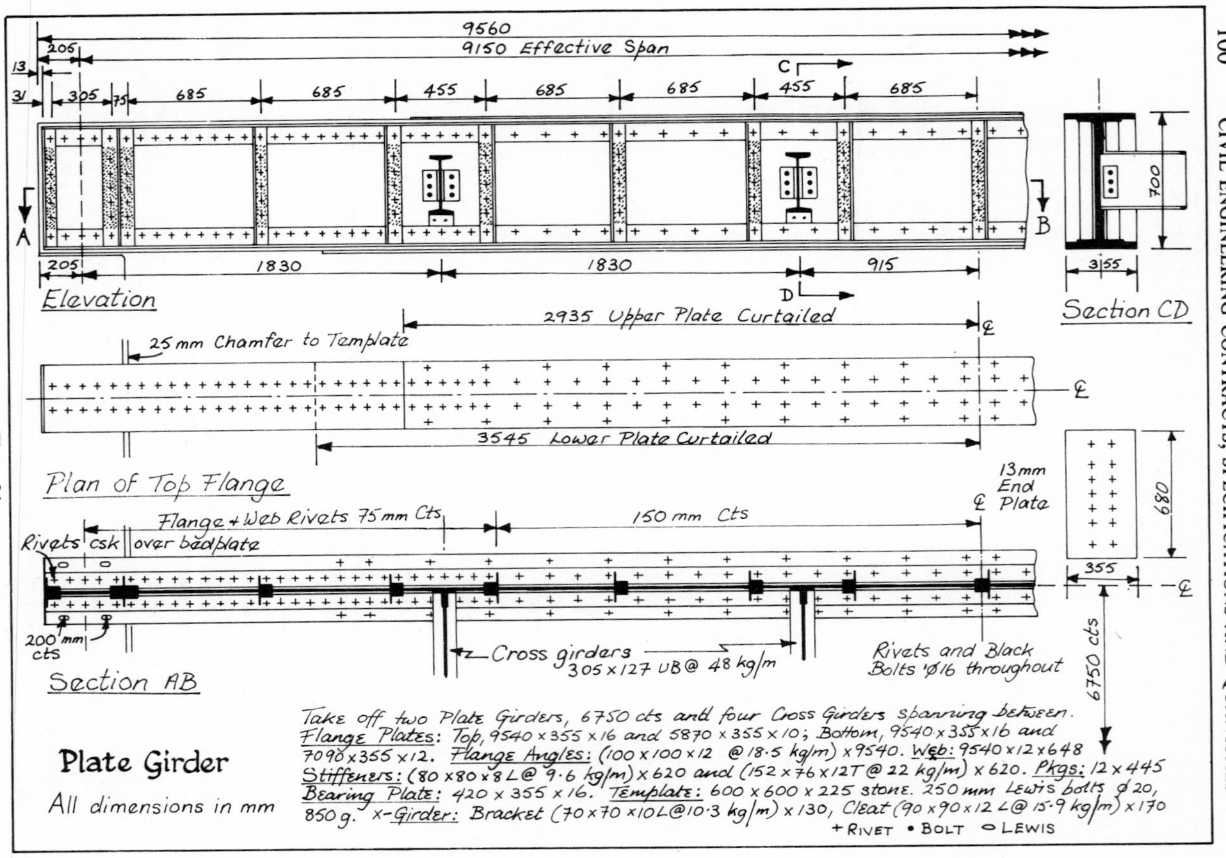
9560
9150 Effective Span
13
31
205
305 75 685 685 455 685 685 455 685
C
A
B
205 1830 1830 915
D
Elevation
700
355
Section CD
2935 Upper Plate Curtailed
25 mm Chamfer to Template
3545 Lower Plate Curtailed
Plan of Top Flange
13mm End Plate
680
355
Flange + Web Rivets 75 mm Cts
150 mm Cts
Rivets csk over bedplate
200 mm cts
Cross girders 305 x 127 UB @ 48 kg/m
Rivets and Black Bolts ø16 throughout
6750 cts
Section AB
Take off two Plate Girders, 6750 cts and four Cross Girders spanning between.
Flange Plates: Top, 9540 x 355 x 16 and 5870 x 355 x 10; Bottom, 9540 x 355 x 16 and 7090 x 355 x 12. Flange Angles: (100 x 100 x 12 @ 18·5 kg/m) x 9540. Web: 9540 x 12 x 648
Stiffeners: (80 x 80 x 8 L @ 9·6 kg/m) x 620 and (152 x 76 x 12T @ 22 kg/m) x 620. Pkgs: 12 x 445
Bearing Plate: 420 x 355 x 16. Template: 600 x 600 x 225 stone. 250 mm Lewis bolts ø 20, 850 g. X-Girder: Bracket (70 x 70 x 10 L @ 10·3 kg/m) x 130, Cleat (90 x 90 x 12 L @ 15·9 kg/m) x 170
+ RIVET • BOLT ○ LEWIS
Plate Girder
All dimensions in mm

FIG. 31.

MATERIAL FOR STEELWORK

Estimate No.
Order No.
Date. 27.5.74

Plate Girders in Annexe
to Factory Q
In 2 No. main girders and
4 No. Cross Girders:—

Sheet No 1.
Drwg No 1.
T.O. by DWRB.

Mark	Description	Number	Kind	Size	Length	Wt/m	Wt.	Source
	Flange angles	8/	L	100×100×12	9·540	18·5	1412·0	Stock.
	End angles	8/	L	80×80×8	0·620	9·6	47·9	
	Stiffeners	4/13/	L	80×80×8	0·620	9·6	311·5	
	ditto	8/	T	152×76×12	0·620	22·0	109·6	
	Flange pl. upper	2/	Pl	355×10	5·870	26·1	306·4	
	2nd ditto	2/	Pl	355×16	9·540	44·8	854·8	
	Flange pl. lower	2/	Pl	355×16	9·540	44·8	854·8	
	2nd ditto	2/	Pl	330×12	7·090	35·7	506·2	
	Webs	2/	Pl	648×12	9·540	65·0	1240·2	
	End packings	8/	Pl	75×12	0·445	7·6	27·2	
	Tee packings	8/	Pl	150×12	0·445	15·2	54·4	
	Angle Stiffr pkgs.	4/13/	Pl	75×12	0·445	7·6	176·8	
	Bearing pl	4/	Pl	355×16	0·420	48·2	80·9	
	End pl	4/	Pl	355×13	0·650	41·6	108·2	
	Rivet Heads Fl	16/112/	R	16 dia		3·7 kg/100	66·3	
	do . Web	8/95/	R	16 dia		3·7 kg/100	28·1	
	do . Stiffrs	4/5/19/	R	16 dia		3·7 kg/100	14·1	
	do . End	8/14/	R	16 dia		3·7 kg/100	4·1	
	Lewis bolts	16/	L.B.	20 dia		0·85 kg /each	13·6	
							6081·9	
	Cleats	16/	L	90×90×12	0·170	15·9	43·2	
	Brackets	8/	L	70×70×10	0·130	10·3	10·7	
	Joists	4/	I	305×127	6·740	48·0	1294·0	
	Rivet Heads	32/	R.	16 dia			1·2	
	Bolts	8/9/	B	16 dia		0·21 kg /each	15·1	
							1364·2	
				Total Steelwk			7537 kg	

Hoisting:—
Wt. of one main Girder 3041 kg
Wt. of one Cross Girder 341 kg

FIG. 32.

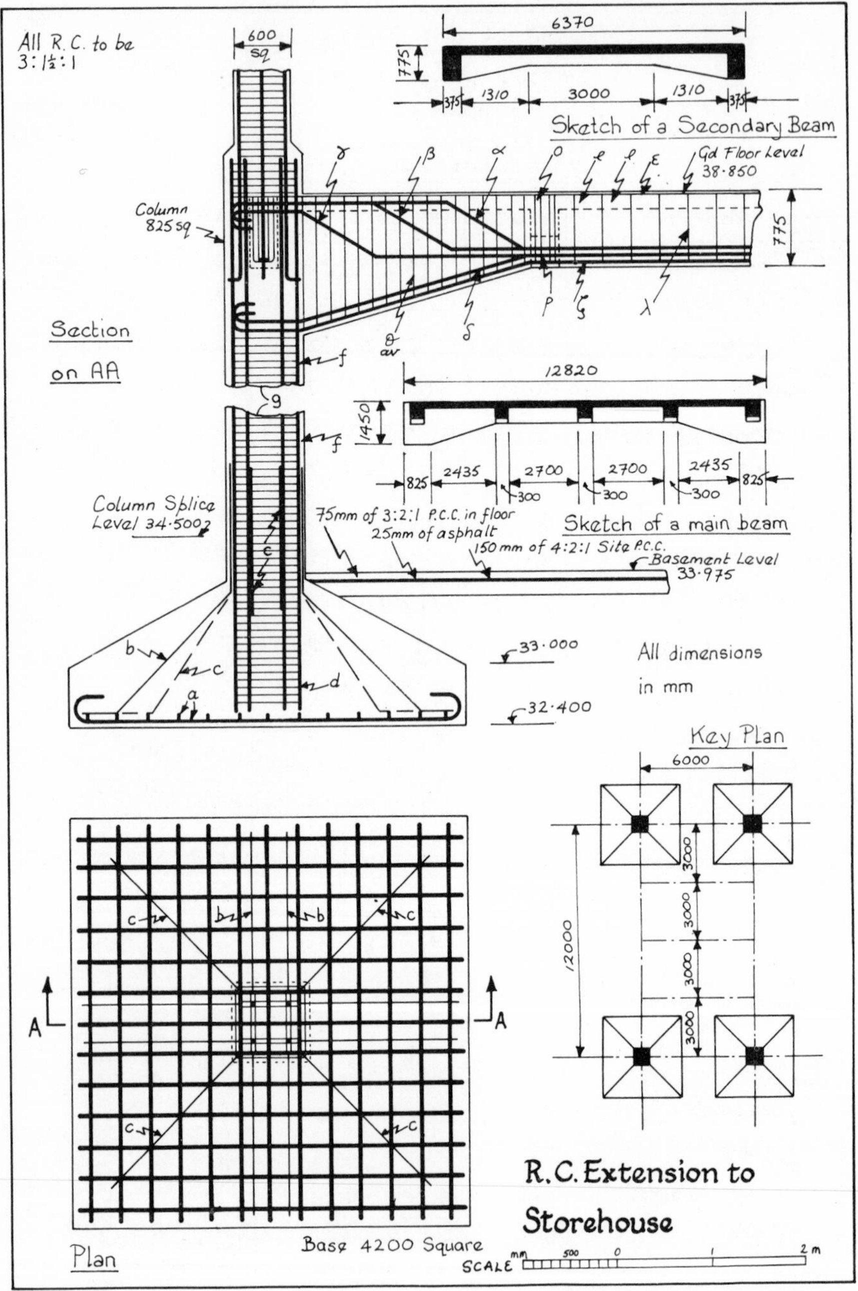

FIG. 33.

(*Fig. 34: See envelope inside back cover*)

Metric
Bar schedule ref: 033 · 01 Rev: A
Date: 23 May 1973

Site ref: R. C. Extension to Store House

Member	Bar mark	Type and size	Number of members	Number of bars in each	Total number of bars	Length of each bar† (mm)	Shape code	A* (mm)	B* (mm)	C* (mm)	D* (mm)	E/r* (mm)
Column foundations	a	Y50	4	26	104	4975	33	4125				
do	b	Y25	4	8	32	3450	49	375	1275	1800	265	890
do	c	Y25	4	4	16	3675	49	600	1275	1800	420	890
Col. reinf. splice	e	Y25	4	4	16	1500	20	1500				
Column reinforcement	d	Y40	4	16	64	1950	20	1950				
do	f	Y40	4	16	64	4750	20	4750				
Column binding	g	Y8	4	552	2208	1800	81	725	040			
Slab reinforcement	h	Y12	2	25	50	3575	43	675	240	1500	100	775
do	i	Y12	2	26	52	3775	33	3550				
do	j	Y12	2	25	50	3675	43	775	200	1500	100	775
do	k	Y12	2	26	52	4125	33	3900				
Slab distance bars	l	Y8	4	10	40	6300	20	6300				
Sec. beam dist. bars	m	Y8	2	3	6	6725	20	6725				
do	n	Y8	3	3	9	6300	20	6300				
Sec. beam reinforcement	o	Y32	2	4	8	7450	43	590	600	4500	300	590
do	p	Y32	2	4	8	7425	43	725	1150	3075	325	725
do	w	Y32	3	4	12	6975	43	340	600	4500	300	340
do	x	Y32	3	4	12	6925	43	475	1150	3075	325	475
Sec. beam stirrups	q	Y10	10	19	190	1200	60	375	150			
do	r,t	Y10	4	35	140	1275	38	560	150			
do	s,u,v	Y10	4 4	45 } 18 }	252	1500	60	675	150			

All bending dimensions are in accordance with BS 4466:1969
*Specified to the nearest 5 mm
†Specified to the nearest 25 mm

FIG. 35 (*a*).

Metric

Bar schedule ref: 0 3 3 | 0 2 — Rev: A

Date: 23 May 1973

Site ref: R. C. Extension to Store House

Member	Bar mark	Type and size	Number of members	Number of bars in each	Total number of bars	Length of each bar† (mm)	Shape code	A* (mm)	B* (mm)	C* (mm)	D* (mm)	E/r* (mm)
Main beam stirrups	λ	Y10	8	9	72	1800	72	710	200			
do	θ	Y10	8	9	72	2500	38	1150	200			
Main beam stirrups	θ	Y10	8	8	64	3150	38	1480	200			
Main beam spliced reinf.	α	Y40	2	4	8	5025	41	1425	975	2290	580	
do		Y40	2	2	4	6450	20	6450				
do	β	Y40	2	4	8	4650	41	1875	975	1460	586	
do		Y40	2	2	4	7200	20	7200				
do	γ	Y40	2	4	8	4650	41	2625	975	715	580	
do		Y40	2	2	4	7200	20	7200				
do	δ	Y40	2	4	8	5000	41	1425	2450	775	675	
do		Y40	2	2	4	6450	20	6450				
do	ζ	Y40	2	8	16	5050	41	1425	2575	725	675	
do		Y40	2	4	8	6300	20	6300				
Main beam dist. bars	∈	Y8	2	6	12	6525	20	6525				

All bending dimensions are in accordance with BS 4466:1969

*Specified to the nearest 5 mm

†Specified to the nearest 25 mm

FIG. 35 (*b*).

Timesing	Dimensions	Squaring	Description
			Extension to Storehouse.
	12.82 6.82 0.15	13.1	4:2:1 Site Conc
4/	1.05 1.05 0.15	0.6	Ddt last where columns
		12.5	
	12.82 6.82	87.4	25 mm asphalt D.P.C.
4/	0.88 0.88	3.1	Ddt last where columns
		84.3	
	12.82 6.82 0.08	7.7	3:2:1 conc. in floor
4/	0.83 0.83 0.08	0.2	Ddt. last where columns
		7.5	
	31.50 0.25	7.9	Shuttering at edges – vertical
4/	4.20 4.20 0.60	42.3	3:1½:1 R.C. in column fdn.
4/4/	4.20 0.60	40.3	Shuttering to do. – vertical
4/⅙/	4.20 4.20 0.90	10.6	Conc. a.b. in column fdn. 0.825 4.200 4.200
4/4/½/⅙/	2.51 2.51 0.90	15.1	
4/⅙/	0.82 0.82 0.90	0.4	
		26.1	
4/4/	2.51 1.95	78.3	Sloping shuttering to do.
4/	0.83 0.83 4.88	13.5	Conc. a.b. in columns to ground floor level
4/4/	0.83 4.95	65.6	Shuttering to do. – vertical
4/	0.38 1.28	1.9	Ddt. shuttering where main beams
4/	0.30 0.60	0.7	do. where sec beams
4/2/	0.60 0.18	0.9	do. where slab
		3.5	

Timesing	Dimensions	Squaring	Description
	12.30 6.38 0.18	14.1	Conc. a.b. in floor slab
4/	0.60 0.58 0.18	0.3	Ddt. last where columns
		13.8	
4/	2.70 5.68	61.3	Horizontal shuttering to do.
	32.70 0.18	5.9	Vertical shuttering to outer edges of do.
2/	5.18 0.30 0.28	0.9	Conc. a.b. in sec. beams between columns
2/2/½/	1.10 0.30 0.28	0.2	do. haunches
		1.1	
2/	5.25 0.30	3.2	Shuttering under do.
2/2/	5.18 0.28	5.8	Side shuttering to do.
2/2/½/	1.10 0.28	1.2	do. haunches
		7.0	
3/	5.62 0.30 0.28	1.4	Conc. a.b. in sec beams between main beams
3/2/½/	1.32 0.30 0.32	0.4	do. haunches
		1.8	
3/	5.70 0.30	5.1	Shuttering under do.
3/2/	5.62 0.22	7.4	Side shuttering to do.
3/2/½/	1.48 0.32	2.8	do. haunches
		10.2	
2/	11.18 0.38 0.60	5.1	Conc. a.b. in main beams
2/2/½/	2.45 0.38 0.68	1.3	do. haunches.
		6.4	
2/	11.40 0.38	8.7	Shuttering under do.
2/2/	11.18 0.60	26.9	Side shuttering to do.
2/2/½/	2.45 0.68	6.7	do. haunches
		33.6	
2/3/	0.30 0.60	1.1	Ddt. last where ends of sec. beams

FIG. 36. (*Fig. 37: See envelope inside back cover*)

			BRICK CHIMNEY
			Ex. n.e. 1·500 deep & R.F.I.R. & Ex. 1·500–3·000 deep & R.F.I.R.:
π/1/4/	7·32 7·32 1·50	63·1	Base
	7·70 2·34 1·50	27·0	Flue
	0·55 2·34 1·50	1·9	Access well
		92·0	
			Ex. 3·000–4·500 deep & R.F.I.R.:
π/1/4/	7·32 7·32 1·50	63·1	Base
	7·70 2·34 0·97	17·5	Flue
	0·55 2·34 0·51	0·7	Access well
		81·3	
π/1/4/	7·32 7·32 0·99	41·7	Ex. 4·500–6·000 deep & R.F.I.R.–Base
			Additional Ex. for timbering & workg space:
π/	7·32 5·50	126·5	Base
2/	7·70 4·00	61·6	Sides of flue
2/	0·56 3·50	3·9	Sides of Access well
		192·0	
π/1/4/	7·32 7·32 0·92	38·7	3:2:1 P.C.C. in fdns & ddt R.F.I.R. & add C.A. – Base
	8·84 2·34 0·22	4·7	4:2:1 do & do & do – Flue 0·225 thick
	2·06 2·34 0·15	0·7	3:2:1 do & do & do – Access well 0·152 thick

π/1/2/	2·98 0·36 0·08	0·2	3:1 P.C.M. fillet at necking
π/1/12/	6·33 6·33 1·07	11·2	Brickwork in h.l.m. to circular footings & ddt R.F.I.R. & add C.A.
π/1/12/	6·33 4·58 1·07	8·1	4·575 14 courses 6·330
π/1/12/	4·58 4·58 1·07	6·2	
		25·5	
π/1/12/	1·37 1·37 0·92	0·5	Ddt. bkwk. in h.l.m. where soot pocket & fire bkwk.
π/1/12/	1·37 2·74 0·92	0·9	2·745 12 courses 1·372
π/1/12/	2·74 2·74 0·92	1·8	
		3·2	
			Bkwk. in h.l.m. to chimney:
π/	3·52 0·90 7·32	72·9	K to L 4·575 4·270 2)8·845(4·422 0·900 Mean dia. 3·522
π/	3·36 0·79 6·10	50·6	L to M 4·270 4·015 2)8·285(4·142 0·787 3·355
π/	3·21 0·68 6·10	41·5	M to N 4·015 3·760 2)7·775(3·887 0·675 3·212
π/	3·07 0·56 6·10	33·0	N to O 3·760 3·505 2)7·265(3·632 0·562 3·070
π/	2·93 0·45 6·10	25·2	O to P 3·505 3·250 2)6·755(3·377 0·450 2·927
π/	2·78 0·34 6·10	18·0	P to Q 3·250 2·995 2)6·245(3·122 0·337 2·785
		241·2	Carried forward

FIG. 38 (*a*).

BRICK CHIMNEY ②

		241·2	Brought forward
π/	2·73 0·22 1·98	3·8	Q to beginning of reinforced bkwk 2·995 2·916 2)5·911(2·956 0·225 End of reinf. bkwk to R 2·731
π/	2·54 0·22 0·92	1·6	2·784 2·745 2)5·528(2·764 0·225 2·539
		246·6	
2/	1·00 1·60 2·00	6·4	Ddt chimney bkwk where flue + access openings + firebrick
2/ π/ 1/8/	0·92 1·83 1·83	2·4	
		8·8	
π/ 1/2/	2·24 0·28 0·38	0·4	Soot rings
π/	2·54 0·76 0·08	0·5	Soot ring slabs
	8·97 1·83 0·23	3·8	Bkwk fdns. to flue & ddt. R.F.I.R. & add C.A.
	4·24 0·58 0·23	0·6	do. to access well & do. & do. 2/1·322 1·601 2·644 4·245
	4·24 0·34 3·28	4·7	Bkwk in access well walls & do. & do.
		9·1	
			Ddt. R.F.I.R. & add C.A.:
π/ 1/4/	4·50 4·50 3·51	55·8	where chimney bkwk
	1·22 0·92 3·36	3·7	where access space
	9·18 1·60 1·98	29·1	where flue
π/ 1/8/	9·18 1·60 1·60	9·2	
		97·8	

			Reinforced bkwk in necking etc:
π/	2·68 0·22 0·38	0·7	5 courses. Mean dia. 2·680
π/ 1/12/	2·92 2·92 0·53		7 courses corbelled 2·925 to 3·202 dia.
π/ 1/12/	2·92 3·20 0·53	3·9	
π/ 1/12/	3·20 3·20 0·53		
π/ 1/12/	2·44 2·44 0·53		Ddt last for chimney opening. 2·443 to 2·422 dia
π/ 1/12/	2·44 2·42 0·53	2·4	
π/ 1/12/	2·42 2·42 0·53		
π/	2·82 0·39 0·15	0·5	2 courses Mean dia. 2·818
π/	2·73 0·34 1·30	3·8	17 courses Mean dia. 2·730
π/ 1/12/	3·07 3·07 0·69		9 courses corbelled 3·072 to 3·450 dia.
π/ 1/12/	3·07 3·45 0·69	5·8	
π/ 1/12/	3·45 3·45 0·69		
π/ 1/12/	2·36 2·36 0·69		Ddt last for chimney opening 2·360 to 2·332 dia.
π/ 1/12/	2·36 2·33 0·69	3·0	
π/ 1/12/	2·33 2·33 0·69		
π/	2·90 0·56 0·15	0·8	2 courses Mean dia. 2·900

FIG. 38 (*b*).

			BRICK CHIMNEY (3)
			Fire brick lining in heat resisting mortar:
π/1/12/	1·37 1·37 0·61		8 courses over circular fdns at soot pocket 2·287 to 1·372 dia.
π/1/12/	1·37 2·29 0·61	1·6	
π/1/12/	2·29 2·29 0·61		
π/1/12/	1·14 1·14 0·46		Ddt last where soot pocket. 6 courses 1·830 to 1·143 dia.
π/1/12/	1·14 1·83 0·46	0·8	
π/1/12/	1·83 1·83 0·46		
			Fire brick a.b. in chimney lining:
π/	2·04 0·22 6·86	9·9	S to T Mean dia. 2·038 7·320 0·460 6·860
π/	2·03 0·11 9·76	6·8	T to U Mean dia. 2·033
		16·7	
2/	0·96 0·22 1·83	0·8	Ddt last where flue & access
2/π/1/8/	2·03 0·22 1·83	0·7	do. do. arches
		1·5	

2/π/1/2/	1·37 1·32 0·31	1·8	Firebrick a.b. in 4 ring arches, circular in plan, through wall & lining
π/1/2/	1·27 9·18 0·34	6·2	do. in 3 ring arch over flue, up to chimney face
	10·45 0·22 5·26	12·4	do. in walls & floor of flue 1·830 1·830 1·601 5·261
π/1/8/	0·92 0·34 0·97	0·1	Firebk. in fireclay, access wall, circular
	0·97 0·34 1·84	0·6	rectangular do.
			Segmental C.I. cap ring 25 mm thick
π/	2·52 0·23	1·8	top
π/	2·77 0·18	1·6	side
		0·2	add for flanges
		3·6	@ 183 kg/m²
		24 No	24 M bolts to do. 90 mm long @ 0·84 kg each
		60·0	Rivetted & welded copper lightening conductor, incl. fixing to chimney bkwk. & earthing connections
		1 No	Copper point to do.

FIG. 38 (c).

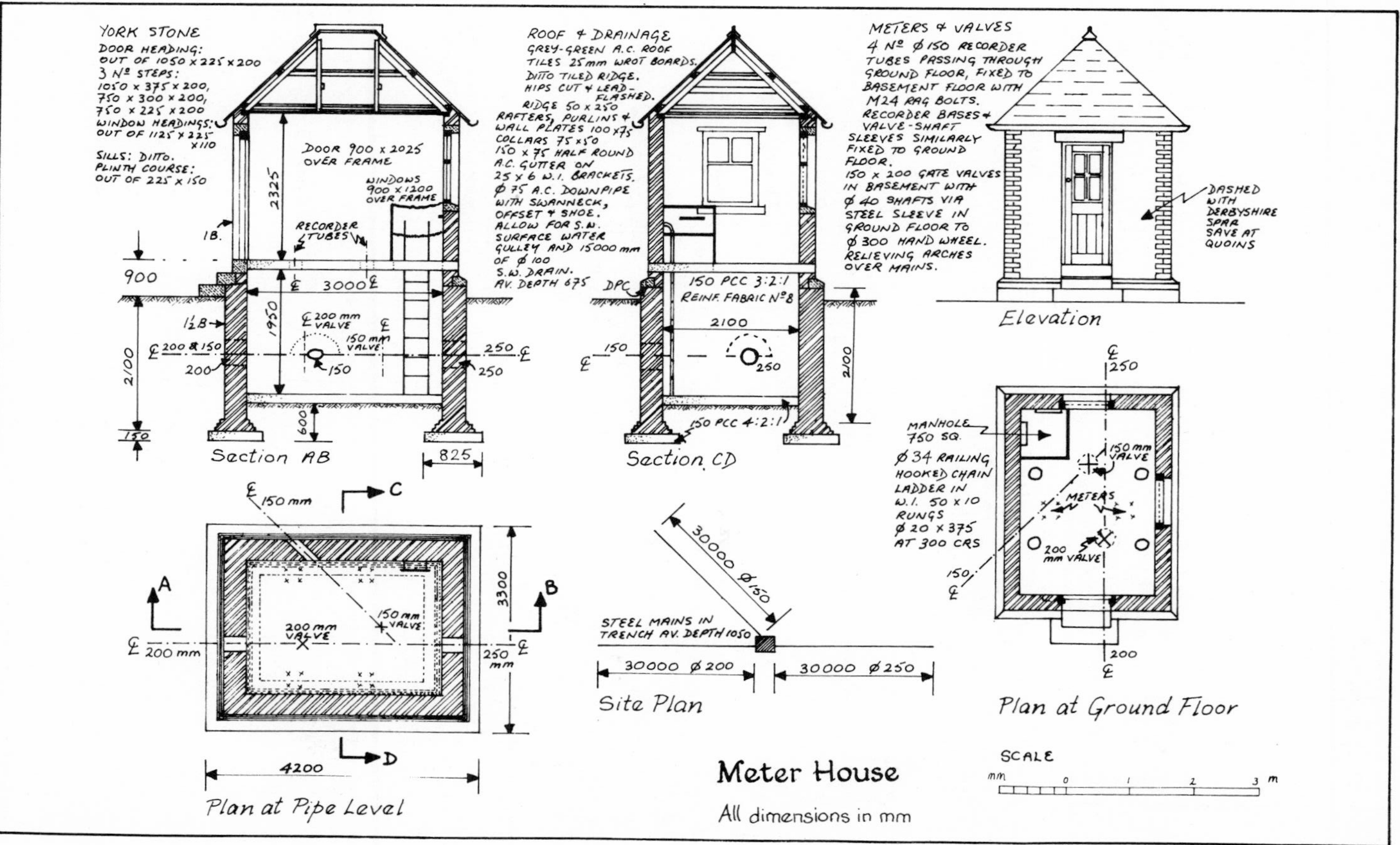
YORK STONE
DOOR HEADING: OUT OF 1050 x 225 x 200
3 Nº STEPS: 1050 x 375 x 200, 750 x 300 x 200, 750 x 225 x 200
WINDOW HEADINGS: OUT OF 1125 x 225 x 110
SILLS: DITTO.
PLINTH COURSE: OUT OF 225 x 150
DOOR 900 x 2025 OVER FRAME
WINDOWS 900 x 1200 OVER FRAME
RECORDER TUBES
200 mm VALVE
150 mm VALVE
Section AB
ROOF & DRAINAGE
GREY-GREEN A.C. ROOF TILES 25 mm WROT BOARDS.
DITTO TILED RIDGE. HIPS CUT & LEAD-FLASHED.
RIDGE 50 x 250
RAFTERS, PURLINS & WALL PLATES 100 x 75
COLLARS 75 x 50
150 x 75 HALF ROUND A.C. GUTTER ON 25 x 6 W.I. BRACKETS.
Ø 75 A.C. DOWNPIPE WITH SWANNECK, OFFSET & SHOE.
ALLOW FOR S.W. SURFACE WATER GULLEY AND 15000 mm OF Ø 100 S.W. DRAIN. AV. DEPTH 675
DPC
150 PCC 3:2:1 REINF. FABRIC Nº 8
150 PCC 4:2:1
Section CD
METERS & VALVES
4 Nº Ø 150 RECORDER TUBES PASSING THROUGH GROUND FLOOR, FIXED TO BASEMENT FLOOR WITH M24 RAG BOLTS.
RECORDER BASES & VALVE-SHAFT SLEEVES SIMILARLY FIXED TO GROUND FLOOR.
150 x 200 GATE VALVES IN BASEMENT WITH Ø 40 SHAFTS VIA STEEL SLEEVE IN GROUND FLOOR TO Ø 300 HAND WHEEL.
RELIEVING ARCHES OVER MAINS.
DASHED WITH DERBYSHIRE SPAR SAVE AT QUOINS
Elevation
MANHOLE 750 SQ.
Ø 34 RAILING HOOKED CHAIN LADDER IN W.I. 50 x 10 RUNGS Ø 20 x 375 AT 300 CRS
METERS
Plan at Ground Floor
Plan at Pipe Level
STEEL MAINS IN TRENCH AV. DEPTH 1050
30000 Ø150
30000 Ø200
30000 Ø250
Site Plan
Meter House
All dimensions in mm
SCALE

FIG. 39 (*a*).

			Meter House (1)
	4.20 3.30 1.65	22.87	Ex & C.A.
	11.70 0.88 0.60	6.18	Ex. in trench + R.F.I.R. 2/3.30 6.60 15.00 4/0.825 3.30 11.70
	14.02 0.25 1.65	5.77	Ddt Ex. + C.A. Add Ex. + R.F.I.R. (outside Basement) 15.00 4/0.244 0.98 14.02
	14.02 0.88 0.15	1.86	Ddt Ex. in trench + R.F.I.R. Add Ex. in trench + C.A. and 4:2:1 conc. in founds.
	14.02 0.58 0.23	1.87	Ddt Ex. in trench + R.F.I.R. Add Ex. in trench + C.A. + Bkwk in footings
	14.02 0.35 0.23	1.13	Ddt Ex. in trench + R.F.I.R Add Ex. in trench + C.A. + Bkwk in c.m.
	3.00 2.10 0.15	0.94	4:2:1 conc. Basement floor
	3.45 2.55 0.15	1.32	Ditto Meter Room floor
4/2/	0.23 0.12 0.08	0.02	Ddt where facing bks at corners
	0.75 0.75 0.15	0.08	Ddt where M H
	0.75 0.23 0.15	0.32	Ddt where part of top step. Add York Stone Dressings
	11.70 0.34 2.10	8.35	Bkwk in c.m. in 1½ bk Basement walls
	11.10 0.23 2.40	6.13	Ditto in 1 bk. Upper walls
2/	1.20 0.90 0.23	0.50	Ddt. last where windows
	2.03 0.90 0.23	0.42	Ddt. where door
	0.75 0.15 0.23	0.03	Ddt. where 2nd step
		0.95	
	10.64	10.64	E.O. Bkwk for beam filling 2/3.00 6.00 2/2.10 4.20 4/0.11 0.44 10.64

			E.O. Bkwk in c.m. for York Stone Dressings
2/2	1.13 0.23 0.11	0.11	Window Heads + Sills
	1.05 0.23 0.20	0.05	Door Head
	0.75 0.23 0.05	0.01	Part of top step
	11.25 0.23 0.15	0.39	Plinth course 2/3.68 7.35 2/2.78 5.55 12.90 4/0.23 0.90 12.00 less step 0.75 11.25
		0.56	
4/	2.55	10.20	E.O. Bkwk for red pressed quoins
2/	3.11 2.55	15.88	Dashed spar Sides 2/0.17 3.45 0.34 3.11
2/	2.21 2.55	11.27	Ends 2.55 0.34 2.21
2/2/	1.05 0.12	0.50	Reveals + windows
2/	1.95 0.12	0.47	Reveals + door
		28.12	
2/	0.80 1.40	2.24	Ddt last: Windows
	0.75 2.33	1.75	Door + steps
		3.99	
	0.75 0.30 0.20	0.04	York Stone Dressings Second step
	1.05 0.38 0.20	0.08	Bottom Step
		0.12	
	11.54 0.34	3.92	Horiz. D.P.C. 2/3.00 6.00 2/2.10 4.20 1.34 11.54
		1 No	Framed + glazed door 1.950 x 0.750 incl. fixing furniture + glazing
		2 No	Framed windows 1.200 x 0.900 incl. fixing + glazing

FIG. 39 (*b*).

			METER HOUSE (2)
	0·90	0·90	100 x 100 fir in door frame
2/	1·94	3·88	
		4·78	
			Fir framed in roof:
	10·60	10·60	100 x 75 plate 6·00
4/	1·58	6·32	rafters 4·20
4/	2·40	9·60	trips 0·40 10·60
2/	3·30	6·60	purlins
2/	2·25	4·50	do
2/	2·40	4·80	do
2/	1·20	2·40	do
2/	1·65	3·30	do
		48·12	
2/	1·65	3·30	75 x 50 collars
	0·98	0·98	250 x 50 ridge
2/½/	4·65 2·10	9·76	25 unwrot boarding + A.C. roof tiles
2/½/	2·93 2·10	6·15	3·75 0·90 4·65
		15·91	
	13·36	13·36	E.O. tiles for double course at eaves 2/3·75 7·50 2/2·93 5·86 13·36
	0·98	0·98	A.C. ridge tiles
		2No	E.O. ridge tiles for ends
4/	2·48	9·92	A.C. Hip tiles + lead soakers
	13·35	13·35	150 x 75 H.R.A.C. Gutter
		4No	Ditto E.O. for angles
		1No	75 A.C. swanneck + jtg.
		1No	75 A.C. offset + jtg
		1No	75 A.C. shoe
	1·80	1·80	75 A.C. downpipe + jtg
		3No	75 Holderbats + fixing
		10No	25 x 6 W.I. Gutter brackets + fixing
		1No	100 G.S. Gulley
	13·50	13·50	100 G.S. drain in trench av. 675 deep
2/	0·68	1·36	34 dia tube rail + fixing
	0·38	0·38	
		1·74	
		1No	1.050 standard do.do.
	3·00	3·00	W.I. ladder 50 x 10 flats 20 dia. rungs at 300 ctrs + fixing

2/	0·75	1·50	Safety chain
		4No	Hooks + fixing
		4No	P+F 150 Recorder tubes incl. holes for same in 150 concrete floor + all connections
		2No	P&F Recorders incl. all connections
		1No	150 full way valve with 38 dia shaft sleeves through 150 conc. floor + 300 dia handwheel
		1No	Ditto but 200 valve
			Steel main in trench av. 1.000 deep incl. handling laying + jointing
	31·50	31·50	250 dia
	32·75	32·75	200 dia
	32·90	32·90	150 dia
		1No	E.O. steel main for 250 x 150 branch junct.
		1No	E.O. steel main for 250 x 200 taper piece
			Build main in wall 1½B thick incl. turning relieving arch over main
		1No	250 straight
		1No	200 straight
		1No	150 45° skew
2/	2	4No	C_3s sash frames
2/2/	2	8No	do squares
2/	2	4No	do large squares
	4·95 0·25	1·24	C_3s x 1·1 Frame
2/	1·95 0·75	2·92	C_3s x 1·1 Door
2/	0·80 0·45	0·72	Ddt x 1·1 Glass
2/	4	8No	C_3s Squares

FIG. 39 (*c*).

(*Figs.* 40, 41: *See envelope inside back cover*)

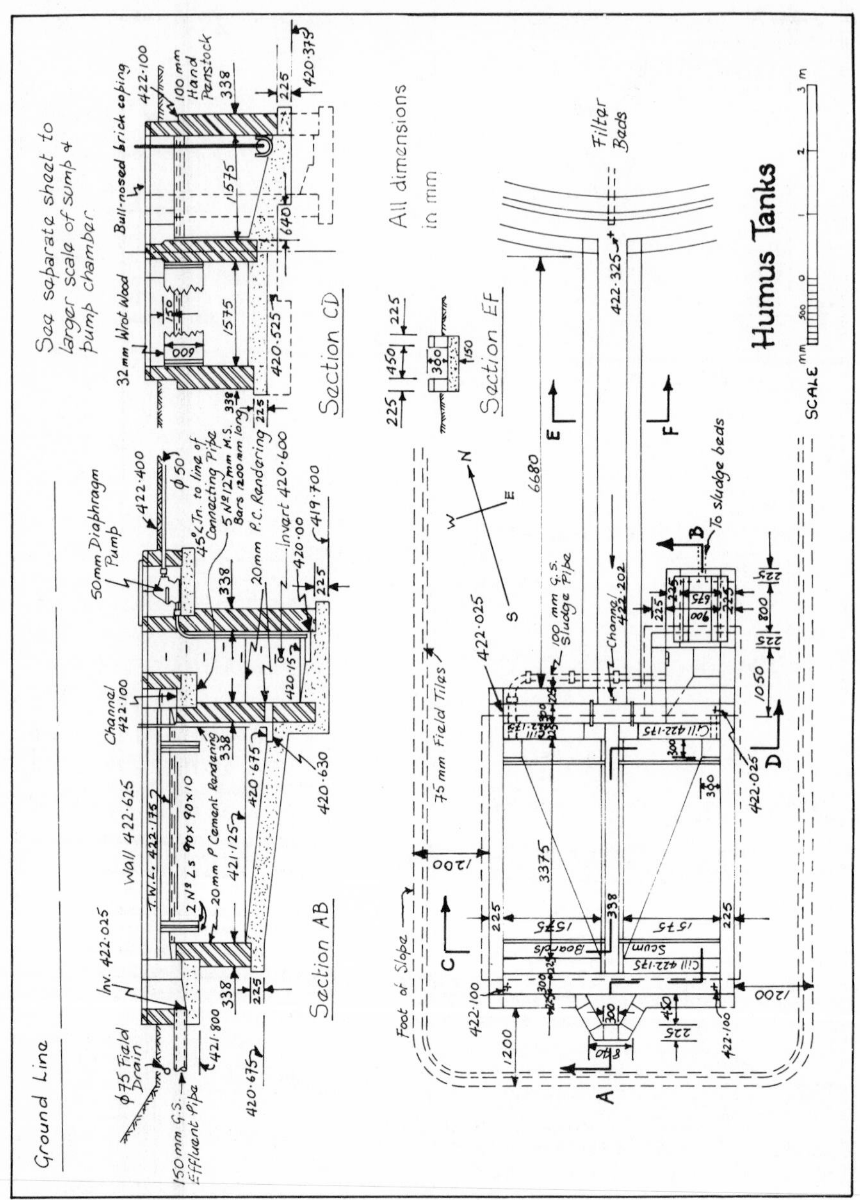
Humus Tanks
Section AB
Section CD
Section EF
All dimensions in mm
See separate sheet to larger scale of sump & pump chamber
Ground Line
Filter Beds
To sludge beds
75 mm Field Tiles
Foot of Slope
100 mm G.S. Sludge Pipe
150 mm G.S. Effluent Pipe
φ75 Field Drain
50 mm Diaphragm Pump
Bull-nosed brick coping
100 mm Hand Penstock
32 mm Wrot Wood
20 mm P Cement Rendering
20 mm P.C. Rendering
2 Nº Ls 90 x 90 x 10
5 Nº 12 mm M.S. Bars 200 mm long
SCALE

Fig. 42.

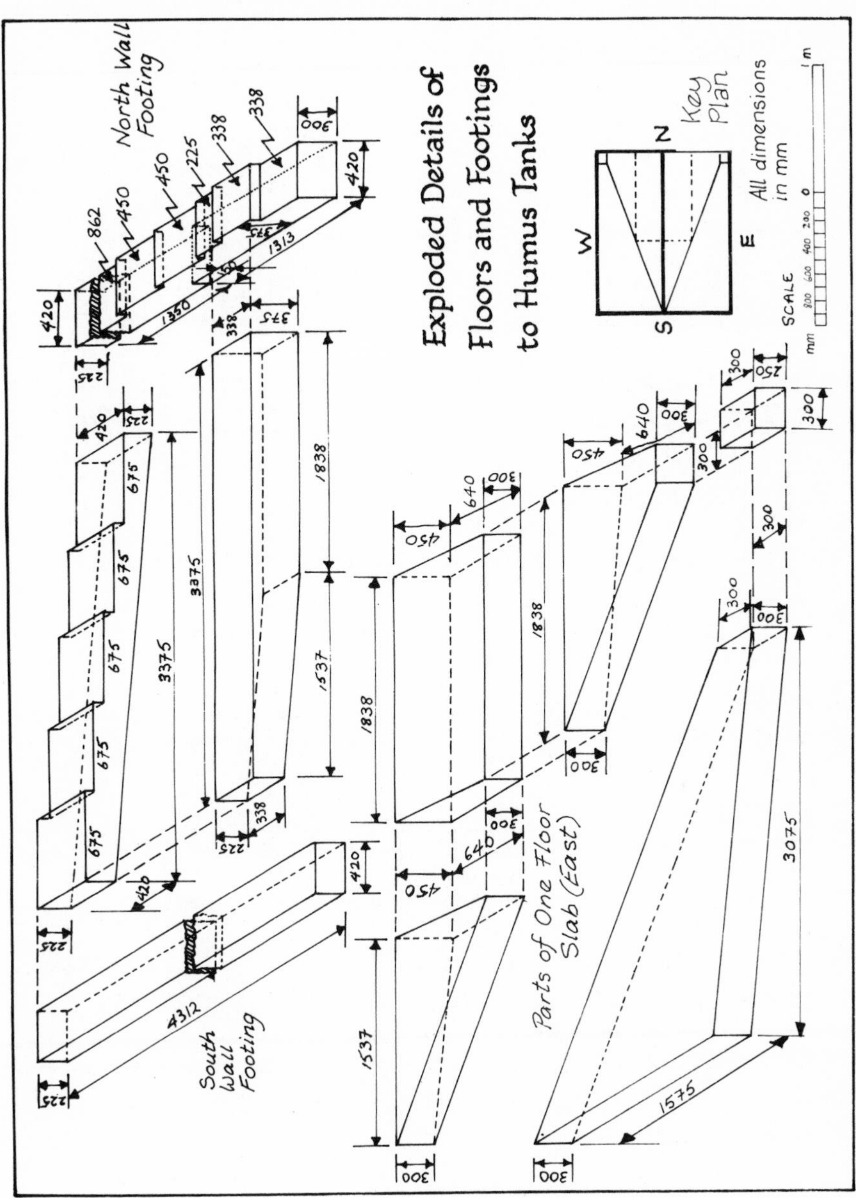
Exploded Details of Floors and Footings to Humus Tanks
North Wall Footing
South Wall Footing
Parts of One Floor Slab (East)
Key Plan
N
S
W
E
All dimensions in mm
SCALE
mm

FIG. 43.

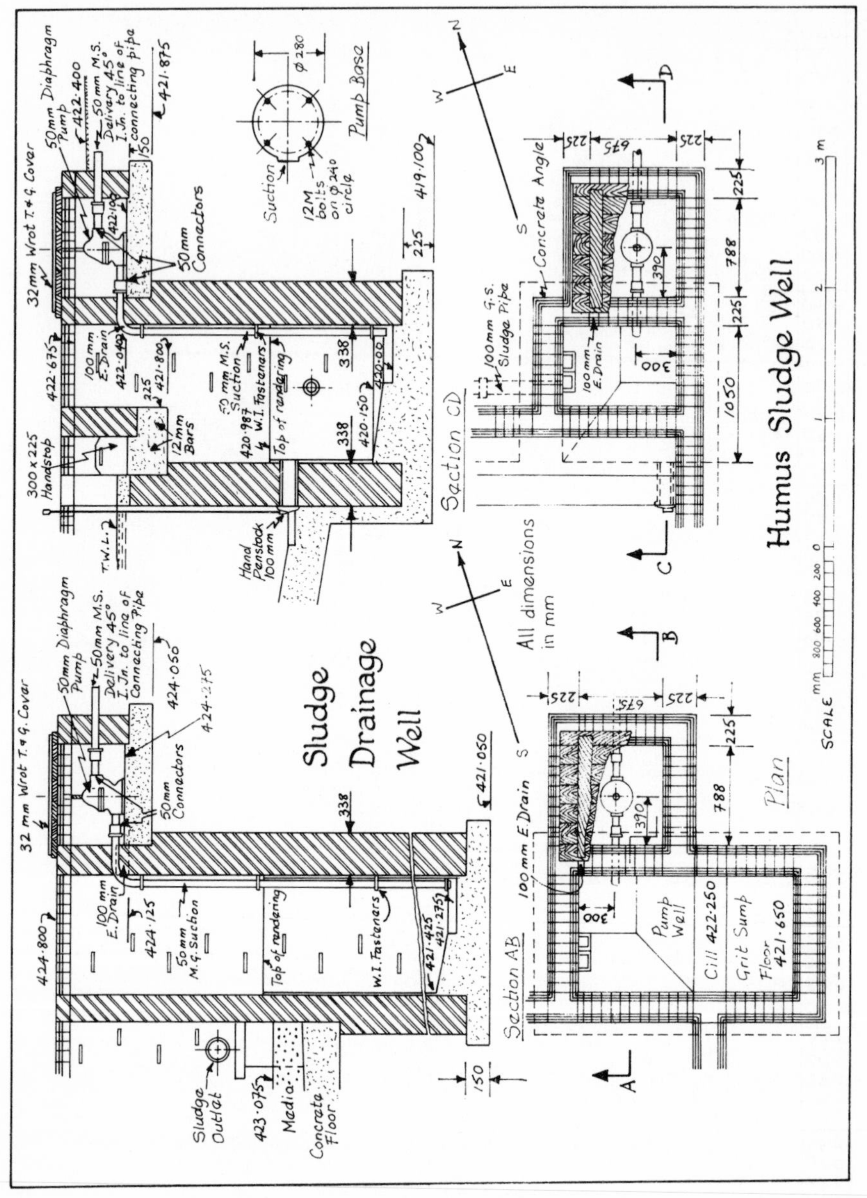

FIG. 44.

(*Fig. 45: See envelope inside back cover*)

			Sewage Disposal Works (1)
			Detritus Tank: av G.L. 424·875 Settling Tank: 424·725 Sludge Manhole: 424·725 Dosing Chamber: 424·575
			Ex. n.e. 1·500 deep & C.A:
	1·80 1·20 1·12	2·42	Detritus Tank 0·600 2/0·225 0·450 2/0·075 0·150 1·200
½/	0·60 1·80 1·12	0·60	Inlet 1·200 0·300 0·450 0·225 0·150 0·075 1·800 0·600
	6·90 6·04 1·50	62·51	Settling Tank 4/1·350 5·400 1·500 6·900 2/0·825 1·650 2/1·350 2·700 1·688 6·038
	1·50 0·98 1·12	1·65	Sludge Manhole 2/0·225 0·450 2/0·075 0·150 0·900 1·500
	1·42 1·95 0·90	2·49	Dosing Chamber 2/0·225 0·450 1·125 2/0·075 0·150 0·225 1·350 0·075 1·950 1·425
	0·52 0·52 0·60	0·16	Rest Bend
		69·83	
			Ddt. Ex. 1·500 deep & C.A. Add Ex. n.e. 1·500 deep & R.F.I.R:
	5·40 0·08 0·90	0·39	Detritus Tank 2/1·800 3·600 2/0·600 0·450 0·150 5·400
	3·45 0·08 0·98	0·27	Sludge Manhole 2/1·050 2·100 1·500 3·600 2/0·075 0·150 3·450
	4·65 0·08 0·68	0·26	Dosing Chamber 2/1·450 2·850 1·950 4·800 2/0·075 0·150 4·650
	12·45 0·15 0·22	0·41	To sides where conc. backing 13·800 1·350 12·450
	0·30 0·30 0·22	0·02	say round Rest bend
		1·35	

			Ex. 1·500 to 3·000 deep & C.A:
	6·90 6·04 0·75	31·26	S.T. to 422·475
	4·20 4·39 0·75	13·83	S.T. to 421·725
	0·52 0·52 0·22	0·06	Rest bend
		45·15	
			Ex. 3·000 to 4·500 deep & C.A:
	4·20 4·39 0·60	11·06	S.T. to 421·125
	1·50 1·69 0·22	0·56	S.T. to 420·900
		11·62	
			E.O. Ex. for removing turf & topsoil & laying aside for reuse:
	1·80 1·20	2·16	Detritus Tank
½/	0·60 1·80	0·54	Inlet
	6·90 6·04	41·68	Settling Tank
	1·50 0·98	1·47	S.M.H.
	1·42 1·95	2·77	Dosing Chamber
		48·62	
	0·90 0·90	0·81	Prepare fdn. for conc. flag.
			Mass conc. 4:2:1
	1·50 1·69 0·22	0·56	S.T. base to 421·125
	4·20 4·39 1·35	24·89	do. to 422·475
	6·90 6·04 1·42	59·18	do. to 423·900
	1·20 0·22 0·08	0·02	Under S. Wall of D.T. to 423·975
	5·30 0·30 0·08	0·13	Under N. Channel to 423·975
		84·78	

FIG. 46 (*a*).

S.D. Works

			Ddt. last:
	23.78 0.22 0.08	0.42	where 225 (1B) wall 2/6.900 13.800 2/6.038 12.075 25.875
2/	4.95 0.22 0.08	0.17	where 225 N. & S. Cills 1.200 24.675 4/0.225 0.900 23.775
	5.85 0.34 0.60	1.19	where 338 (1½B) dividing walls
	4.50 0.34 0.45	0.69	do
	3.60 0.34 0.52	1.74	do
	2.60 0.34 0.52	0.46	do
	1.70 0.34 0.52	0.30	do
2/½/6/	5.40 2.48 2.55	11.38	where trapezoids
2/4/½/6/	2.92 1.39 2.55	13.80	do 5.400 0.450 2)5.850 2.925 2.480 0.300 2)2.780 1.390
2/½/6/	0.45 0.30 2.55	0.11	do
	1.35 0.15 0.15	0.03	where S.M.H. side walls & benching
		30.29	
			4:2:1 conc. in fdns:
	1.80 1.20 0.22	0.48	D.T.
½/	0.60 1.80 0.22	0.24	Inlet
	1.50 1.05 0.15	0.24	S.M.H.
	1.42 1.95 0.22	0.61	D.C.
	0.52 0.52 0.22	0.06	
		1.67	

②

			4:2:1 conc. in benching & channel filling laid to falls:
½/	0.30 0.90 0.95	0.13	D.T. inlet
	1.80 0.60 0.08	0.09	D.T. floor to 424.050
½/	0.75 0.60 0.45	0.10	D.T. triangular ramp
½/	0.75 0.60 1.05	0.24	D.T. trapezoid ramp 0.600 0.450 1.050
	5.30 0.30 0.64		N. Channel above 424.050 av. 0.640 deep.
	5.30 0.30 0.79	2.27	S. Channel above 423.900 av. 0.790 deep
	0.90 0.90 0.30	0.24	S.M.H. av. 0.300 deep
	1.12 1.35 0.38	0.57	D.C.
		3.64	
	0.68 0.60 0.08	0.03	Ddt. last where D.C. outlet
	12.45 0.15 0.60	1.12	4:2:1 conc. in backing to E & W walls 13.800 1.350 12.450
	0.60 0.90	0.54	Use & waste of shuttering to vertical face - D.T.
4/	1.40 3.52	19.71	do. but to sloping faces - S.T.
2/	2.92 3.30	19.27	do. do. - S.T.
		38.98	
	0.90 0.90	0.81	Precast conc. draining flag av. 75 mm thick P & F on prepared fdn
	0.22 10.02 0.08	0.18	Precast conc. coping to cills av. 60 mm deep Inlet N chl 0.600 N chl. 2/2.186 4.372 S chl 2/2.524 5.048 10.020 2.524 0.338 2.186

FIG. 46 (b).

Timesing	Dimensions	Squaring	Description
	S.D. Works		Bkwk in cement mortar 338 mm (1½B):
	5.85 0.68	3.98	Dividing wall below 424.050
	4.50 0.45	2.02	do
	3.60 0.52		do
	2.60 0.52	4.11	do
	1.70 0.52		do
		10.11	
			Ditto but 225 mm (1B):
	5.85 1.28	7.49	D.T. — Inlet 0.525, 0.450, 0.525
	23.78 1.42	33.77	S.T. walls — E 2.025, S 1.200, W 2.025 = 6.750
4/	2.52 0.90	9.07	Chl. walls — 4/0.225 0.900 = 5.825
2/	0.34 0.52	0.35	N. Chl. wall returns to dividing wall
	5.85 1.28	7.49	Dividing wall above 423.975
	3.15 1.50	4.72	S.M.H. 0.900, 1.350, 0.900 = 3.150
	4.05 0.98	3.96	D.C. 1.125, 1.800, 1.125 = 4.050
		66.85	
			Ddt last:
	0.60 0.45	0.27	where cill to 424.800
2/	0.22 0.15	0.07	where ends of 225 × 150 perf. channel
		0.34	
	42.31	42.31	E.O. Bkwk for D.B.N. coping — D.T. 5.850; S.T. 23.780, 5.850, 0.340, 0.340; S.M.H. 3.150; D.C. 4.050 = 43.360; Cill 1.050; 42.310
		11 No	E.O. D.B.N. coping for mitred + angled blocks - square
		4 No	do but skew
		3 No	E.O. D.B.N. coping for stop-end blocks on dividing walls and returns

Timesing	Dimensions	Squaring	Description
		2 No	150 mm G.S.W. pipes in short lengths + build into 225 mm wall ③
		1 No	100 mm do. do.
		4 No	Build 100 mm pipe into 225 mm wall - square
		1 No	do. but skew
		1 No	Build 50 mm pipe into 225 mm wall
		1 No	Build 100 mm pipe into 338 mm wall
			20 mm cement rendering in two coats:
2/	1.80 1.12	4.03	D.T. sides
	0.90 0.28	0.25	D.T. inlet face av. 275 mm.
2/	0.22 0.34	0.15	Ends of cill into N. Channel
	11.20 0.52	5.82	N. Channel walls 0.600, 10.600 = 11.200
2/2/	0.22 0.42	0.37	Faces of returns + ends of cills. N.
	31.52 1.28	40.35	Sides of S.T. and div. wall to 423.900 — 4/5.400 21.600; 4/2.480 9.920 = 31.520
2/½/	5.85 2.55	14.92	Dividing wall below 423.900
2/2/	0.22 0.42	0.37	Ends of S. cills
	11.20 0.52	5.82	S. chl. walls
	3.60 0.22	0.79	S.M.H. 4/0.900 3.600
	4.95 0.52	2.57	D.C. 2/1.125 2.250; 2/1.350 2.700 = 4.950
		75.44	
			Ddt. last:
2/½/	0.75 0.45		D.T. where ramps
2/½/	0.75 1.05	1.12	do.
	0.60 0.34	0.20	D.T. where inlet to N. chl.
2/2/	2.20 0.42	3.70	where N. cills b.s. taken
2/2/	2.52 0.42	4.23	where S. cills b.s. taken
		9.25	

FIG. 46 (c).

S.D. Works

	6·30	6·30	100 mm G.S. Sludge pipe in trench av. 900 mm deep
		3 No	E.O. for bends
		1 No	P&F 100 mm Penstock with 1·350 stem & ⌀ 225 mm handwheel incl. 100 mm spigot piece and building in & holding brackets.
		1 No	P&F screen of 10 mm. bars at 20 mm ctrs. M.S. 900 mm long & 600 mm wide
		1 No	P&F 225 x 150 mm Perf. channel M.S. 1·050 long
		2 No	P&F Channel Handstops C.I. 375 x 300 mm incl. building in.
4/3/	2·52	30·24	300 x 40 wrot. scum board & fixing
2/4/2/	0·90	14·40	90 x 90 x 10 EA @ 13·4 kg/m & fixing
		16 No	20M x 90 @ 0·42 kg B.H.N. & W
		32 No	20M x 150 @ 0·59 kg Rag bolts & fixing
		2 No	P&F ranges of 100 mm C.I. sludge pipe incl. vent pipe and blank flange & Y branch joint
		4 No	100 mm pipe holderbats & fixing
		2 No	100 mm sluice valves & turnkeys P.&F.
		1 No	150 mm C.I. closing siphon incl. vent & test bend, p.c. & fixing

Percolating Filter ④
Formation Level 422·400

			Ex. n.e. 1·500 & C.A.:
π/½/	6·64 6·64 0·15		Filter 6·300 + 0·338 = 6·638
π/½/	6·64 6·64 0·30	31·17	do
π/	6·90 0·52 0·15	1·69	channel 6·638 + 0·262 = 6·900
π/½/	6·72 0·22 0·08	0·19	do. fillet
	6·68 0·90 0·29	1·80	Straight chl av. 288 mm deep
	0·45 0·38 0·22	0·04	Pier
		34·89	
½/	13·28 0·30 0·15	0·30	Ddt. last where step on filter base
			4:2:1 conc. laid to falls in floors & channels:
π/½/	6·64 6·64 0·28		Filter N. part
π/½/	6·64 6·64 0·38	45·60	do. S. part
½/	13·28 0·30 0·15	0·31	do. step
π/	6·90 0·52 0·15	1·69	channel
π/½/	6·72 0·22 0·08	0·19	do. fillet
	6·68 0·90 0·15	1·00	straight channel
		48·79	
	0·45 0·38 0·15	0·03	4:2:1 conc. in fdns to pier
		3 No	Precast conc. pier caps to suit 100 mm pipe
		2 No	do. but 50 mm pipe

Fig. 46 (*d*).

S.D. Works			
π/½	12.95 0.34 0.15	1.04	Circular honeycombed Bkwk in cem. mortar – filter wall, S. part
			Circular brickwork in cem. mortar pointed on seen face – 1½B:
π/½/	12.95 0.15	3.05	Filter, N. part
π	12.95 0.98	39.87	do. above 422.625
		42.92	
			Do. but 1B:
π/	12.95 0.60	24.41	Filter above 423.600
π/	7.05 0.30	6.64	Chl. 6.638 0.300 0.112 7.050
		31.05	
	0.45 0.30	0.14	Ddt. last where outlet
			E.O. Circular Bkwk. for D.B.N. coping:
π/	12.95	62.83	Filter
π/	7.05		Chl.
	0.45	0.45	Ddt. last where outlet
π/	13.18	41.41	E.O. Circular Bkwk for splayed plinth course
			Bkwk in cement mortar – 1B:
2/	0.30 0.30	0.18	Ends of circular chl.
2/	6.68 0.30	4.01	straight chl.
		4.19	
			E.O. Bkwk for D.B.N. coping:
2/	0.30	13.96	Ends of circ. chl.
2/	6.68		Straight chl.
		4 No	E.O. D.B.N. coping for angled & mitred blocks
	0.56 0.60	0.34	2½B in distributor pier
	0.22 2.55	0.56	1B in test of piers 0.525 0.600 0.450 0.300 0.675 2.550
		1 No	Build 150 mm pipe into 338 mm wall
		1 No	Build 50 mm do. do.

			(5)
π/	6.30 6.30	124.69	75 mm floor tiles
			Ddt. last:
	0.56 0.56	0.31	where distributor
4/	0.22 0.22	0.19	where piers
		0.50	
			Washed clinker filtering medium:
π/	6.30 6.30 0.22	27.43	60 to 40 mm. av. 225 mm. deep
π/	6.30 6.30 1.28	159.60	10 to 20 mm. av. 1.275 deep
			Ddt. last:
	0.56 0.56 0.60	0.19	where distributor pier
	0.22 0.22 1.88	0.09	where piers
π/2/	0.08 0.08 0.90	0.04	where distributor & protection pipe
π/	6.22 0.10 0.10	0.20	where inlet pipe
π/	6.08 0.05 0.05	0.05	where 50 mm drain
		0.57	
	10.95	10.95	150 mm C.I. socketted pipe incl. laying & jtg & bedding on piers
		1 No	P.& F. 150 mm sluice valve on same
		1 No	P.& F. Rotary distributor for 12.600 dia. bed
		1 No	P.& F. 50 mm sluice valve & turnkey incl. connections to distributor
	0.90	0.90	100 mm G.S. protection pipe & stopeye incl. jointing & fixing
	5.85	5.85	50 mm C.I. socketted pipe incl. laying of jtg. and bedding on piers
		1 No	50 mm C.I. Bend

FIG. 46 (*e*).

(6)

S.D. Works.

Humus Tank

Formation Level 422·400

			Ex. n.e. 1·500 deep & C.A.:
	4·31 4·20 1·50	27·15	Humus tank 2/0·075 0·150 3/0·075 0·150 2/0·338 0·676 3/0·338 1·014 3·375 2/1·575 3·150 4·201 4·314
	1·39 1·73 1·50	3·61	Humus sludge well 0·975 2/0·075 0·150 0·225 2/0·338 0·676 0·112 0·900 0·075 1·726 1·387
	0·90 1·28 0·52	0·60	Pump chamber 0·600 2/0·075 0·150 0·225 2/0·225 0·450 0·075 0·675 0·900 1·275
	0·34 2·40 0·60	0·49	Inlet channel 0·525 4·312 0·187 1·725 0·338 2·587 0·187 2·400
	0·34 3·94 0·60	0·80	Outlet channel 4·312 0·875 3·937
½/	0·45 1·65 0·60	0·22	Outlet bay 0·525 1·125 1·650
		32·87	
			Ddt. Ex. n.e. 1·500 & C.A. Add Ex. n.e. 1·500 & R.F.I.R.:
	0·08 16·75 1·20	1·61	H.T. where 1½B 8·400 8·650 17·050 4/0·075 0·300 16·750
	0·08 1·58 1·20	0·15	Ddt. this where HSW on N. side 0·675 0·900 1·575
	0·08 2·48 0·30	0·06	Ddt. excess where inlet chl. N. side 2·400 0·075 2·475
	0·08 3·94 0·30	0·09	Ddt. excess where outlet chl. S. side
		0·30	
	0·20 16·30 0·30	0·98	H.T. a.b. where 1B 17·050 4/0·188 0·752 16·298
	0·20 1·35 0·30	0·08	Ddt. excess where HSW N. side 1·575 2/0·112 0·224 1·351
	0·20 2·59 0·30	0·16	do. where inlet chl. 2·400 0·187 2·587
	0·20 3·94 0·30	0·24	do. where outlet chl.
		0·48	

	0·08 4·35 1·20	0·42	H.S.W. a.b. to 422·100 W. 1·387 N. 1·725 E. 1·387 4·499 2/0·075 0·150 4·349
	0·08 1·12 0·52	0·05	Ddt. excess where pump chr. on N. side 0·450 0·675 1·125
	0·20 3·00 0·30	0·18	H.S.W. a.b. 4·500 2/0·187 0·374 4·126 P.Ch. 1·125 3·001
	0·08 2·92 0·38	0·09	Pump chr.
		0·27	
			Ex. 1·500 to 3·000 deep & C.A:
	0·42 4·31 0·22	0·40	H.T. S. wall ftg.
	3·38 4·31 0·38	5·54	Floors and E. s/w wall ftgs 0·225 0·525 2)0·750 0·375
	0·42 1·35 0·52	0·29	N. wall ftgs up to H.S.W.
	0·42 1·32 0·38	0·21	do
	1·95 1·72 1·20	4·02	H.S.W. 1·387 0·412 0·150 1·949
		10·46	
½/	1·62 1·85 0·15	0·22	Ddt. at centre wall & on either side where level base
	0·15 1·72 0·52	0·13	Ddt. at S. side H.S.W. where twice taken
		0·35	
			Ddt Ex. 1·5–3·0m & C.A. Add Ex. 1·5–3·0 m & R.F.I.R.
2/	2·70 0·08 0·19	0·08	Side walls steps 4/0·675 0·075 0·150 2·700 0·225 0·300 4)0·750(0·188
	0·08 2·32 0·19	0·04	N. wall av. 0·188 0·562 0·450 0·450 0·862 2·324
	0·08 4·84 0·52	0·20	H.S.W. where tank 1·462 1·725 1·800 4·987 2/0·075 0·150 4·837
	0·08 5·88 0·45	0·21	H.S.W. below tank 1·950 2·975 1·950 5·875
		0·53	

FIG. 46 (*f*).

			S.D. Works
	2·10	2·10	100 mm G.S. sludge pipe in trench av. 1·800 deep
		1 No	E.O. for 90° bend
			Conc. 4:2:1 in ftgs & fdns:
2/	3·38 0·42 0·22	0·62	H.T. Side walls av. 225 mm.
	0·42 4·31 0·22	0·40	do. S. wall
	0·42 2·66 0·30	0·34	do. N. wall av. 300 mm
	1·54 0·34 0·30	0·16	do. Division wall S. part av. 300 mm
	1·84 0·34 0·38	0·24	do. do. N. part
	1·95 1·72 0·22	0·74	H.S.W.
	1·10 1·28 0·15	0·21	P. Chr
	0·52 2·60 0·22	0·30	Inlet Chl. up to H.S.W.
	0·52 3·94 0·22	0·45	Outlet Chl.
½/	0·45 1·65 0·25	0·09	Outlet chl. bay
		3·55	
	0·52 1·35 0·22	0·15	Reinf. conc. 4:2:1 in chl. over H.S.W. incl. shuttering
5/	1·20	6·00	12 mm M.S. bars @ 0·87 kg/m
			4:2:1 conc. in floors laid to falls and benching:

B C
A D
E

H.T. Floors.

2/	3·08 0·94 0·30	1·74	Slabs A 1·575 0·300 2)1·875(0·938 (7)
2/	0·77 0·65 0·30	0·30	Slabs B 2)1·538(0·769
2/⅓/	0·77 0·65 0·15	0·05	Pyramids B
2/	1·84 0·65 0·38	0·91	Prisms C
2/	1·07 0·65 0·30	0·42	Slabs D 0·300 2)2·138(1·07
2/⅓/	1·07 0·65 0·15	0·07	Pyramids D
	0·30 0·30 0·25	0·02	Sump E
	1·05 0·90 0·12	0·11	H.S.W. av. 125 mm thick
	0·80 0·68 0·06	0·03	P. Cht. av. 60 mm thick
2/	3·49 0·30 0·04	0·08	Channel av. 40 mm 1·575 0·338 1·575 3·488
	0·45 0·56 0·04	0·01	Outlet Bay av. 40 mm 0·300 0·825 2)1·125(0·562
		3·74	
	0·15 1·58 0·45	0·11	Conc. 4:2:1 in backing to H.S.W. S. wall. 1·725 2/0·075 0·150 1·575
	0·22 5·74 0·08	0·10	Precast conc. cills av. 60 mm thickness 3/0·338 1·014 0·225 1·239; 3·488 3·488 6·976 1·239 5·737
			Bkwk in cem. mortar 1B:
2/	3·38 0·52	3·52	Side walls 422·625 422·100 0·525
	3·38 0·22	0·74	Dividing wall 422·625 422·400 0·225
	10·39 0·60	6·23	N. s/s Chls. 422·625 422·025 0·600
	1·25 0·82	1·02	do. between cills 422·625 421·800 0·825
	5·75 0·30	1·72	Cills 422·100 421·800 0·300
			N: 0·525 3·937 0·525; S: 0·525 1·462 0·525 0·375 0·525 1·462 0·525; 10·386
		13·23	Carried forward

FIG. 46 (g).

			S.D. Works
		13·23	Brought forward
	1·50 0·52	0·78	H.S.W. where no P. Cbr or Chl. 422·625 422·100 0·525; 0·638 0·862 1·500
	1·12 0·75	0·84	do. where P. Cbr. 422·625 421·875 0·750; 0·225 0·675 0·225 1·125
	2·70 0·60	1·62	P. Cbr 422·625 422·025 0·600; 0·787 1·125 0·787 2·699
		16·47	
	0·45 0·42	0·19	Ddt. where chl. opening
			Bkwk. a.b. 1½B:
2/	3·38 1·35	9·13	Side walls 422·100 420·750 1·350
	3·38 1·50	5·07	Dividing wall 422·400 420·900 1·500
	2·59 1·08	2·80	Under N. cill up to H.S.W. 421·800 420·720 1·080
	4·16 0·90	3·74	Under S. cill 421·800 420·900 0·900 | 4·126 1·575 2·587
	2·40 1·88	4·51	H.S.W. where channel 421·800 419·925 1·875
	1·12 1·95	2·18	do. where P. Chr. 421·875 419·925 1·950 | 2/0·412 0·824; 1·575 2·399
	1·62 2·18	3·53	do. remainder 422·100 419·925 2·175
		30·96	
	27·07	27·07	E.O. Bkwk for D.B.N. coping | 6·750 3·375 10·386 1·238 2·625 2·700 27·074
		10 No	E.O. coping for angled & mitred blocks
		3 No	E.O. coping for stop ends, dividing wall & returns
		4 No	E.O. coping for skew blocks outlet bay
		3 No	Build 100 mm pipe into 338 mm wall
		2 No	do. 50 mm pipe do. do. 225 mm wall.
		1 No	do. 100 mm pipe do. do.
		1 No	do. 150 mm pipe do. do.

			(8) 20 mm rendering in two coats:
2/	4·95 1·72	17·03	H.T. 3·375 1·575 4·950
2/	4·95 1·58	15·64	do.
	3·90 0·90	3·51	H.S.W. 2/0·900 1·800; 2/1·050 2·100; 3·900
	15·72 0·58	9·12	Chls 7·575 8·150 15·725
		45·30	
	5·75 0·45	2·59	Ddt last where cill openings
		2 No	C.I. Channel hand-stops 300 x 225 incl. fixing
		2 No	P.& F. 100 mm penstocks & bkts with 2·100 stem & 300 mm dia. hand-wheel & 100 mm spigot
	2·40	2·40	50 mm M.S. suction pipe
		1 No	E.O. 50 mm pipe for bend
		2 No	do. for connections 50 mm
		3 No	50 mm pipe clamps
		1 No	P.& F. 50 mm diaphragm pump & connections
		4 No	12M x 125 @ 0·28 kg Rag Bolts
		7 No	2·3 kg step irons
	1·00 1·00	1·00	Wrot. T.& G. double battened 32mm wood cover
2/4/2/	0·90	14·40	90 x 90 x 10L to A @ 13·4 kg/m & fixing

Fig. 46 (*h*).

	Dimensions	Squared	Description
			S.D. Works
			Sludge Drying Beds. G.L. 424·350
			Ex. n.e. 1·500 & C.A:
	9·68 8·55 1·50	124·15	Beds 3/2·925 8·775 4/0·225 0·900 9·675 8·100 0·450 8·550
	7·20 0·68 1·12	5·48	Inlet chl. 6·750 0·450 7·200 ; 3/0·150 0·450 0·225 0·675
	7·20 0·10 0·38	0·27	Under inlet chl.
	1·31 1·54 1·50	3·03	Pump well incl. cill 0·900 0·338 0·075 1·313 ; 0·075 0·900 0·225 0·225 0·112 1·537
	1·72 0·98 1·50	2·53	Grit well excl. cill 0·900 0·450 0·225 0·150 1·725 ; 0·562 0·225 0·112 0·075 0·975
	0·90 1·28 0·30	0·35	Pump Cbr. 0·788 0·112 0·676 0·225 0·901 ; 0·675 0·450 0·150 1·275
		135·81	
			Ddt. Ex. n.e. 1·500 & C.A. Add Ex. n.e. 1·500 & R.F.I.R:
	5·96 0·20 0·98	1·17	Well etc. where 225 mm wall. W. 1·312 N{1·538 0·975} E 1·725 S 0·975 6·525
	6·30 0·08 0·52	0·26	do. where 338mm 3/0·187 6·525 0·561 5·964 ; 3/0·075 6·525 0·225 6·300
	2·92 0·08 0·15	0·04	Round P. Cbr. 0·900 1·275 0·900 3·075 ; 3/0·075 0·150 2·925
		1·47	
			Ddt. this twice taken at P. cbr. S. side:
	0·20 1·12 0·30	0·07	where 225 mm wall
	0·12 1·12 0·68	0·09	where 338 mm wall
		0·16	

	Dimensions	Squared	Description
			Ex. 1·500–3·000 deep & C.A: (9)
	9·68 8·55 0·30	24·83	Beds
	7·20 0·10 0·30	0·22	Under inlet chl
L 2/3/	0·45 8·55 0·15	0·87	Under media chls av. 0·450 wide
	1·72 1·69 1·50	4·36	P. wall incl. cill conc. 0·900 0·675 0·150 1·725 ; 0·075 0·338 0·900 0·225 0·150 1·688
	1·72 0·82 1·42	2·00	Grit sump 0·975 0·150 0·825
		32·28	
			Ddt. this where twice taken at beds S. of P.W.
	0·42 1·55 0·30	0·20	
			Ddt. Ex. 1·500-3·000 & C.A. Add Ex. 1·500-3·000 & R.F.I.R:
	4·95 0·08 1·50	0·59	P.W. S. 1·688 W. 1·725 N. 1·688 5·101 ; 2/0·075 0·150 4·951
	3·22 0·08 1·28	0·33	G.S. 0·825 1·725 0·825 3·375 0·150 3·225
		0·92	
			Ddt. this where twice taken S&W of P.W. 1·538 0·338 1·876
	1·88 0·08 0·30	0·05	
			Ex. 3·000-4·500 & C.A. P.W.
	1·78 1·69 0·30	0·90	
			Ddt. Ex. 3·000-4·500 & C.A. Add Ex. 3·000-4·500 & R.F.I.R. P.W.
	4·95 0·08 0·15	0·06	
			100 mm G.S. Sludge pipe in trench av. 1·875 deep
	7·95	7·95	
			E.O. Ex. for stripping turf & topsoil and laying aside for reuse
	9·68 8·55	82·76	
	7·20 0·68	4·90	
	1·31 1·54	2·02	
	1·72 0·98	1·69	
	0·09 1·28	0·11	
		91·48	

FIG. 46 (i).

S.D. Works			
			4:2:1 conc. in fdns:
	7.20 0.68 0.15	0.73	Inlet channel.
	7.20 0.10 0.68	0.49	Under do.
	9.68 8.55 0.22	18.21	Bed floors
½/3/	0.45 8.55 0.15	0.87	Under media chls
	1.72 1.69 0.15	0.44	P.W.
	1.72 0.98 0.15	0.25	Grit sump
	1.72 0.15 0.22	0.06	Under do.
	1.09 1.28 0.15	0.21	P. Cbr. 0.788 0.225 0.075 1.088
		21.26	
			Ddt. last
	0.35 1.46 0.22	0.11	Bed floors at S. side of P.W. 0.225 0.900 0.338 1.463
3/	0.10 8.32 0.10	0.25	where media chls av. 100 mm deep
		0.36	
			4:2:1 conc. in floors laid to falls & benching:
3/2/½/	1.46 8.10 0.08	2.84	Beds 2)2.925(1.462 av. 75 mm thick
2/	6.75 0.15 0.20	0.40	Inlet chl
2/½/	6.75 0.15 0.15	0.15	do.
	0.90 0.90 0.08	0.06	P.W.
2/⅙/	0.90 0.45 0.15	0.02	do. prismoids
4/2/⅙/	0.68 0.45 0.10	0.04	do. do.
2/⅙/	0.45 0.45 0.05	0.00	do. do.
	0.90 0.58 0.08	0.04	
		3.35	carried forward

		3.55	Brought forward (10)
	0.80 0.68 0.08	0.04	P. Cbr.
		3.59	
	0.90	0.90	Precast conc. cill
			Bkwk in cem. mortar 1B:
	8.10 1.42	11.50	Inlet chl. 7.200 0.450 0.450 8.100
	51.75 2.02	104.54	Bed walls & division walls 2/9.675 19.350 4/8.100 32.400 51.750
	4.72 1.42	6.70	P.W. & Grit sump W. 0.900 N. 1.688 E. 0.900 S. 0.562
	0.90 0.98	0.88	Cill 3/0.275 4.050 0.675 4.725
	2.70 0.60	1.62	P. Cbr. W. 0.788 N 1.125 E 0.788 2.701
	0.22 0.45	0.10	Pier
		125.34	
	1.12 0.68	0.76	**Bkwk. a.b. ½B:** under P. Cbr. S. side
			Bkwk. a.b. 1½B:
	5.06 0.82	4.15	P.W. & Grit sump to bottom of beds 4.050 1.012 5.062
	6.53 0.98	6.40	do. to bottom of sump W. 0.900 N. 1.688 E. 0.900 S. 1.688 4/0.338 1.352 6.528
	3.83 0.38	1.46	P.W. only 1.125 0.900 1.125
3/	0.34 0.45	0.46	Piers 2/0.338 0.676 3.826
		12.47	
			20 mm. cem. rendering in two coats:
	14.40 1.01	14.54	Inlet chl. 2/6.750 13.500 2/0.450 0.900 14.400 1.425 0.412 1.013
3/	22.05 1.91	126.35	Beds 2/2.925 5.850 2/8.100 16.200 22.050 1.988 0.075 1.913
	2.70 1.80	4.86	P.W.
	0.90 0.75	0.68	do. cill
	2.02 1.50	3.03	Grit sump 2/0.562 1.124 0.900 2.024
	0.90 0.52	0.47	do. cill
		149.93	

FIG. 46 (j).

S.D.	Works		
3/	8.10	24.30	75 mm field tiles laid falls in & incl. channel av. depth 100 mm in conc. floor to sludge beds
3/	2.92 8.10 0.26	18.45	8–20 mm washed clinker for media av. 260 mm deep & 60–40 mm over tiles
		3 No	Provide 150 mm pipe in short lengths & build into 225 mm walls
		3 No	Build 50 mm pipe into 225 wall
		4 No	do. 100 do. do.
		1 No	do. do. 338 wall
	8.10	8.10	Lay & joint 100 mm G.S. sludge pipe in trench av. 1.875 deep
		1 No	E.O. for 100 mm bend
		2 No	E.O. for 100 x 100 junct.
		5 No	150 mm M.S. H.R. chl. Handstops. P.&F.
	3.90	3.90	50mm M.S. suction & delivery pipe incl. jointing & fixing
		1 No	E.O. for 50mm bend
		2 No	E.O. for 50mm connections
		4 No	50 mm W.I. pipe clamps & fixings
		1 No	P.&F. 50 mm diaphragm pump & connections
		4 No	12M x 125 @ 0.28 kg Rag Bolts
	1.00 1.00	1.00	Wrot. T.&G. double battened 32mm wood cover
		21 No	Step irons 2.3 kg
			GENERAL
		689.0	Bulk Ex. to form level 422.400 for filter bed & humus tanks. See fig 9.10.
			E.O. Excavation for stripping turf & topsoil laying aside & reusing:
π/	10.12 10.12	321.74	Circular
½/	13.20 20.55	135.63	Trapezium
		457.37	
0.0268	20.25 20.25	10.99	Ddt last where twice taken - segment

	11.02	11.02	100 mm G.S.W. sludge drainage pipe & in trench av. 0.900 deep (11)
		2 No	E.O. for bends
	15.00	15.00	50 mm Galv.I. humus sludge pipe & in trench av. 0.600 deep
		1 No	E.O. for tail bend
		1 No	E.O. for insp. junction
	22.58	22.58	50 mm Galv.I. sludge drainings return & in trench av. 0.150 deep
		1 No	E.O. for bend
		1 No	E.O. for insp. junction
	72.00	72.0	75mm E.W. field drains & in trench av. 0.450 deep
	72.00 0.30 0.30	6.48	Clinker filling over field drains
Say	100.00 1.25	125.00	75 mm consolidated clinker over paths
	81.00 1.50	121.50	Turfing side slopes av. 1.500 on face
			PROVISIONAL
			Additional excav. for timbering & wkg space:
	25.95 2.25	58.39	S.T. 424.725 2/6.900 13.800 422.475 2/6.075 12.150 2.250 25.950
	17.18 1.35	23.19	S.T. 422.475 2/4.200 8.400 421.125 2/4.388 8.776 1.350 17.175
	6.38 0.22	1.43	S.T. 421.125 2/1.500 3.000 420.900 2/1.688 3.376 0.225 6.376
	4.20 1.12	4.70	D.T. 424.875 2/1.800 3.600 423.750 2/0.600 1.200 1.125 0.450 S.M.H. taken already 1.050 4.200
2/	1.05 1.12	2.35	sides 424.725 423.600 1.125
2/	1.42 0.90	2.56	D.C. sides 424.575 423.675 0.900
		92.62	
	2.70 1.95	5.26	H.T. N. 422.400 420.450 av. 1.950
2/	3.38 1.88	12.71	do. E&W. 422.400 420.525 1.875
		17.97	carried forward

FIG. 46 (*k*).

S.D. Works (12)

Dimensions	Squaring	Description
	17.97	Brought forward
4.42 1.72	7.60	do. S. 422.400 − 420.675 = 1.725; 1.425 + 1.575 + 1.425 = 4.425
4.42 2.70	11.93	H.S.W. 422.400 − 419.700 = 2.700
1.58 0.68	1.07	do. under H.T. 420.375 − 419.700 = 0.675
	38.57	
36.45 1.80	65.61	S.D.B. 424.350 − 422.550 = 1.800; 2/9.675 = 19.350; 2/8.550 = 17.100; 36.450
5.92 3.00	17.76	P.W. & G.S. 1.275 + 2.475 + 1.275 + 0.900 = 5.925; 424.350 − 421.350 = 3.000
1.58 1.50	2.37	do. under S.D.B. 422.550 − 421.050 = 1.500
	85.74	
		Ramp on side slope to filter bed at gradient of 1 in 10:
15.00 1.80	27.00	4:2:1 P.C.C. 0.150 thick 50 mm. clinker under
15.00 1.80 0.75	20.25	Ex. av. 750 mm deep for do.
	8 No	Precast conc. steps 1.200 × 0.375 × 0.200 in flight leading to humus tank incl. building & setting
3.85	3.85	Precast conc. curbs 300 × 75 to do.

Compliance with Conditions of Contract.

- Dealing with water
- Watching & Lighting
- Clearing site
- Offices, canteen & sanitary accom^n^
- Protection of cement
- Adjacent property
- Statutory obligations

FIG. 46 (*l*).

CHAPTER XIV

UNITS OF MEASUREMENT AND EXAMPLES—(*continued*)

ROADS AND PAVINGS

14.01 The measurement of excavation, filling and fabric reinforcement has been described in the previous chapter. The following units of measurement are usual in roadwork and pavings generally:—

Roads and paving	Sq. m
Concrete foundations to pavings	Sq. m
Ditto to kerbs and channels	Lin. m
Kerbs and channels	Lin. m
Expansion joints	Lin. m

All rates include for making good up to kerbs and channels, manholes and the like.

14.02 Macadam Roads.—Items for macadam roads should state the nature and thickness of bottoming and finishing coats and it should be stated that the rates are to include for any preparation of the bed for receiving the macadam surface.

14.03 Asphalt Surfaces.—The quality and composition of the asphalt should be stated together with the number of coats and the finished thickness. Any special surface finish should be specified. The rates to cover making good to kerbs, channels, manholes and the like.

14.04 Concrete Roads.—For concrete roads the composition and thickness of the concrete should be stated. The rates should cover for any preparation of the bed, for waterproof paper if used, and for finishing the surface in a specified manner to camber or otherwise. Channels formed in concrete are measured per linear metre extra over the rate for the concrete. Separate items should be provided for reinforcement of concrete roads.

14.05 Pavings.—The material to be used in pavings, whether setts, flags or slabs should be stated and the method of bedding and grouting. Separate items should be included for paving between railway or tram rails, and these rates should cover the cost of trimming up to rails.

14.06 Kerbs and Channels.—The size and nature of kerbs and channels should be stated with the method of laying and jointing. Curved work is measured separately if less than 10m radius, and separate items should be included for curves with radius of 5m or less. Channels in sett pavings are measured by the linear yard extra over the cost of pavings. Manholes of 1 sq. m or less and gulleys of 1 lin. metre or less are not deducted from measurements of paved surfaces.

SEWERS AND DRAINS

14.07 Earthenware and pre-cast concrete sewers and drains are measured per linear metre complete, the rate including for all laying and jointing, but not for excavation and reinstatement which have been dealt with in Chapter VI. Bends, junctions and fittings are numbered and measured extra over plain pipe. Cuts are taken by number.

14.08 Cast Iron Sewers and Drains.—The units are:—

Pipes supplied and delivered	Lin. m (effective length)
Making up pieces and pipes not of standard length	Number of each
Standard bends, tees and specials ..	,, ,, ,,
Non-standard bends, tees and specials ..	,, ,, ,,
Distributing and laying pipes, including bends, etc.	Lin. m as laid.
Jointing, including materials	Number of joints
Supports and brackets	Number of each type
Penstocks	Number of each type

14.09 Small Sewers—Small sewers and drains are frequently measured by the linear metre, including all excavation and reinstatement. In this case the average depth to invert should be stated. A subsidiary bill in the description column should accompany the item in the bill of quantities giving the detailed measurements for one linear metre of the work. Manholes should be measured in detail as in Figs. 24 (*a*) and 24 (*b*).

14.10 Pipes of different classes as defined in the British Standards should be kept separate.

PIPES AND PIPE LINES

14.11 The units of measurement for cast iron pipes are the same as for cast iron sewers and drains already described. For steel, wrought iron, pre-cast concrete and composite pipes the units are:—

Pipes supplied and delivered	Linear metre (effective length)
Making up pieces and collars (including all pipes not of standard length), supplied and delivered	Number of each type

Bends, tees and other specials, supplied and delivered	Number of each type
Taking delivery of pipes, etc., and transporting (where pipes are supplied to the contractor)	Linear metre (effective length)
Distributing and laying pipes, bends, tees and specials	Linear metre of pipe line as laid
Jointing, including jointing material, bolts and other fastenings	Number of joints
Brackets, slings and other supports supplied and fixed	Number of each type
Insulating covering for pipes	Linear metre of pipe line
Valves, expansion joints, anchors and similar fittings, supplied and fixed	Number of each type

As for small sewers and drains, pipe lines may be measured per linear metre of completed work, in which case the method of separation of items referred to under "Sewers and Drains" should be followed.

RAILWAY TRACKWORK

14.12 Track materials are frequently measured as supplied and delivered to the contractor at a specified point in which case the following units are used:—

Rails, Steel Sleepers, Guard Rails, ...	Tonne
Ordinary chairs, spikes, chair screws, track bolts and nuts, fishplates, fishbolts and nuts, other bolts, nuts and washers, sleeper plates, tie plates, packing plates, anchors	Number

Rails should be fully described, whether bullheaded or flat-bottomed, and the mass per metre given. For steel sleepers, ordinary chairs, spikes, chair screws, track bolts and nuts, fishplates and fishbolts and nut the weight of each should be stated.

Timber Sleepers (stating dimensions) ..	Number
Crossing timbers	Cubic metre
Keys, trenails	Number
Switches complete, diamond crossings, or elbows of various angles	Number of sets
Crossings of various angles	Number of each angle

For ballasting and laying tracks the units are:—

Ballast of specified material and size, including distribution and spreading	Cubic metre
Ballast for boxing up and labour distributing and spreading	,, ,,
Laying plain track	Linear metre

Laying Guard Rails (extra to laying track)	Linear metre of guard rail
Bending rails to radius of less than 300 metres extra over laying..	Linear metre of track
Timber for fixing accessories	Cubic metre

The laying of switches, crossings and elbows should be treated as extra over the laying of plain track, and items for fixing accessories should be taken separately, the number of each type being given.

CHAPTER XV

ABSTRACTING AND BILLING

15.01 Abstract sheets are prepared for the purpose of listing items in some predetermined order, usually approximating to the order in which the work is carried out. One or more abstract sheets are used for each class of work.

After the dimension sheets have been squared and checked, each item is transferred to an abstract sheet which is ruled with vertical columns, each column being read from top to bottom and the columns from left to right.

15.02 To avoid errors in transferring the items from the dimension sheets, the description should first be written on the abstract with the dimension entered beneath it, the two being separated by a horizontal line as shown in Figs. 47 (*b*) and 48.

When both description and dimension have been entered on the abstract sheet, but not before, the item on the dimension paper should be crossed out by drawing a vertical line through the squaring column as shown in Fig. 47 (*a*).

In cases where the same dimension applies to two descriptions, a vertical line should be drawn through the first description when, with the dimension, it is transferred, and the vertical line through the squaring column drawn only after the second description and dimension have been abstracted.

15.03 The general rule for abstracting the items for any particular trade or class of work is that cubic dimensions come before super, super before linear, and linear before numbers. This order should not be considered as fixed as it may frequently be necessary to vary it to suit the particular work

Detailed order of items in the Abstract.

15.04 PRELIMINARIES.—As a general rule preliminary items are not abstracted but are written directly on the bill from the specification and conditions of contract. Items which might appear in the abstracts would include the following: provision for hoarding and protection; sinking trial holes, temporary buildings; preparing means of access, work to existing structures, watching and lighting; pumping and insurance.

15.05 EXCAVATION.—The items for excavation will be somewhat in the following order: surface excavation, super items coming before cube, excavation in foundations, excavation in trenches according to depth of digging, excavation in underpinning, tunnels or headings, excavation in rock or hard materials, excavation in compressed air, excavation affected by tides. In cases where some of the material is returned and rammed and the remainder carted away, the item of return and ram should come before cart away in each case.

2/	6·00		Exc. n.e. 1·500 & C.A.
½/	1·20		&
	0·30	2·16	4:2:1 conc in fdns.

FIG. 47 (*a*).

Exc. n.e. 1·500 & C.A.		4:2:1 conc. in fdns.
2·16		2·16

FIG. 47 (*b*).

15.06 CONCRETE.—The order of abstracting concrete work is as follows: cube items, square items under 300mm thick, concrete in pier holes, grillages, underpinning or backing to walls, shuttering. Concrete in special work such as tunnel linings, concrete surrounds, channels and gutters. Items involving extra labour such as special facework, bedding and grouting baseplates, mortices for bolts, joggles and dowels.

15.07 REINFORCED CONCRETE.—For reinforced concrete the order will be: cube items followed by square items, shuttering, bar or rod reinforcement, items of special work, square items coming before numbered items.

15.08 BRICKWORK.—Enter the items in the brickwork abstract in the following order: general brickwork, brickwork battered or circular on plan, brickwork in backing to masonry and underpinning, special facings, the cheapest first, special brickwork such as manholes, wells, chimney shafts, arches, sewers and tunnel lining, running items such as plinths, corbels, bullnoses and copings, numbered items such as holes, and building-in items of ironwork.

15.09 MASONRY.—The order of the items will be: rubble masonry, ashlar masonry, facework to concrete and rubble, stone in bands, plinths, copings, voussoirs, steps and similar work, items incidental to the building-in of ironwork, numbered items under each of these headings. Where more than one kind of stone is used, the cheapest should come first.

15.10 STEEL AND IRONWORK.—The abstracts for steel and ironwork will usually be in the order of cast iron, wrought iron and steel. Items which are to be billed by weight should come first, followed by linear and numbered items. If steel joists are billed according to size the smallest sizes will come first, followed by rods, angles, tees, channels, rivetted girders, stanchions and roof trusses.

15.11 TIMBER.—The order of abstracting is deal, oak, teak and other hard wood. Cube items come before square items and work such as housing treads and risers will, if not included in the general price, be numbered.

Name of Job or Trade : Trade

Date.
Initials or Signature.

4:2:1 conc.		3:2:1 R.C.			1B. in cm.		1½B do.		2B do.
	Ddt		Ddt			Ddt		Ddt	
400	150	10	35		15	10	120	15	30
200	75	90			20	5	45	10	15
50	15	75			40	25	70	25	10
650	240	175			35	40	30		55
240		35			110		10		m^2
410		140			40		180		
m^3		m^3			70		455		
					m^2		25		
							430		
							m^2		

FIG. 48.

15.12 SEWERS AND DRAINS.—On the abstract the main divisions for sewers and drains will be earthenware pipes, pre-cast concrete tubes and cast iron, in this order. These are taken according to the size of the pipe, beginning with the smallest diameter in each case. Next are taken bends, junctions, fittings, jointing and supports. Manholes should be taken off separately, the order of the items in the abstract being: excavation, concrete, brickwork, benching, building-in of pipes, rendering, foot irons, covers.

15.13 PIPES AND PIPE LINES.—The items for pipes and pipe lines should be kept in the following order: ordinary cast iron pipes arranged according to size and depth of cutting, spun cast iron pipes, cast iron pipes with special joints, steel pipes, cast iron bends and fittings, composite pipes, sluice valves, washouts, air valves, hydrants and other fittings.

15.14 RAILWAY TRACKWORK.—The abstract should commence with excavation and filling together with the items of ballasting. Then should follow rails, bullheaded before flat-bottomed, steel sleepers, guard rails, fishplates, chains, switches and crossings, spikes, concrete sleepers, timber sleepers, timber for accessories.

EXAMPLES OF ABSTRACTING

15.15 To illustrate the method of abstracting, certain abstracts for the dimension sheets shown in Figs. 24 (*a*) and 24 (*b*) are given. This example includes a variety of work and materials and therefore well illustrates the procedure to be followed. Figs. 24 (*a*) and 24 (*b*) are reproduced in Figs. 49 (*a*) and 49 (*b*) to show the method of marking off the items on the dimension sheets. The first dimension of 16·8 applies to the four items of excavation in the description column. To prepare the abstract sheet the first description is transferred as shown in the first column of Fig. 50 (*a*) and a line is drawn beneath it. The dimension of 16·8 is written beneath this line and a vertical line is drawn through the first description, viz.: "Ex. n.e. 1·5m deep and C.A." The next three items in the description column are abstracted in a similar manner and after the last item is transferred a vertical line is drawn through the dimension in the squaring column. The next three items are abstracted and written under the appropriate heading on the abstract sheet, each item in the dimension paper being crossed out after it is transferred as shown in Figs. 50 (*a*) and 50 (*b*).

The fifth item of 2·3 is a deduction from the item of 15·8 immediately above. Deductions are written in a special column headed "Ddt." at the side of the item on the abstract sheet from which the deduction is to be made. The sum of the items in this column is deducted from the main item when working up the abstracts.

For the item of 18·5 a new heading is required on the abstract sheet, viz.: "Ex. n.e. 1·5m deep and R.F.I.R." The dimension is entered as a deduction against "Ex. n.e. 1·5m deep and C.A." and as an addition under

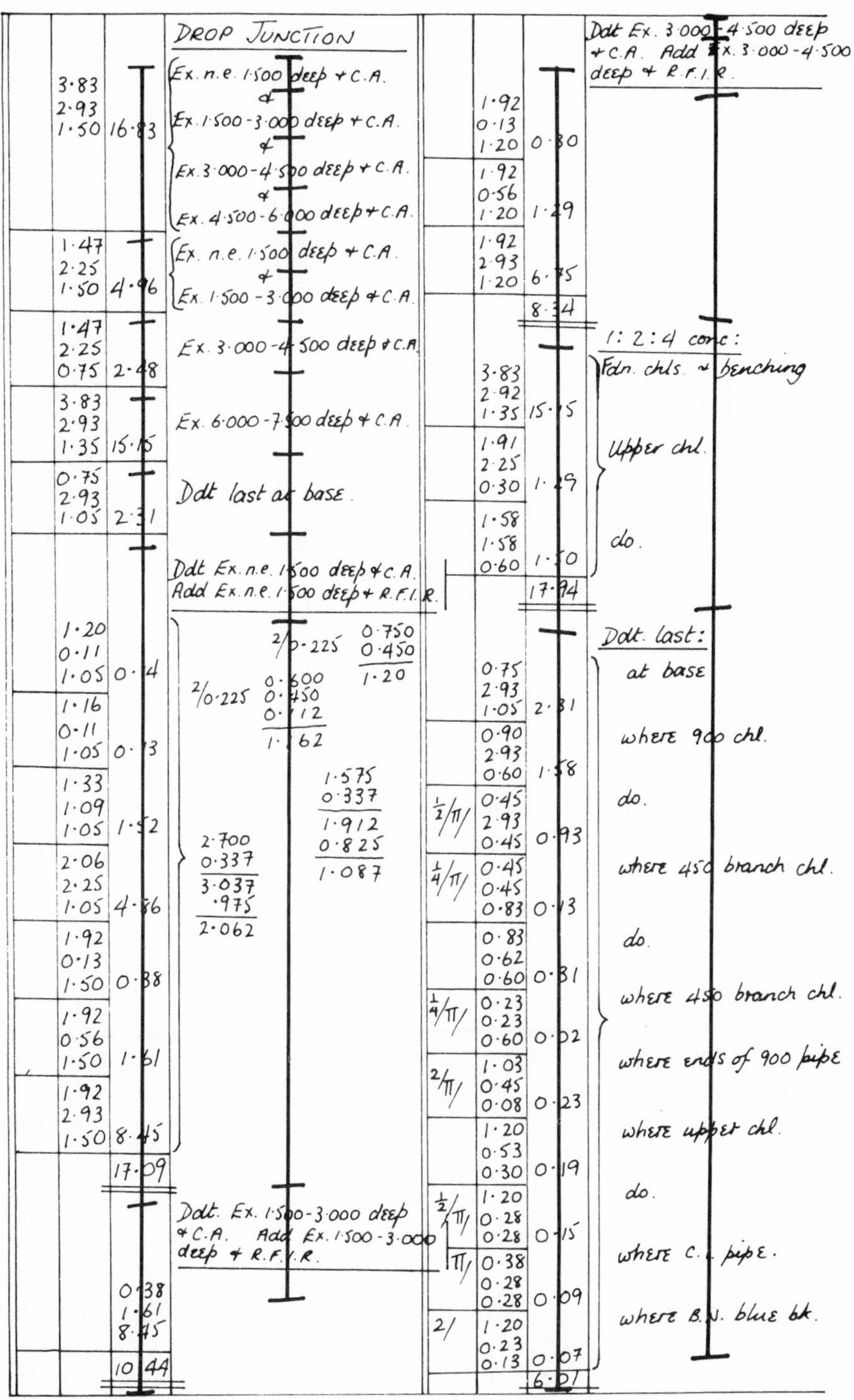
DROP JUNCTION
3·83 2·93 1·50 16·83
Ex. n.e. 1·500 deep + C.A. & Ex. 1·500-3·000 deep + C.A. & Ex. 3·000-4·500 deep + C.A. & Ex. 4·500-6·000 deep + C.A.
1·47 2·25 1·50 4·96
Ex. n.e. 1·500 deep + C.A. & Ex. 1·500-3·000 deep + C.A.
1·47 2·25 0·75 2·48
Ex. 3·000-4·500 deep + C.A.
3·83 2·93 1·35 15·15
Ex. 6·000-7·500 deep + C.A.
0·75 2·93 1·05 2·31
Ddt last at base.
Ddt Ex. n.e. 1·500 deep + C.A. Add Ex. n.e. 1·500 deep + R.F.I.R.
1·20 0·11 1·05 0·14
1·16 0·11 1·05 0·13
1·33 1·09 1·05 1·52
2·06 2·25 1·05 4·86
1·92 0·13 1·50 0·38
1·92 0·56 1·50 1·61
1·92 2·93 1·50 8·45
17·09
2/0·225 0·750 0·450 1·20
2/0·225 0·600 0·450 0·112 1·162
1·575 0·337 1·912 0·825 1·087
2·700 0·337 3·037 ·975 2·062
Ddt. Ex. 1·500-3·000 deep + C.A. Add Ex. 1·500-3·000 deep + R.F.I.R.
0·38 1·61 8·45 10·44
1·92 0·13 1·20 0·30
1·92 0·56 1·20 1·29
1·92 2·93 1·20 6·75
8·34
Ddt Ex. 3·000-4·500 deep + C.A. Add Ex. 3·000-4·500 deep + R.F.I.R.
1: 2: 4 conc:
Fdn. chls. & benching 3·83 2·92 1·35 15·15
Upper chl. 1·91 2·25 0·30 1·29
do. 1·58 1·58 0·60 1·50
17·94
Ddt. last:
at base 0·75 2·93 1·05 2·31
where 900 chl. 0·90 2·93 0·60 1·58
do. ½/π/ 0·45 2·93 0·45 0·93
where 450 branch chl. ¼/π/ 0·45 0·45 0·83 0·13
do. 0·83 0·62 0·60 0·31
where 450 branch chl. ¼/π/ 0·23 0·23 0·60 0·02
where ends of 900 pipe 2/π/ 1·03 0·45 0·08 0·23
where upper chl. 1·20 0·53 0·30 0·19
do. ½/π/ 1·20 0·28 0·28 0·15
where C.I. pipe. π/ 0·38 0·28 0·28 0·09
where B.N. blue bk. 2/ 1·20 0·23 0·13 0·07
6·07

FIG. 49 (*a*).

			3:2:1 conc. incl. shuttering:
	3.83 2.93 0.30	3.37	Lower chamber roof
	4.20 2.25 0.30	2.83	Upper chamber roof
	1.20 1.05 0.15	0.19	Under M.H. cover
	0.13 1.05 0.15	0.02	Round R.S.J.
		6.41	
			Ddt. last:
	1.15 1.58 0.30	0.54	Lower chamber roof
	0.75 0.60 0.30	0.14	Upper chamber roof.
		0.68	
			Fabric No. 62:
		3.37 2.83	
		6.20	
			Ddt. last:
		0.54 0.14	
		0.68	
	2.48	2.48	203 x 102 R.S.J. @ 25.3 kg/m
	1.05	1.05	127 x 76 R.S.J. @ 13.4 kg/m
		18.No.	2.5 kg. step irons
		2 No.	Hooks
		1 No.	Chain 1.750 long
		1 No.	C.I. Manhole cover + seating, wt/325 kg
		6 No.	150 x 24M Rag bolts 1.1 kg each.

			Eng. Blue Bk. in walls in cement mortar:
	11.70 1.50	17.55	2 Bk Lower Chamber 2/2.925 5.850; 2/2.025 4.050; 4/0.450 1.800; 11.700
2/	0.90 0.60	1.08	Arches
		18.63	
	6.65 0.45	2.99	1½ Bk Shaft 2/1.125 2.250; 2/1.575 3.150; 4/0.312 1.248; 6.648
	9.80 2.10	20.58	Upper Chamber 2/2.700 5.400; 2/1.575 3.150; 4/0.312 1.248; 9.798
	4.45 0.30	1.34	do 2/1.125 1.250; 1.575; 2/0.312 0.624; 4.449
		24.91	
			Ddt last where inlet pipe
π/	0.35 0.35	0.38	
			Manhole shaft 1 Bk. 2/0.750 1.500; 2/0.600 1.200; 4/0.225 0.900; 3.600
	3.60 0.75	2.70	
π/	0.46 0.27	0.39	E.O. bkwk for gauged arch in two rings in 1½ bk walls 0.300; 0.050; 0.117; 0.457
2/ ½/π/	0.68 0.35	0.75	do. but three rings in 2 Bk wall. 0.450; 0.063; 0.169; 0.682
2/	1.20	2.40	Bullnosed Bk. on edge to chl.
	0.45	0.45	450 dia. C.I. flanged pipe
	2.25	2.25	
		2.70	
		1 No.	450 dia. C.I. flanged 90° bend.
		2 No.	Pipe brackets 510 int. dia. bolted in halves P. & F.

FIG. 49 (*b*).

the heading of excavate and return, fill-in and ram. The items for concrete, brickwork and ironwork are abstracted in a similar manner and no further explanation is necessary. Further typical abstracts are shown in Figs. 51 (*a*), (*b*) and (*c*). The numbers in circles refer to the page of the taking-off sheet.

Drop Junction : Excavator

Ex. n.e. 1·500 deep & R.F.I.R.	Ex. 1·500 – 3·000 deep & R.F.I.R.	Ex 3·000 – 4·500 deep & R.F.I.R.			
17·09	10·44	8·34			

Ex. n.e. 1·500 deep & C.A.		Ex. 1·500 – 3·000 deep & C.A.		Ex. 3·000 – 4·500 deep & C.A.		Ex. 4·500 – 6·000 deep & C.A.		Ex. 6·000 – 7·500 deep & C.A.	
	Ddt.		Ddt.		Ddt		Ddt		Ddt
16·83	17·09	16·83	10·44	16·83	8·34	16·83	nil	15·15	2·31
4·96		4·96		2·48				2·31	
21·79		21·79		19·31				12·84	
17·09		10·44		8·34					
4·70		11·35		10·97					

FIG. 50 (*a*).

WORKING-UP THE ABSTRACTS

15.16 The working-up of the abstracts, sometimes called "casting and reducing," proceeds after all the items have been transferred from the dimension paper to the abstract sheets and checked. The various columns of dimensions are added up, deductions made where necessary, and the net amounts reduced to the appropriate units for billing. The totals in the "deduction" columns should be cut out by drawing a vertical line through them after each has been transferred and deducted from the item in the "additions" column.

15.17 In some cases it may be easier to take off brickwork by the metre super, specifying the brick thickness, rather than to take off by the metre cube, which involves repeated multiplication by the wall thickness.

Drop Junction: Concretor, Bricklayer, Steelworker

Conc. 1:2:4 in chls + fdns		Eng. Blue Brickwork in cem. mortar			
		1 Bk	1½ Bk		2 Bk
17·94 6·01 11·93 m³	Ddt 6·01	2·70 m²	24·91 0·38 24·53 m²	Ddt 0·38	18·63 m²

Do. in roof slabs incl. shuttering but 1:2:3		E.O. Bkwk 2 ring gauged arch 1½B		B.N. bk on edge to chl.
6·41 0·68 5·73 m³	Ddt. 0·68	0·39 m²		2·40 m

M.S. Fabric No. 62		Do. 3 ring 2B		Steel in R.S.J.	
				203 × 102 @ 25·3	127 × 76 @ 13·4
6·20 0·68 5·52 m³	Ddt 0·68	0·75 m²		2·48 @ 25·3 62·7 kg	1·05 @ 13·4 14·9
				76·7 kg	

FIG. 50 (*b*).

15.18 Ironwork which must be billed by weight should be reduced on the abstract sheets using weights of 785kg, 770kg and 725kg per sq. metre 100mm thick for steel, wrought iron and cast iron respectively.

Sewage Disposal Works : Excavator

27.6.73
[signature]

Bulk Ex.	Ex. n.e. 1·500 + R.F.I.R.		Ex. 1·500–3·000 + R.F.I.R.		Ex. 3·000–4·500 + R.F.I.R.	Provisional Excavation for ramp.	E.O. Ex for removing turf + topsoil + laying aside for reuse	Prepare fdn for conc. flag	Turfing side slopes	Provisional Additional Ex. for timbering and working space
689 (11) m³	1·35 (1) 1·61 (6) 0·98 (6) 0·42 (6) 0·27 (6) 1·47 (9) 6·10 0·99 5·11 m³	Ddt 0·30 (6) 0·48 (6) 0·05 (6) 0·16 (9) 0·99	0·53 (6) 0·92 (9) 1·45 0·05 1·40 m³	Ddt 0·05 (9)	0·06 (9) neglect	20·25 (12) m³	48·62 (1) 91·48 (9) 457·37 (11) 597·47 Ddt 10·99 (11) 597·47 10·99 586·48 m²	0·81 (1) m²	121·50 (11) m²	92·62 (11) 38·57 (12) 85·74 (12) 216·93 m²
	Ex. n.e. 1·500 + C.A.		Ex. 1·500–3·000 + C.A.		Ex. 3·000–4·500 + C.A.					
	69·83 (1) 34·89 (4) 32·87 (6) 0·30 (6) 0·48 (6) 0·05 (6) 135·81 (9) 0·16 (9) 274·39 6·50 267·89 m³	Ddt 1·45 (1) 0·30 (4) 1·61 (6) 0·98 (6) 0·42 (6) 0·27 (6) 1·47 (9) 6·50	45·15 (1) 10·46 (6) 32·28 (9) 0·05 (9) 87·94 2·00 85·94 m³	Ddt 0·35 (6) 0·53 (6) 0·20 (9) 0·92 (9) 2·00	11·62 (1) 0·90 (9) 12·52 0·06 12·46 m³ Ddt 0·06 (9)					

FIG. 51 (*a*).

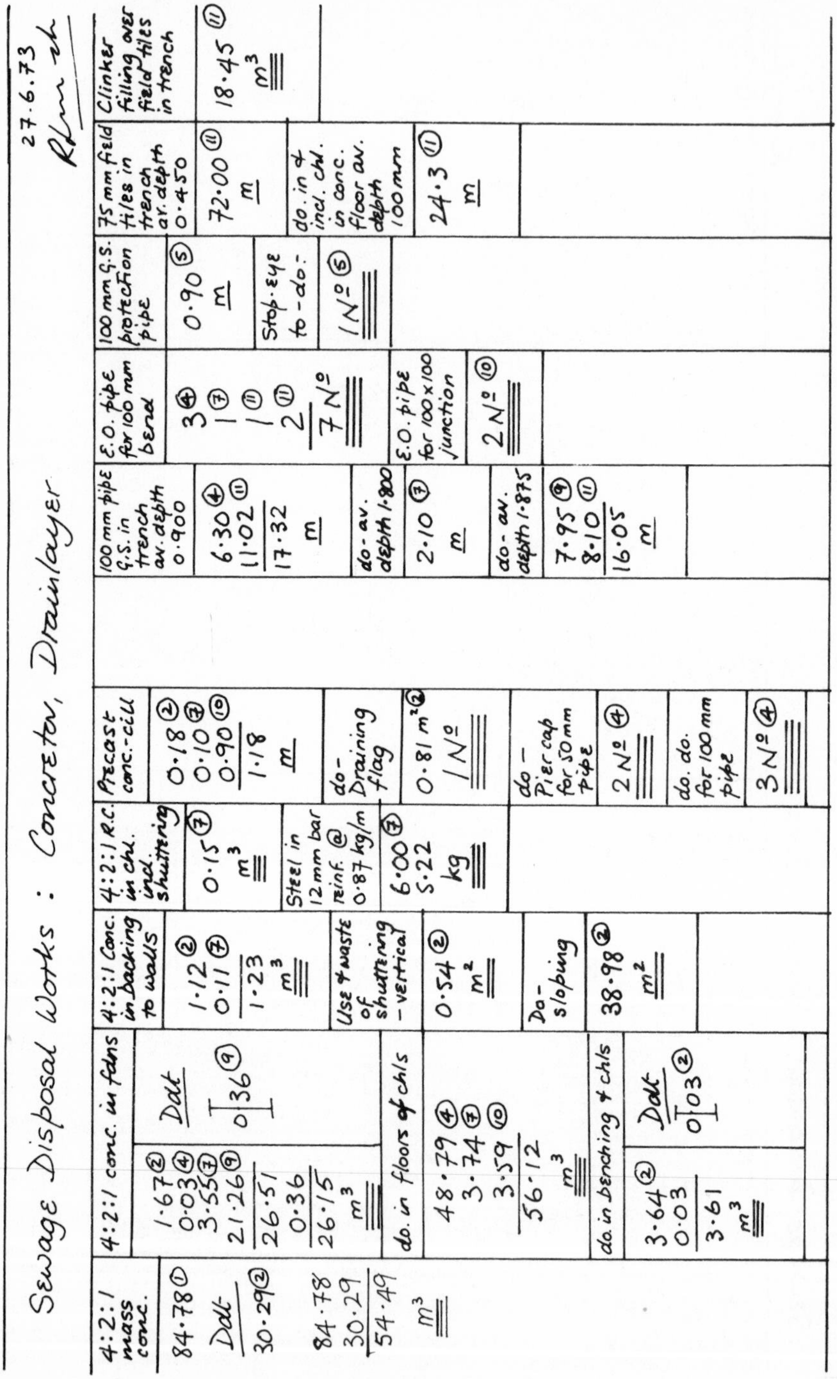

Sewage Disposal Works : Concretor, Drainlayer

27.6.73
R [signature]

4:2:1 mass conc.

84·78 (1)
Ddt
30·29 (2)

84·78
30·29
54·49
m³

4:2:1 conc. in fdns

1·67 (2)
0·03 (4)
3·55 (7)
21·26 (9)
26·51
0·36
26·15
m³

Ddt
0·36 (9)

do. in floors of chls

48·79 (4)
3·74 (7)
3·59 (10)
56·12
m³

do. in benching & chls

3·64 (2)
0·03
3·61
m³

Ddt
0·03 (2)

4:2:1 Conc. in backing to walls

1·12 (2)
0·11 (7)
1·23
m³

Use & waste of shuttering – vertical

0·54 (2)
m²

Do – sloping

38·98 (2)
m²

4:2:1 R.C. in chl. incl. shuttering

0·15 (7)
m³

Steel in 12 mm bar reinf. @ 0·87 kg/m

6·00 (7)
5·22
kg

Precast conc.-cill

0·18 (2)
0·10 (7)
0·90 (10)
1·18
m

do – Draining flag

0·81 m² (2)
1 Nº

do – Pier cap for 50 mm pipe

2 Nº (4)

do. do. for 100 mm pipe

3 Nº (4)

100 mm pipe G.S. in trench av. depth 0·900

6·30 (4)
11·02 (11)
17·32
m

do – av. depth 1·800

2·10 (7)
m

do – av. depth 1·875

7·95 (9)
8·10 (11)
16·05
m

E.O. pipe for 100 mm bend

3 (4)
1 (7)
1 (11)
2 (11)
7 Nº

E.O. pipe for 100 x 100 junction

2 Nº (10)

100 mm G.S. protection pipe

0·90 (5)
m

Stop-eye to -do-

1 Nº (5)

75 mm field tiles in trench av. depth 0·450

72·00 (11)
m

do. in & incl. chl. in conc. floor av. depth 100 mm

24·3 (11)
m

Clinker filling over field tiles in trench

18·45 (11)
m³

FIG. 51 (*b*).

Sewage Disposal Works : Bricklayer

27. 6. 73
R [signature]

Brickwork in cement mortar

½B	1B		1½B
0·76 (10)	66·85 (3)	Ddt	10·11 (3)
m²	4·19 (5)	0·34 (3)	30·96 (8)
	16·47 (8)	0·19 (8)	12·47 (10)
	125·34 (10)	0·53	53·54
	212·85		m²
	0·53		
	212·32		
	m²		

Do. circular		Do. circular
31·05 (5)	Ddt	42·92 (5)
0·14	0·14 (5)	m²
30·91		
m²		

Do. do. honeycomb
1·04 (5)
m³

Bkwk in piers in cem. mortar

1B	2½B
0·56 (5)	0·34 (5)
m²	m²

E.O. Bkwk for 225 mm D.B.N. coping
42·31 (3)
13·96 (5)
27·07 (8)
83·34
m

E.O. circ.^r bkwk for do.	
62·83 (5)	Ddt
0·45	0·45 (5)
62·38	
m	

E.O. do. for splayed plinth course

41·41 m (5)

E.O. D.B.N. coping for mitred angle block – square
11 (3)
4 (5)
10 (8)
25 N°

do – skew
4 (3)
4 (8)
8 N°

E.O. D.B.N. coping for stop ends
3 (3)
3 (8)
6 N°

G.S. pipe in short lengths & build into 1B wall

ϕ 100 mm	ϕ 150 mm
1 N° (3)	2 (3)
	3 (10)
	5 N°

Build end of pipe into 1B wall

ϕ 50 mm	ϕ 100 mm	ϕ 150 mm
1 (3)	4 (3)	1 N° (8)
2 (8)	1 (8)	
3 (10)	4 (10)	
6 N°	9 N°	

Do. skew

	1 N° (3)

Build end of pipe into 1½ B wall

ϕ 50 mm	ϕ 100 mm	ϕ 150 mm
1 N° (5)	1 (3) 3 (8) 1 (10)	1 N° (5)
	5 N°	

20 mm cem. rendering in two coats

	Ddt
75·44 (3)	9·25 (3)
45·30 (8)	2·59 (8)
149·93 (10)	11·84
270·67	
11·84	
258·83	
m²	

FIG. 51 (*c*).

WRITING THE BILL OF QUANTITIES

15.19 The writing of the Bill of Quantities, or billing as it is called, is the operation of transferring all items from the abstract sheets to bill paper. A specimen ruling of bill paper is shown in Fig. 52; column 1 is for the number of the item, column 2 for the description, column 3 for the quantity, column 4 for the unit of measurement, column 5 for the rate, and column 6 for the amount in pounds and pence.

1	2	3	4	5	6	

FIG. 52.

15.20 The heading of the Bill will state the name of the employer, the nature of the work and the name of the responsible Engineer, followed by the "Preliminaries" which are all the general items in the specification and conditions of contract which a contractor may wish to price. These items comprise such work as setting out, sinking trial holes, allowance for watching and lighting, testing of materials, provision of machinery and plant, pumping, making good defects during the period of maintenance, reinstatement, etc. The items will vary with every contract, but they will usually include all work for which no measurement is given in the bill.

15.21 A clause is frequently inserted in the bill immediately following the "Preliminaries" advising the person tendering before commencing to price the bill to read the conditions of contract and the specification and to include against the various items in the "Preliminaries," such sum as he thinks necessary to cover his liabilities in respect of the terms of the conditions of contract and specification applying thereto. In some cases it may be necessary to insert a short preamble at the beginning of each trade or class of work, briefly describing the materials and workmanship and referring the tenderer to the specification for further information.

15.22 METHOD OF BILLING.—The items on the abstract sheets are transferred to the bill in the same order as on the abstracts and as each item is transferred it is cut out by a vertical line through the abstract. The pages of the Bill will be numbered and each page, except the first and last of each trade or section, will begin with "Brought Forward" and end with "Carried Forward".

15.23 There is no rule as to the accuracy with which items should be entered in the dimension columns of the Bill as it depends upon the accuracy of taking-off. The following may, however, be regarded as good practice. Items in cubic metres to the nearest $\frac{1}{10}$ cubic metre. Items in linear dimensions to the nearest decimetre and weight to the nearest kilogram. Care must be taken in using these rules where the bill includes a large number of small items, as the errors may not cancel out in such cases. Fig. 53 shows how typical items would be entered on the Bill.

Item No.	**BILL OF QUANTITIES for NAME OF WORKS**	*Quant*	*Unit*	*Rate*	£	*p*
	NAME OF EMPLOYER (NAME OF ENGINEER)					
4	Allow for setting out works.					
7	Excavate to foundations, return, fill in and ram around footings.	40	cu.m			
61	80 mm of clean broken stone, to 25 mm British Standard gauge, well rammed and consolidated to receive concrete under floors.	10	sq.m			
85	Labour and materials to forming 100 mm diameter half-round channel in concrete floor.	5	m			
103	Stone in templates under bearings of girders.	12	cu.m			
104	Labour to sinking holes 150 mm deep in stone templates for 25 mm diameter ragged Lewis bolts.	8	No.			
273	Provide and fix on concrete manhole shaft, one cast iron manhole cover of pattern approved by the Engineer.	40	kg			

FIG. 53.

15.24 SUMMARY.—The totals obtained in the Bill for each trade or class of work are often brought together in a summary, and the grand total at the end of the summary is carried to the Form of Tender.

15.25 DAYWORK.—If a considerable amount of daywork is likely to be required, it is usual to include after the summary a schedule of daywork prices for labour and material. Such a schedule takes the form of a list of the various classes of workmen likely to be engaged on the work, and the contractor fills in the rate per hour which he will require for such labour. A similar schedule of materials likely to be required is prepared which the contractor prices on a unit basis. It should be stated that the prices are to include for profit, tackle, tools and general foreman's superintendence. Foremen on the works are usually charged as ordinary workmen.

15.26 As an example of billing the complete Bill for the Sewage Disposal Works taken off in Figs. 46 (*a*) to (*l*) is given in the following pages. In accordance with the standard method of measurement of Civil Engineering Quantities, fractions are expressed in decimals, and the ruling of the form is that suggested in the Report.

BILL OF QUANTITIES

for the Proposed Sewage Disposal Works at Coat Park in the Urban District of Hart on Cleve, to be carried out under the supervision of R. Q. Vectorston, Esq., B.Sc., C.Eng., M.I.C.E., Engineer to the Urban District Council, and in accordance with the Drawings, Specification and Conditions of Contract prepared by him.

Instructions to persons tendering.

The above documents will be available for inspection at the Offices of the Urban District Council for 28 days commencing 30th September, 1974, during office hours, on payment of £5, which will be returned on receipt of a *bona-fide* tender.

The sealed tender, endorsed "Tender for Coat Park Sewage Disposal Works," and addressed to the Clerk, Hart on Cleve U.D.C. Offices, Chat Road, Hart on Cleve, must arrive not later than 9 a.m. on the 30th November, 1974.

Tenders must be on the Form supplied herewith and must be accompanied by the fully priced Bill of Quantities and by the names and addresses of the Sureties.

Preamble.

(*a*) Attention is directed to the form of contract, the conditions of contract, the specification, and the drawings, and these documents are to be read in conjunction with the Bill of Quantities.

(*b*) The prices and rates to be inserted in the Bill of Quantities are to be the full inclusive value of the work described under the several items, including all costs and expenses which may be required in and for the construction of the work described, together with all general risks, liabilities and obligations (such as temporary buildings, fencing, watching, lighting, insurances, labour regulations, order of procedure, indemnity, maintenance and the like) set forth or implied in the documents on which the tender is to be based; where special risks, liabilities and obligations cannot be dealt with as above, then the price thereof is to be separately stated in the item or items provided for the purpose.

(*c*) A price or rate is to be entered against each item in the Bill of Quantities, whether quantities are stated or not. Items against which no price is entered are to be considered as covered by other prices or rates in the bill.

(*d*) Any special methods of measurement used are stated at the head of or in the text of the Bill of Quantities for the trades or items affected. All other items are measured net in accordance with the drawings and no allowance has been made for waste.

(*e*) The quantities of work and material in the Bill of Quantities are not to be considered as limiting or extending the amount of work to be done and material to be supplied by the contractor.

(*f*) General directions and descriptions of work and material given in the specification are not necessarily repeated in the Bill of Quantities. Reference is to be made to the specification for this information.

(*g*) Provisional sums and prime cost items (if any) are to be dealt with as provided for in the conditions of contract and in the specification.

PRELIMINARY ITEMS

Item No.	*Description*	*Quant.*	*Unit*	*Rate*	£	*p*
1	Allow for visiting the site and ascertaining the nature of the works and the character of the subsoil and for verifying and examining the drawings and specification and providing working or progress drawings as required by the Conditions of Contract.					
2	Allow for setting out the works from lines marked by the Engineer and for the accurate transfer of levels from bench marks furnished to the Contractor including for pegs, templates, profiles and all other equipment for setting out.					
3	Allow for assisting to measure any part of the works					
4	Allow for providing all special machinery plant tools and equipment and other matters and things (not included in other items or covered in general rates and prices) necessary for the proper, safe, entire and expeditious performance completion and maintenance of the works.					
5	Allow for giving all notices and paying all fees required by law to any persons or bodies so entitled in respect of operations under this contract.					
6	Allow for indemnifying the Council against all claims for accidents and damages from whatever cause, for the interruption of traffic, gas, and water, and for interference with drainage, telephonic and electric lighting wires and allow for taking all precautions to prevent damage to persons and property in connection with the execution of this contract.					
7	Allow for and make such arrangements as will avoid any interference with the carrying on of the sewage disposal under the existing scheme until the completion of provision of such temporary work, bridges, crossings and diversions as may be necessary.					
8	Allow for making good all surfaces of lands in or through which the works are performed and for making good injury or damage to property or land occasioned by the execution of the works or by extraordinary traffic arising therefrom.					
	Carried forward ..					

Item No.	Description	Quant	Unit	Rate	£	p
	Brought forward ..					
9	Allow for clearing the site before the commencement of the works and for removing from time to time all surplus condemned and objectionable material and rubbish and for removing old material which shall remain the property of the Council to such places of disposal as the Engineer may order and for leaving the works clean and tidy at the end of the contract.					
10	Allow for keeping the works clear of water from whatever source and sewage and for ascertaining the amount of water and sewage to be so dealt with.					
11	Allow for making good damage caused by floods.					
12	Provide and lay on all water required for mixing materials and for canteens and other purposes in connection with the works and pay the Water Company's charges thereon.					
13	Allow for work specified to be done by the Contractor but for which no separate items is given in the Bill of Quantities.					
	Excavator					
14	Bulk excavation to formation for Filter Bed and Humus Tanks.	689	cu.m			
15	Excavate to a depth not exceeding 1·500 metres and return, fill in and ram.	5·1	cu.m			
16	Excavate ditto and cart away to spoil.	268	cu.m			
17	Excavate from a depth of 1·500 metres and not exceeding 3·000 metres and return, fill in and ram.	1·4	cu.m			
18	Excavate ditto and cart away to spoil.	85·9	cu.m			
19	Excavate from a depth of 3 metres and not exceeding 4·500 metres and cart away to spoil.	12·5	cu.m			
20	Provisional item. Excavation for ramp.	20·3	cu.m			
21	Extra over excavation for labour to removing turf and top soil, laying aside selected material for reuse on side slopes and carting remainder to spoil.	587	sq.m			
22	Turfing side slopes.	121·5	sq.m			
23	Prepare foundation to receive concrete draining flag.	1	sq.m			
24	Provisional item. Additional excavation for timbering and working space.	217	sq.m			
	Concretor and Reinforced Concretor					
25	Mass concrete in Settling Tanks.	54·5	cu.m			
	Carried forward ..					

Item No.	*Description*	*Quant.*	*Unit*	*Rate*	£	*p*
	Brought forward ..					
26	Concrete in foundations.	26·2	cu.m			
27	Concrete laid to falls in floors and channels.	56·1	cu.m			
28	Concrete laid to falls in benching and channel filling in small quantities.	3·6	cu.m			
29	Concrete in backing to walls.	1·2	cu.m			
30	Use and waste of shuttering to vertical face of concrete, including all necessary strutting.	0·5	sq.m			
31	Ditto, but sloping faces.	39	sq.m			
32	Reinforced concrete in channel, including all formwork.	0·2	cu.m			
33	12 mm diameter mild steel bar reinforcement.	5·2	kg			
34	Precast concrete in sills 225 mm wide and 60 mm average depth.	1·2	m			
35	Precast concrete in draining flag average 75 mm thick and 900 mm square laid on prepared foundation.	1	No.			
36	Precast concrete in caps to piers as saddles to suit 50 mm diameter pipe.	2	No.			
37	Ditto to suit 100 mm diameter pipe.	3	No.			
38	Provisional item. 150 mm thick concrete ramp at a gradient of 1 in 10 on side slope to Filter formation including 50 mm thickness of consolidated 40 mm clinker under.	27	sq.m			
39	Provisional item. Build flight of steps leading to Humus Tank formation from Filter Bed formation level. Provide, lay and set 8 No. precast concrete steps, 1·200 by 0·375 by 0·200 m, together with 3·850 metres of precast concrete curb, 75 mm wide by 300 mm deep, including all bedding, jointing, cramps and dowels.	1	No.			
	Drainlayer					
40	100 mm diameter glazed stoneware pipe laid to fall and jointed in and including trench average 900 mm deep excavated and refilled.	17·3	m			
41	Ditto, but average 1·800 m deep.	2·1	m			
42	Ditto, but average 1·875 m deep.	16	m			
43	Extra over above pipe for 100 mm diameter bends.	7	No.			
44	Extra over above pipe for junctions 100 mm by 100 mm diameter.	2	No.			
45	100 mm diameter glazed stoneware protection pipe, including jointing.	0·9	m			
46	Glazed stoneware stop eye for protection pipe.	1	No.			
	Carried forward ..					

Item No.	Description	Quant.	Unit	Rate	£	p
	Brought forward ..					
47	75 mm diameter earthenware field tiles laid to fall and butt-jointed in and including trench average 450 mm deep, excavated and refilled with clinker and soil.	72	m			
48	Clinker filling over field tiles.	18·5	cu.m			
49	75 mm diameter earthenware field tiles laid to fall and butt-jointed in and including forming channel in concrete floor average 100 mm deep, and filling over tiles with 60 – 40 mm clinker average depth 50 mm.	24	m			
	Bricklayer					
50	Engineering brickwork in cement mortar, in walls, pointed on seen faces, ½ brick thick.	0·8	sq.m			
51	Ditto, but 1 brick thick.	212·3	sq.m			
52	Ditto, but 1½ bricks thick.	53·5	sq.m			
53	Circular ditto, 1 brick thick.	30·9	sq.m			
54	Circular ditto, 1½ bricks thick.	42·9	sq.m			
55	Honeycombed circular ditto, 1½ bricks thick.	1	cu.m			
56	Engineering brickwork as before in piers, 1 brick thick.	0·6	sq.m			
57	Ditto, but 2½ bricks thick.	0·4	sq.m			
58	Extra over engineering brickwork in walls for double bull-nosed coping set and pointed in cement mortar.	83·3	m			
59	Extra over circular engineering brickwork for ditto.	62·4	m			
60	Extra over coping for square-mitred angle blocks.	25	No.			
61	Extra over coping for skew-mitred angle blocks.	8	No.			
62	Extra over coping for stop end blocks.	6	No.			
63	Extra over circular engineering brickwork for double splayed plinth course in cement mortar pointed on seen face.	41·4	m			
64	Provide 100 mm diameter glazed stoneware pipe in short lengths and build into brick wall 225 mm thick.	1	No.			
65	Ditto, but 150 mm diameter.	5	No.			
66	Build end of pipe into 225 mm thick brick wall for 50 mm diameter pipes.	6	No.			
67	Ditto, for 100 mm diameter pipes.	9	No.			
68	Ditto, for 150 mm diameter pipe.	1	No.			
69	Build end of pipe into 338 mm thick brick wall for 50 mm diameter pipe.	1	No.			
70	Ditto, for 100 mm diameter pipes.	5	No.			
71	Ditto, for 150 mm diameter pipe.	1	No.			
	Carried forward ..					

Item No.	*Description*	*Quant.*	*Unit*	*Rate*	£	*p*
	Brought forward ..					
72	Build end of 100 mm diameter pipe skew into 225 mm thick brick wall.	1	No.			
73	20 mm thick cement rendering in two coats.	258·8	sq.m			
	Sewage Pipelayer and Ironworker					
74	50 mm diameter cast iron coated spigot and socket pipes, including laying and jointing with lead and spun yarn and bedding on piers.	6	m			
75	Ditto, but 150 mm diameter.	11	m			
76	Extra over 50 mm diameter cast iron pipe for bend.	1	No.			
77	50 mm diameter galvanised iron screw-jointed pipe in and including trench average 150 mm deep excavated and refilled.	23	m			
78	Ditto, but average 600 mm deep.	15·3	m			
79	Extra over galvanised pipe for bends.	2	No.			
80	Extra over galvanised pipe for junctions.	2	No.			
81	50 mm diameter mild steel screw-jointed coated suction pipe.	6·5	m			
82	Extra over above pipe for bends.	2	No.			
83	Extra over above pipe for special connections.	4	No.			
84	Ranges of cast iron coated flange-jointed sludge pipe together with bends, vent, blank flange and Y-junction as shown and including all fixing and jointing.	2	No.			
85	Pipe clamps and fixing for 50 mm diameter pipe.	7	No.			
86	Ditto for 100 mm diameter pipe.	6	No.			
87	50 mm sluice valve and turnkey, including flanged joints and fixing.	1	No.			
88	100 mm sluice valves and turnkeys, including fixing.	2	No.			
89	150 mm ditto.	1	No.			
90	100 mm penstock with 1·350 m stem and 225 mm diameter handwheel, together with 100 mm diameter spigot, including all building in, jointing, fixing and holding brackets.	1	No.			
91	Ditto, but 2·100 m stems and 300 mm handwheels.	2	No.			
92	Provide and fix 150 mm diameter cast iron coated dosing siphon together with vent and rest bend.	1	No.			
93	Provide and fix rotary sewage distributor for 12·600 m diameter bed. Prime cost £350.	1	No.			
	Carried forward ..					

Item No.	Description	Quant.	Unit	Rate	£	p
	Brought forward ..					
94	Provide and fix 50 mm diaphragm pumps as shown with all connections complete.	2	No.			
95	Provide and fix mild steel screen 900 mm long and 600 mm wide of 10 mm dia. coated mild steel bars at 25 mm centres.	1	No.			
96	Provide and fix 225 mm by 150 mm coated mild steel perforated channel 1·050 m long.	1	No.			
97	Provide and fix 375 mm by 300 mm cast iron coated channel handstops, including all necessary cutting out in brickwork and concrete and making good.	4	No.			
98	Provide 32 mm wrot tongued and grooved creosoted battened cover 1 metre square.	2	No.			
99	300 mm by 40 mm wrot scumboards, including fixing.	53	m			
100	90 mm by 90 by 10 mm rolled mild steel (Grade 43) equal angles, including fixing.	0·47	tonne			
101	20 M by 90 mm black bolts with hexagonal heads and nuts and tapered washers, having a mass of 0·42 kg each.	32	No.			
102	12 M by 125 mm ragged Lewis bolts, including fixing. Mass 0·28 kg each.	8	No.			
103	20 M by 150 mm ditto. Mass 0·59 kg each.	64	No.			
104	Provide and fix 2·3 kg wrought iron step irons.	28	No.			
	Miscellaneous					
105	75 mm floor drainage tiles in Filter Bed including laying and fitting.	124·7	sq.m			
106	Hard burnt clinker filtering medium graded 60 mm to 40 mm in bed average 225 mm	27·4	cu.m			
107	Ditto, 20 mm to 10 mm in bed average 1·275 m deep.	160	cu.m			
108	Ditto, 20 mm to 8 mm in bed average 260 mm deep.	18·5	cu.m			
109	75 mm consolidated thickness of hard burnt clinker, graded 20 mm to 10 mm on footpaths.	125	sq.m			
	Total forward to Form of Tender ..			£		

DAYWORK SCHEDULE

Preamble

(i) The time of gangers working with their gangs is to to be paid for under appropiate items, but the time of foreman and walking gangers is not to be included but is to be covered by superintendance.

(ii) Overtime is to be paid for in the same proportion as it is to the workmen.

(iii) The rates for heavy plant are to apply only to plant which the contractor has available upon the site.

(iv) The rates for material are to cover delivery at the usual points at which materials are received on the site and not for distribution to the individual sites, the cost of which is chargeable in addition.

(v) Daywork rates are to cover the use of the Contractor's wagons and temporary tracks available on the site.

(vi) The cost of fencing, watching and lighting is to be borne upon the rates for daywork.

(vii) The rates are to cover insurances, use and maintenance of ordinary plant, superintendance, overhead charges and profit.

Item No.	*Description*	*Quant*	*Unit*	*Rate*
	Labour			
110	Navvy or excavator.	—	hour	
111	General labourer (all trades).	—	hour	
112	Drain layer.	—	hour	
113	Pipe layer and pipe jointer.	—	hour	
114	Concretor.	—	hour	
115	Pavior.	—	hour	
116	Pavior's labourer.	—	hour	
117	Bricklayer.	—	hour	
118	Bricklayer's labourer.	—	hour	
119	Mason.	—	hour	
120	Mason's labourer.	—	hour	
121	Carpenter and joiner.	—	hour	
122	Ditto labourer.	—	hour	
123	Plumber.	—	hour	
124	Plumber's labourer.	—	hour	
125	Founder and smith.	—	hour	
126	Roofer.	—	hour	
127	Electrician.	—	hour	
128	Painter and glazier.	—	hour	
129	Waterproofer.	—	hour	

Item No.	*Description*	*Quant.*	*Unit*	*Rate*
	Brought forward ..			
	Materials			
130	Sand.	—	tonne	
131	Portland Cement.	—	tonne	
132	Rapid-hardening Portland Cement.	—	tonne	
133	Lime.	—	tonne	
134	Aggregate.	—	tonne	
135	Furnace clinker.	—	tonne	
136	Quarry dressed stone.	—	cu.m	
137	Timber left in trenches.	—	cu.m	
138	Pitch pine sheet piling 300mm × 150mm 3–6m long.	—	cu.m	
139	Ditto, 6–9m long.	—	cu.m	
140	Timber pile 300mm × 300mm, including handling, pitching and driving, not exceeding 9m long.	1	No.	
141	Ditto, 9–12m long.	1	No.	
142	Sawn fir timber.	—	cu.m	
143	Timber whitewood for joiner's work..	—	cu.m	
144	Nails and spikes.	—	kg	
145	Reinforced concrete pile 300mm × 300mm including handling, pitching and driving, not exceeding 9m long.	1	No.	
146	Ditto, 9–12m long.	1	No.	
147	Lead wool.	—	kg	
148	Sheet lead.	—	kg	
149	Spun yarn.	—	kg	
150	Cast iron.	—	kg	
151	Clay puddle.	—	cu.m	
152	Common bricks.	1000	No.	
153	Engineering bricks.	1000	No.	
154	Slates.	1000	No.	
	Plant (including operator, attendance and fuel)			
155	Horse and cart.	—	day	
156	Motor lorry, 4 cu.m. tipping.	—	day	
157	Motor lorry, 10 tonne.	—	day	
158	Pump, capacity 25000 litres per hour, working.	—	hour	
159	Ditto, standing by.	—	hour	
160	Oxyacetylene plant.	—	hour	

APPENDIX A

CONDITIONS OF CONTRACT

DEFINITIONS AND INTERPRETATION

1. (1) In the Contract (as hereinafter defined) the following words and expressions shall have the meanings hereby assigned to them except where the context otherwise requires:— **Definitions.**

(a) " Employer " means ....

of..........

and includes the Employer's personal representatives or successors;

(b) " Contractor " means the person or persons firm or company whose tender has been accepted by the Employer and includes the Contractor's personal representatives successors and permitted assigns;

(c) " Engineer " means ....
or other the Engineer appointed from time to time by the Employer and notified in writing to the Contractor to act as Engineer for the purposes of the Contract in

place of the said.......... ;

(d) " Engineer's Representative " means a person being the resident engineer or assistant of the Engineer or clerk of works appointed from time to time by the Employer or the Engineer and notified in writing to the Contractor by the Engineer to perform the functions set forth in Clause 2(1);

(e) " Contract " means the Conditions of Contract Specification Drawings Priced Bill of Quantities the Tender the written acceptance thereof and the Contract Agreement (if completed);

(f) " Specification " means the specification referred to in the Tender and any modification thereof or addition thereto as may from time to time be furnished or approved in writing by the Engineer;

(g) " Drawings " means the drawings referred to in the Specification and any modification of such drawings approved in writing by the Engineer and such other drawings as may from time to time be furnished or approved in writing by the Engineer;

(h) " Tender Total " means the total of the Priced Bill of Quantities at the date of acceptance of the Contractor's Tender for the Works;

(i) " Contract Price " means the sum to be ascertained and paid in accordance with the provisions hereinafter contained for the construction completion and maintenance of the Works in accordance with the Contract;

(j) " Permanent Works " means the permanent works to be constructed completed and maintained in accordance with the Contract;

(k) " Temporary Works " means all temporary works of every kind required in or about the construction completion and maintenance of the Works;

(l) " Works " means the Permanent Works together with the Temporary Works;

(m) " Section " means a part of the Works separately identified in the Appendix to the Form of Tender;

(n) " Site " means the lands and other places on under in or through which the Works are to be executed and any other lands or places provided by the Employer for the purposes of the Contract;

(o) " Constructional Plant " means all appliances or things of whatsoever nature required in or about the construction completion and maintenance of the Works but does not include materials or other things intended to form or forming part of the Permanent Works.

(2) Words importing the singular also include the plural and *vice-versa* where the context requires. **Singular and Plural.**

(3) The headings and marginal notes in the Conditions of Contract shall not be deemed to be part thereof or be taken into consideration in the interpretation or construction thereof or of the Contract. **Headings and Marginal Notes.**

(4) All references herein to clauses are references to clauses numbered in the Conditions of Contract and not to those in any other document forming part of the Contract. **Clause References.**

(5) The word " cost " when used in the Conditions of Contract shall be deemed to include overhead costs whether on or off the Site except where the contrary is expressly stated. **Cost.**

ENGINEER'S REPRESENTATIVE

Functions and Powers of Engineer's Representative.

2. (1) The functions of the Engineer's Representative are to watch and supervise the construction completion and maintenance of the Works. He shall have no authority to relieve the Contractor of any of his duties or obligations under the Contract nor except as expressly provided hereunder to order any work involving delay or any extra payment by the Employer nor to make any variation of or in the Works.

Appointment of Assistants.

(2) The Engineer or the Engineer's Representative may appoint any number of persons to assist the Engineer's Representative in the exercise of his functions under sub-clause (1) of this Clause. He shall notify to the Contractor the names and functions of such persons. The said assistants shall have no power to issue any instructions to the Contractor save in so far as such instructions may be necessary to enable them to discharge their functions and to secure their acceptance of materials or workmanship as being in accordance with the Specification and Drawings and any instructions given by any of them for those purposes shall be deemed to have been given by the Engineer's Representative.

Delegation by Engineer.

(3) The Engineer may from time to time in writing authorise the Engineer's Representative or any other person responsible to the Engineer to act on behalf of the Engineer either generally in respect of the Contract or specifically in respect of particular Clauses of these Conditions of Contract and any act of any such person within the scope of his authority shall for the purposes of the contract constitute an act of the Engineer. Prior notice in writing of any such authorisation shall be given by the Engineer to the Contractor. Such authorisation shall continue in force until such time as the Engineer shall notify the Contractor in writing that the same is determined. Provided that such authorisation shall not be given in respect of any decision to be taken or certificate to be issued under Clauses 12(3) 44 48 60(3) 61 63 and 66.

Reference to Engineer or Engineer's Representative.

(4) If the Contractor shall be dissatisfied by reason of any instruction of any assistant of the Engineer's Representative duly appointed under sub-clause (2) of this Clause he shall be entitled to refer the matter to the Engineer's Representative who shall thereupon confirm reverse or vary such instruction. Similarly if the Contractor shall be dissatisfied by reason of any act of the Engineer's Representative or other person duly authorised by the Engineer under sub-clause (3) of this Clause he shall be entitled to refer the matter to the Engineer for his decision.

ASSIGNMENT AND SUB-LETTING

Assignment.

3. The Contractor shall not assign the Contract or any part thereof or any benefit or interest therein or thereunder without the written consent of the Employer.

Sub-Letting.

4. The Contractor shall not sub-let the whole of the Works. Except where otherwise provided by the Contract the Contractor shall not sub-let any part of the Works without the written consent of the Engineer and such consent if given shall not relieve the Contractor from any liability or obligation under the Contract and he shall be responsible for the acts defaults and neglects of any sub-contractor his agents servants or workmen as fully as if they were the acts defaults or neglects of the Contractor his agents servants or workmen. Provided always that the provision of labour on a piece-work basis shall not be deemed to be a sub-letting under this Clause.

CONTRACT DOCUMENTS

Documents Mutually Explanatory.

5. The several documents forming the Contract are to be taken as mutually explanatory of one another and in case of ambiguities or discrepancies the same shall be explained and adjusted by the Engineer who shall thereupon issue to the Contractor appropriate instructions in writing which shall be regarded as instructions issued in accordance with Clause 13.

Supply of Documents.

6. Upon acceptance of the Tender 2 copies of the drawings referred to in the Specification and of the Conditions of Contract the Specification and (unpriced) Bill of Quantities shall be furnished to the Contractor free of charge. Copyright of the Drawings and Specification and of the Bill of Quantities (except the pricing thereof) shall remain in the Engineer but the Contractor may obtain or make at his own expense any further copies required by him. At the completion of the Contract the Contractor shall return to the Engineer all Drawings and the Specification whether provided by the Engineer or obtained or made by the Contractor.

Further Drawings and Instructions.

7. (1) The Engineer shall have full power and authority to supply and shall supply to the Contractor from time to time during the progress of the Works such modified or further drawings and instructions as shall in the Engineer's opinion be necessary for the purpose of the proper and adequate construction completion and maintenance of the Works and the Contractor shall carry out and be bound by the same.

Notice by Contractor.

(2) The Contractor shall give adequate notice in writing to the Engineer of any further drawing or specification that the Contractor may require for the execution of the Works or otherwise under the Contract.

(3) If by reason of any failure or inability of the Engineer to issue at a time reasonable in all the circumstances drawings or instructions requested by the Contractor and considered necessary by the Engineer in accordance with sub-clause (1) of this Clause the Contractor suffers delay or incurs cost then the Engineer shall take such delay into account in determining any extension of time to which the Contractor is entitled under Clause 44 and the Contractor shall subject to Clause 52(4) be paid in accordance with Clause 60 the amount of such cost as may be reasonable. If such drawings or instructions require any variation to any part of the Works the same shall be deemed to have been issued pursuant to Clause 51. **Delay in Issue.**

(4) One copy of the Drawings and Specification furnished to the Contractor as aforesaid shall be kept by the Contractor on the Site and the same shall at all reasonable times be available for inspection and use by the Engineer and the Engineer's Representative and by any other person authorised by the Engineer in writing. **One Copy of Documents to be kept on Site.**

GENERAL OBLIGATIONS

8. (1) The Contractor shall subject to the provisions of the Contract construct complete and maintain the Works and provide all labour materials Constructional Plant Temporary Works transport to and from and in or about the Site and everything whether of a temporary or permanent nature required in and for such construction completion and maintenance so far as the necessity for providing the same is specified in or reasonably to be inferred from the Contract. **Contractor's General Responsibilities.**

(2) The Contractor shall take full responsibility for the adequacy stability and safety of all site operations and methods of construction provided that the Contractor shall not be responsible for the design or specification of the Permanent Works (except as may be expressly provided in the Contract) or of any Temporary Works designed by the Engineer. **Contractor Responsible for Safety of Site Operations.**

9. The Contractor shall when called upon so to do enter into and execute a Contract Agreement (to be prepared at the cost of the Employer) in the form annexed. **Contract Agreement.**

10. If the Tender shall contain an undertaking by the Contractor to provide when required 2 good and sufficient sureties or to obtain the guarantee of an Insurance Company or Bank to be jointly and severally bound with the Contractor in a sum not exceeding 10 per cent of the Tender Total for the due performance of the Contract under the terms of a Bond the said sureties Insurance Company or Bank and the terms of the said Bond shall be such as shall be approved by the Employer and the provision of such sureties or the obtaining of such guarantee and the cost of the Bond to be so entered into shall be at the expense in all respects of the Contractor unless the Contract otherwise provides. **Sureties.**

11. (1) The Contractor shall be deemed to have inspected and examined the Site and its surroundings and to have satisfied himself before submitting his tender as to the nature of the ground and sub-soil (so far as is practicable and having taken into account any information in connection therewith which may have been provided by or on behalf of the Employer) the form and nature of the Site the extent and nature of the work and materials necessary for the completion of the Works the means of communication with and access to the Site the accommodation he may require and in general to have obtained for himself all necessary information (subject as above-mentioned) as to risks contingencies and all other circumstances influencing or affecting his tender. **Inspection of Site.**

(2) The Contractor shall be deemed to have satisfied himself before submitting his tender as to the correctness and sufficiency of the rates and prices stated by him in the Priced Bill of Quantities which shall (except in so far as it is otherwise provided in the Contract) cover all his obligations under the Contract. **Sufficiency of Tender.**

12. (1) If during the execution of the Works the Contractor shall encounter physical conditions (other than weather conditions or conditions due to weather conditions) or artificial obstructions which conditions or obstructions he considers could not reasonably have been foreseen by an experienced contractor and the Contractor is of opinion that additional cost will be incurred which would not have been incurred if the physical conditions or artificial obstructions had not been encountered he shall if he intends to make any claim for additional payment give notice to the Engineer pursuant to Clause 52(4) and shall specify in such notice the physical conditions and/or artificial obstructions encountered and with the notice if practicable or as soon as possible thereafter give details of the anticipated effects thereof the measures he is taking or is proposing to take and the extent of the anticipated delay in or interference with the execution of the Works. **Adverse Physical Conditions and Artificial Obstructions.**

(2) Following receipt of a notice under sub-clause (1) of this Clause the Engineer may if he thinks fit *inter alia:*— **Measures to be Taken.**

(a) require the Contractor to provide an estimate of the cost of the measures he is taking or is proposing to take;
(b) approve in writing such measures with or without modification;
(c) give written instructions as to how the physical conditions or artificial obstructions are to be dealt with;
(d) order a suspension under Clause 40 or a variation under Clause 51.

Delay and Extra Cost.

(3) To the extent that the Engineer shall decide that the whole or some part of the said physical conditions or artificial obstructions could not reasonably have been foreseen by an experienced contractor the Engineer shall take any delay suffered by the Contractor as a result of such conditions or obstructions into account in determining any extension of time to which the Contractor is entitled under Clause 44 and the Contractor shall subject to Clause 52(4) (notwithstanding that the Engineer may not have given any instructions or orders pursuant to sub-clause (2) of this Clause) be paid in accordance with Clause 60 such sum as represents the reasonable cost of carrying out any additional work done and additional Constructional Plant used which would not have been done or used had such conditions or obstructions or such part thereof as the case may be not been encountered together with a reasonable percentage addition thereto in respect of profit and the reasonable costs incurred by the Contractor by reason of any unavoidable delay or disruption of working suffered as a consequence of encountering the said conditions or obstructions or such part thereof.

Conditions Reasonably Foreseeable.

(4) If the Engineer shall decide that the physical conditions or artificial obstructions could in whole or in part have been reasonably foreseen by an experienced contractor he shall so inform the Contractor in writing as soon as he shall have reached that decision but the value of any variation previously ordered by him pursuant to sub-clause (2)(d) of this Clause shall be ascertained in accordance with Clause 52 and included in the Contract Price.

Work to be to Satisfaction of Engineer.

13. (1) Save in so far as it is legally or physically impossible the Contractor shall construct complete and maintain the Works in strict accordance with the Contract to the satisfaction of the Engineer and shall comply with and adhere strictly to the Engineer's instructions and directions on any matter connected therewith (whether mentioned in the Contract or not). The Contractor shall take instructions and directions only from the Engineer or (subject to the limitations referred to in Clause 2) from the Engineer's Representative.

Mode and Manner of Construction.

(2) The whole of the materials plant and labour to be provided by the Contractor under Clause 8 and the mode manner and speed of construction and maintenance of the Works are to be of a kind and conducted in a manner approved of by the Engineer.

Delay and Extra Cost.

(3) If in pursuance of Clause 5 or sub-clause (1) of this Clause the Engineer shall issue instructions or directions which involve the Contractor in delay or disrupt his arrangements or methods of construction so as to cause him to incur cost beyond that reasonably to have been foreseen by an experienced contractor at the time of tender then the Engineer shall take such delay into account in determining any extension of time to which the Contractor is entitled under Clause 44 and the Contractor shall subject to Clause 52(4) be paid in accordance with Clause 60 the amount of such cost as may be reasonable. If such instructions or directions require any variation to any part of the Works the same shall be deemed to have been given pursuant to Clause 51.

Programme to be Furnished.

14. (1) Within 21 days after the acceptance of his Tender the Contractor shall submit to the Engineer for his approval a programme showing the order of procedure in which he proposes to carry out the Works and thereafter shall furnish such further details and information as the Engineer may reasonably require in regard thereto. The Contractor shall at the same time also provide in writing for the information of the Engineer a general description of the arrangements and methods of construction which the Contractor proposes to adopt for the carrying out of the Works.

Revision of Programme.

(2) Should it appear to the Engineer at any time that the actual progress of the Works does not conform with the approved programme referred to in sub-clause (1) of this Clause the Engineer shall be entitled to require the Contractor to produce a revised programme showing the modifications to the original programme necessary to ensure completion of the Works or any Section within the time for completion as defined in Clause 43 or extended time granted pursuant to Clause 44(2).

Methods of Construction.

(3) If requested by the Engineer the Contractor shall submit at such times and in such detail as the Engineer may reasonably require such information pertaining to the methods of construction (including Temporary Works and the use of Constructional Plant) which the Contractor proposes to adopt or use and such calculations of stresses strains and deflections that will arise in the Permanent Works or any parts thereof during construction from the use of such methods as will enable the Engineer to decide whether if these methods are adhered to the Works can be executed in accordance with the Drawings and Specification and without detriment to the Permanent Works when completed.

Engineer's Consent.

(4) The Engineer shall inform the Contractor in writing within a reasonable period after receipt of the information submitted in accordance with sub-clause (3) of this Clause either:—

(a) that the Contractor's proposed methods have the consent of the Engineer; or
(b) in what respects in the opinion of the Engineer they fail to meet the requirements of the Drawings or Specification or will be detrimental to the Permanent Works.

In the latter event the Contractor shall take such steps or make such changes in the said methods as may be necessary to meet the Engineer's requirements and to obtain his consent. The Contractor shall not change the methods which have received the Engineer's consent without the further consent in writing of the Engineer which shall not be unreasonably withheld.

Design Criteria.

(5) The Engineer shall provide to the Contractor such design criteria relevant to the Permanent Works or any Temporary Works designed by the Engineer as may be necessary to enable the Contractor to comply with sub-clauses (3) and (4) of this Clause.

Delay and Extra Cost.

(6) If the Engineer's consent to the proposed methods of construction shall be unreasonably delayed or if the requirements of the Engineer pursuant to sub-clause (4) of this Clause or any limitations imposed by any of the design criteria supplied by the Engineer pursuant to sub-clause (5) of this Clause could not reasonably have been foreseen by an experienced contractor at the time of tender and if in consequence of any of the aforesaid the Contractor unavoidably incurs delay or cost the Engineer shall take such delay into account in determining any extension of time to which the Contractor is entitled under Clause 44 and the Contractor shall subject to Clause 52(4) be paid in accordance with Clause 60 such sum in respect of the cost incurred as the Engineer considers fair in all the circumstances.

Responsibility Unaffected by Approval.

(7) Approval by the Engineer of the Contractor's programme in accordance with sub-clauses (1) and (2) of this Clause and the consent of the Engineer to the Contractor's proposed methods of construction in accordance with sub-clause (4) of this Clause shall not relieve the Contractor of any of his duties or responsibilities under the Contract.

Contractor's Superintendence.

15. (1) The Contractor shall give or provide all necessary superintendence during the execution of the Works and as long thereafter as the Engineer may consider necessary. Such superintendence shall be given by sufficient persons having adequate knowledge of the operations to be carried out (including the methods and techniques required the hazards likely to be encountered and methods of preventing accidents) as may be requisite for the satisfactory construction of the Works.

Contractor's Agent.

(2) The Contractor or a competent and authorised agent or representative approved of in writing by the Engineer (which approval may at any time be withdrawn) is to be constantly on the Works and shall give his whole time to the superintendence of the same. Such authorised agent or representative shall be in full charge of the Works and shall receive on behalf of the Contractor directions and instructions from the Engineer or (subject to the limitations of Clause 2) the Engineer's Representative. The Contractor or such authorised agent or representative shall be responsible for the safety of all operations.

Removal of Contractor's Employees.

16. The Contractor shall employ or cause to be employed in and about the execution of the Works and in the superintendence thereof only such persons as are careful skilled and experienced in their several trades and callings and the Engineer shall be at liberty to object to and require the Contractor to remove from the Works any person employed by the Contractor in or about the execution of the Works who in the opinion of the Engineer misconducts himself or is incompetent or negligent in the performance of his duties or fails to conform with any particular provisions with regard to safety which may be set out in the Specification or persists in any conduct which is prejudicial to safety or health and such persons shall not be again employed upon the Works without the permission of the Engineer.

Setting-out.

17. The Contractor shall be responsible for the true and proper setting-out of the Works and for the correctness of the position levels dimensions and alignment of all parts of the Works and for the provision of all necessary instruments appliances and labour in connection therewith. If at any time during the progress of the Works any error shall appear or arise in the position levels dimensions or alignment of any part of the Works the Contractor on being required so to do by the Engineer shall at his own cost rectify such error to the satisfaction of the Engineer unless such error is based on incorrect data supplied in writing by the Engineer or the Engineer's Representative in which case the cost of rectifying the same shall be borne by the Employer. The checking of any setting-out or of any line or level by the Engineer or the Engineer's Representative shall not in any way relieve the Contractor of his responsibility for the correctness thereof and the Contractor shall carefully protect and preserve all bench-marks sight rails pegs and other things used in setting out the Works.

Boreholes and Exploratory Excavation.

18. If at any time during the execution of the Works the Engineer shall require the Contractor to make boreholes or to carry out exploratory excavation such requirement shall be ordered in writing and shall be deemed to be a variation ordered under Clause 51 unless a Provisional Sum or Prime Cost Item in respect of such anticipated work shall have been included in the Bill of Quantities.

Safety and Security.

19. (1) The Contractor shall throughout the progress of the Works have full regard for the safety of all persons entitled to be upon the Site and shall keep the Site (so far as the same is under his control) and the Works (so far as the same are not completed or occupied by the Employer) in an orderly state appropriate to the avoidance of danger to such persons and shall *inter alia* in connection with the Works provide and maintain at his own cost all lights guards fencing warning signs and watching when and where necessary or required by the Engineer or by any competent statutory or other authority for the protection of the Works or for the safety and convenience of the public or others.

Employer's Responsibilities.

(2) If under Clause 31 the Employer shall carry out work on the Site with his own workmen he shall in respect of such work:—

(a) have full regard to the safety of all persons entitled to be upon the Site; and
(b) keep the Site in an orderly state appropriate to the avoidance of danger to such persons.

If under Clause 31 the Employer shall employ other contractors on the Site he shall require them to have the same regard for safety and avoidance of danger.

Care of the Works.

20. (1) The Contractor shall take full responsibility for the care of the Works from the date of the commencement thereof until 14 days after the Engineer shall have issued a Certificate of Completion for the whole of the Works pursuant to Clause 48. Provided that if the Engineer shall issue a Certificate of Completion in respect of any Section or part of the Permanent Works before he shall issue a Certificate of Completion in respect of the whole of the Works the Contractor shall cease to be responsible for the care of that Section or part of the Permanent Works 14 days after the Engineer shall have issued the Certificate of Completion in respect of that Section or part and the responsibility for the care thereof shall thereupon pass to the Employer. Provided further that the Contractor shall take full responsibility for the care of any outstanding work which he shall have undertaken to finish during the Period of Maintenance until such outstanding work is complete.

Responsibility for Reinstatement.

(2) In case any damage loss or injury from any cause whatsoever (save and except the Excepted Risks as defined in sub-clause (3) of this Clause) shall happen to the Works or any part thereof while the Contractor shall be responsible for the care thereof the Contractor shall at his own cost repair and make good the same so that at completion the Permanent Works shall be in good order and condition and in conformity in every respect with the requirements of the Contract and the Engineer's instructions. To the extent that any such damage loss or injury arises from any of the Excepted Risks the Contractor shall if required by the Engineer repair and make good the same as aforesaid at the expense of the Employer. The Contractor shall also be liable for any damage to the Works occasioned by him in the course of any operations carried out by him for the purpose of completing any outstanding work or of complying with his obligations under Clauses 49 and 50.

Excepted Risks.

(3) The " Excepted Risks " are riot war invasion act of foreign enemies hostilities (whether war be declared or not) civil war rebellion revolution insurrection or military or usurped power ionising radiations or contamination by radio-activity from any nuclear fuel or from any nuclear waste from the combustion of nuclear fuel radioactive toxic explosive or other hazardous properties of any explosive nuclear assembly or nuclear component thereof pressure waves caused by aircraft or other aerial devices travelling at sonic or supersonic speeds or a cause due to use or occupation by the Employer his agents servants or other contractors (not being employed by the Contractor) of any part of the Permanent Works or to fault defect error or omission in the design of the Works (other than a design provided by the Contractor pursuant to his obligations under the Contract).

Insurance of Works, etc.

21. Without limiting his obligations and responsibilities under Clause 20 the Contractor shall insure in the joint names of the Employer and the Contractor:—

(a) the Permanent Works and the Temporary Works (including for the purposes of this Clause any unfixed materials or other things delivered to the Site for incorporation therein) to their full value;
(b) the Constructional Plant to its full value;

against all loss or damage from whatever cause arising (other than the Excepted Risks) for which he is responsible under the terms of the Contract and in such manner that the Employer and Contractor are covered for the period stipulated in Clause 20(1) and are also covered for loss or damage arising during the Period of Maintenance from such cause occurring prior to the commencement of the Period of Maintenance and for any loss or damage occasioned by the Contractor in the course of any operation carried out by him for the purpose of complying with his obligations under Clauses 49 and 50.

Provided that without limiting his obligations and responsibilities as aforesaid nothing in this Clause contained shall render the Contractor liable to insure against the necessity for the repair or reconstruction of any work constructed with materials and workmanship not in accordance with the requirements of the Contract unless the Bill of Quantities shall provide a special item for this insurance.

Such insurances shall be effected with an insurer and in terms approved by the Employer (which approval shall not be unreasonably withheld) and the Contractor shall whenever required produce to the Employer the policy or policies of insurance and the receipts for payment of the current premiums.

Damage to Persons and Property.

22. (1) The Contractor shall (except if and so far as the Contract otherwise provides) indemnify and keep indemnified the Employer against all losses and claims for injuries or damage to any person or property whatsoever (other than the Works for which insurance is required under Clause 21 but including surface or other damage to land being the Site suffered by any persons in beneficial occupation of such land) which may arise out of or in consequence of the construction and maintenance of the Works and against all claims demands proceedings damages costs charges and expenses whatsoever in respect thereof or in relation thereto. Provided always that:—

(a) the Contractor's liability to indemnify the Employer as aforesaid shall be reduced proportionately to the extent that the act or neglect of the Employer his servants or agents may have contributed to the said loss injury or damage;

(b) nothing herein contained shall be deemed to render the Contractor liable for or in respect of or to indemnify the Employer against any compensation or damages for or with respect to:—

(i) damage to crops being on the Site (save in so far as possession has not been given to the Contractor);

(ii) the use or occupation of land (which has been provided by the Employer) by the Works or any part thereof or for the purpose of constructing completing and maintaining the Works (including consequent losses of crops) or interference whether temporary or permanent with any right of way light air or water or other easement or quasi easement which are the unavoidable result of the construction of the Works in accordance with the Contract;

(iii) the right of the Employer to construct the Works or any part thereof on over under in or through any land;

(iv) damage which is the unavoidable result of the construction of the Works in accordance with the Contract;

(v) injuries or damage to persons or property resulting from any act or neglect or breach of statutory duty done or committed by the Engineer or the Employer his agents servants or other contractors (not being employed by the Contractor) or for or in respect of any claims demands proceedings damages costs charges and expenses in respect thereof or in relation thereto.

Indemnity by Employer.

(2) The Employer will save harmless and indemnify the Contractor from and against all claims demands proceedings damages costs charges and expenses in respect of the matters referred to in the proviso to sub-clause (1) of this Clause. Provided always that the Employer's liability to indemnify the Contractor under paragraph (v) of proviso (b) to sub-clause (1) of this Clause shall be reduced proportionately to the extent that the act or neglect of the Contractor or his sub-contractors servants or agents may have contributed to the said injury or damage.

Insurance against Damage to Persons and Property.

23. (1) Throughout the execution of the Works the Contractor (but without limiting his obligations and responsibilities under Clause 22) shall insure against any damage loss or injury which may occur to any property or to any person by or arising out of the execution of the Works or in the carrying out of the Contract otherwise than due to the matters referred to in proviso (b) to Clause 22(1).

Amount and Terms of Insurance.

(2) Such insurance shall be effected with an insurer and in terms approved by the Employer (which approval shall not be unreasonably withheld) and for at least the amount stated in the Appendix to the Form of Tender. The terms shall include a provision whereby in the event of any claim in respect of which the Contractor would be entitled to receive indemnity under the policy being brought or made against the Employer the insurer will indemnify the Employer against such claims and any costs charges and expenses in respect thereof. The Contractor shall whenever required produce to the Employer the policy or policies of insurance and the receipts for payment of the current premiums.

Accident or Injury to Workmen.

24. The Employer shall not be liable for or in respect of any damages or compensation payable at law in respect or in consequence of any accident or injury to any workman or other person in the employment of the Contractor or any sub-contractor save and except to the extent that such accident or injury results from or is contributed to by any act or default of the Employer his agents or servants and the Contractor shall indemnify and keep indemnified the Employer against all such damages and compensation (save and except as aforesaid) and against all claims demands proceedings costs charges and expenses whatsoever in respect thereof or in relation thereto.

Remedy on Contractor's Failure to Insure.

25. If the Contractor shall fail upon request to produce to the Employer satisfactory evidence that there is in force the insurance referred to in Clauses 21 and 23 or any other insurance which he may be required to effect under the terms of the Contract then and in any such case the Employer may effect and keep in force any such insurance and pay such premium or premiums as may be necessary for that purpose and from time to time deduct the amount so paid by the Employer as aforesaid from any monies due or which may become due to the Contractor or recover the same as a debt due from the Contractor.

Giving of Notices and Payment of Fees.

26. (1) The Contractor shall save as provided in Clause 27 give all notices and pay all fees required to be given or paid by any Act of Parliament or any Regulation or Bye-law of any local or other statutory authority in relation to the execution of the Works and by the rules and regulations of all public bodies and companies whose property or rights are or may be affected in any way by the Works. The Employer shall repay or allow to the Contractor all such sums as the Engineer shall certify to have been properly payable and paid by the Contractor in respect of such fees and also all rates and taxes paid by the Contractor in respect of the Site or any part thereof or anything constructed or erected thereon or on any part thereof or any temporary structures situate elsewhere but used exclusively for the purposes of the Works or any structures used temporarily and exclusively for the purposes of the Works.

Contractor to Conform with Statutes, etc.

(2) The Contractor shall ascertain and conform in all respects with the provisions of any general or local Act of Parliament and the Regulations and Bye-laws of any local or other statutory authority which may be applicable to the Works and with such rules and regulations of public bodies and companies as aforesaid and shall keep the Employer indemnified against all penalties and liability of every kind for breach of any such Act Regulation or Bye-law. Provided always that:—

(a) the Contractor shall not be required to indemnify the Employer against the consequences of any such breach which is the unavoidable result of complying with the Drawings Specification or instructions of the Engineer;
(b) if the Drawings Specification or instructions of the Engineer shall at any time be found not to be in conformity with any such Act Regulation or Bye-law the Engineer shall issue such instructions including the ordering of a variation under Clause 51 as may be necessary to ensure conformity with such Act Regulation or Bye-law;
(c) the Contractor shall not be responsible for obtaining any planning permission which may be necessary in respect of the Permanent Works or any Temporary Works specified or designed by the Engineer and the Employer hereby warrants that all the said permissions have been or will in due time be obtained.

Public Utilities Street Works Act 1950—Definitions.

27. (1) For the purposes of this Clause:—
(a) the expression " the Act " shall mean and include the Public Utilities Street Works Act 1950 and any statutory modification or re-enactment thereof for the time being in force;
(b) all other expressions common to the Act and to this Clause shall have the same meaning as that assigned to them by the Act.

Notifications by Employer to Contractor.

(2) The Employer shall before the commencement of the Works notify the Contractor in writing:—

(a) whether the Works or any parts thereof (and if so which parts) are Emergency Works; and
(b) which (if any) parts of the Works are to be carried out in Controlled Land or in a Prospectively Maintainable Highway.

If any duly authorised variation of the Works shall involve the execution thereof in a Street or in Controlled Land or in a Prospectively Maintainable Highway or are Emergency Works the Employer shall notify the Contractor in writing accordingly at the time such variation is ordered.

Service of Notices by Employer.

(3) The Employer shall (subject to the obligations of the Contract under sub-clause (4) of this Clause) serve all such notices as may from time to time whether before or during the course of or after completion of the Works be required to be served under the Act.

Notices by Contractor to Employer.

(4) The Contractor shall in relation to any part of the Works (other than Emergency Works) and subject to the compliance by the Employer with sub-clause (2) of this Clause give not less than 21 days' notice in writing to the Employer before:—

(a) commencing any part of the Works in a Street (as defined by Sections 1(3) and 38(1) of the Act); or
(b) commencing any part of the Works in Controlled Land or in a Prospectively Maintainable Highway; or
(c) commencing in a Street or in Controlled Land or in a Prospectively Maintainable Highway any part of the Works which is likely to affect the apparatus of any Owning Undertaker (within the meaning of Section 26 of the Act).

Such notice shall state the date on which and the place at which the Contractor intends to commence the execution of the work referred to therein.

Failure to Commence Street Works.

(5) If the Contractor having given any such notice as is required by sub-clause (4) of this Clause shall not commence the part of the Works to which such notice relates within 2 months after the date when such notice is given such notice shall be treated as invalid and compliance with the said sub-clause (4) shall be requisite as if such notice had not been given.

(6) In the event of such a variation of the Works as is referred to in sub-clause (2) of this Clause being ordered by or on behalf of the Employer and resulting in delay in the execution of the Works by reason of the necessity of compliance by the Contractor with sub-clause (4) of this Clause the Engineer shall take such delay into account in determining any extension of time to which the Contractor is entitled under Clause 44 and the Contractor shall subject to Clause 52 be paid in accordance with Clause 60 such additional cost as the Engineer shall consider to have been reasonably attributable to such delay. **Delays Attributable to Variations.**

(7) Except as otherwise provided by this Clause where in relation to the carrying out of the Works the Act imposes any requirements or obligations upon the Employer the Contractor shall subject to Clause 49(5) comply with such requirements and obligations and shall (subject as aforesaid) indemnify the Employer against any liability which the Employer may incur in consequence of any failure to comply with the said requirements and obligations. **Contractor to Comply with Other Obligations of Act.**

28. (1) The Contractor shall save harmless and indemnify the Employer from and against all claims and proceedings for or on account of infringement of any patent rights design trade-mark or name or other protected rights in respect of any Constructional Plant machine work or material used for or in connection with the Works and from and against all claims demands proceedings damages costs charges and expenses whatsoever in respect thereof or in relation thereto. **Patent Rights.**

(2) Except where otherwise specified the Contractor shall pay all tonnage and other royalties rent and other payments or compensation (if any) for getting stone sand gravel clay or other materials required for the Works. **Royalties.**

29. (1) All operations necessary for the execution of the Works shall so far as compliance with the requirements of the Contract permits be carried on so as not to interfere unnecessarily or improperly with the public convenience or the access to or use or occupation of public or private roads and foot-paths or to or of properties whether in the possession of the Employer or of any other person and the Contractor shall save harmless and indemnify the Employer in respect of all claims demands proceedings damages costs charges and expenses whatsoever arising out of or in relation to any such matters. **Interference with Traffic and Adjoining Properties.**

(2) All work shall be carried out without unreasonable noise and disturbance. The Contractor shall indemnify the Employer from and against any liability for damages on account of noise or other disturbance created while or in carrying out the work and from and against all claims demands proceedings damages costs charges and expenses whatsoever in regard or in relation to such liability. **Noise and Disturbance.**

30. (1) The Contractor shall use every reasonable means to prevent any of the highways or bridges communicating with or on the routes to the Site from being subjected to extraordinary traffic within the meaning of the Highways Act 1959 or in Scotland the Road Traffic Act 1930 or any statutory modification or re-enactment thereof by any traffic of the Contractor or any of his sub-contractors and in particular shall select routes and use vehicles and restrict and distribute loads so that any such extraordinary traffic as will inevitably arise from the moving of Constructional Plant and materials or manufactured or fabricated articles from and to the Site shall be limited as far as reasonably possible and so that no unnecessary damage or injury may be occasioned to such highways and bridges. **Avoidance of Damage to Highways, etc.**

(2) Save insofar as the Contract otherwise provides the Contractor shall be responsible for and shall pay the cost of strengthening any bridges or altering or improving any highway communicating with the Site to facilitate the movement of Constructional Plant equipment or Temporary Works required in the execution of the Works and the Contractor shall indemnify and keep indemnified the Employer against all claims for damage to any highway or bridge communicating with the Site caused by such movement including such claims as may be made by any competent authority directly against the Employer pursuant to any Act of Parliament or other Statutory Instrument and shall negotiate and pay all claims arising solely out of such damage. **Transport of Constructional Plant.**

(3) If notwithstanding sub-clause (1) of this Clause any damage shall occur to any bridge or highway communicating with the Site arising from the transport of materials or manufactured or fabricated articles in the execution of the Works the Contractor shall notify the Engineer as soon as he becomes aware of such damage or as soon as he receives any claim from the authority entitled to make such claim. Where under any Act of Parliament or other Statutory Instrument the haulier of such materials or manufactured or fabricated articles is required to indemnify the highway authority against damage the Employer shall not be liable for any costs charges or expenses in respect thereof or in relation thereto. In other cases the Employer shall negotiate the settlement of and pay all sums due in respect of such claim and shall indemnify the Contractor in respect thereof and in respect of all claims demands proceedings damages costs charges and expenses in relation thereto. Provided always that if and so far as any such claim or part thereof shall in the opinion of the Engineer be due to any failure on the part of the Contractor to observe and perform his obligations under sub-clause (1) of this Clause then the amount certified by the Engineer to be due to such failure shall be paid by the Contractor to the Employer or deducted from any sum due or which may become due to the Contractor. **Transport of Materials.**

Facilities for Other Contractors.

31. (1) The Contractor shall in accordance with the requirements of the Engineer afford all reasonable facilities for any other contractors employed by the Employer and their workmen and for the workmen of the Employer and of any other properly authorised authorities or statutory bodies who may be employed in the execution on or near the Site of any work not in the Contract or of any contract which the Employer may enter into in connection with or ancillary to the Works.

Delay and Extra Cost.

(2) If compliance with sub-clause (1) of this Clause shall involve the Contractor in delay or cost beyond that reasonably to be foreseen by an experienced contractor at the time of tender then the Engineer shall take such delay into account in determining any extension of time to which the Contractor is entitled under Clause 44 and the Contractor shall subject to Clause 52(4) be paid in accordance with Clause 60 the amount of such cost as may be reasonable.

Fossils, etc.

32. All fossils coins articles of value or antiquity and structures or other remains or things of geological or archaeological interest discovered on the Site shall as between the Employer and the Contractor be deemed to be the absolute property of the Employer and the Contractor shall take reasonable precautions to prevent his workmen or any other persons from removing or damaging any such article or thing and shall immediately upon discovery thereof and before removal acquaint the Engineer of such discovery and carry out at the expense of the Employer the Engineer's orders as to the disposal of the same.

Clearance of Site on Completion.

33. On the completion of the Works the Contractor shall clear away and remove from the Site all Constructional Plant surplus material rubbish and Temporary Works of every kind and leave the whole of the Site and Permanent Works clean and in a workmanlike condition to the satisfaction of the Engineer.

LABOUR

Rates of Wages/Hours and Conditions of Labour.

34. (1) The Contractor shall in the execution of the Contract observe and fulfil the obligations upon contractors specified in the Fair Wages Resolution passed by the House of Commons on the 14 October 1946 of which the following is an extract:—

Extract from Fair Wages Resolution.

" 1 (a) The contractor shall pay rates of wages and observe hours and conditions of labour not less favourable than those established for the trade or industry in the district where the work is carried out by machinery of negotiation or arbitration to which the parties are organisations of employers and trade unions representative respectively of substantial proportions of the employers and workers engaged in the trade or industry in the district.

" (b) In the absence of any rates of wages, hours or conditions of labour so established the contractor shall pay rates of wages and observe hours and conditions of labour which are not less favourable than the general level of wages, hours and conditions observed by other employers whose general circumstances in the trade or industry in which the contractor is engaged are similar.

" 2 The contractor shall in respect of all persons employed by him (whether in execution of the contract or otherwise) in every factory workshop or place occupied or used by him for the execution of the contract comply with the general conditions required by this Resolution.

" 3 In the event of any question arising as to whether the requirements of this Resolution are being observed, the question shall, if not otherwise disposed of, be referred by the Minister of Labour and National Service to an independent Tribunal for decision.

" 4 The contractor shall recognise the freedom of his workpeople to be members of Trade Unions.

" 5 The contractor shall at all times during the continuance of a contract display, for the information of his workpeople, in every factory, workshop or place occupied or used by him for the execution of the contract a copy of this Resolution.

" 6 The contractor shall be responsible for the observance of this Resolution by sub-contractors employed in the execution of the contract."

Civil Engineering Construction Conciliation Board.

(2) The wages hours and conditions of employment above referred to shall be those prescribed for the time being by the Civil Engineering Construction Conciliation Board for Great Britain save that the rates of wages payable to any class of labour in respect of which the said Board does not prescribe a rate shall be governed by the provisions of sub-clause (1) of this Clause.

35. The Contractor shall if required by the Engineer deliver to the Engineer or at his office a return in such form and at such intervals as the Engineer may prescribe showing in detail the numbers of the several classes of labour from time to time employed by the Contractor on the Site and such information respecting Constructional Plant as the Engineer may require. The Contractor shall require his sub-contractors to observe the provisions of this Clause. **Returns of Labour and Plant.**

WORKMANSHIP AND MATERIALS

36. (1) All materials and workmanship shall be of the respective kinds described in the Contract and in accordance with the Engineer's instructions and shall be subjected from time to time to such tests as the Engineer may direct at the place of manufacture or fabrication or on the Site or such other place or places as may be specified in the Contract. The Contractor shall provide such assistance instruments machines labour and materials as are normally required for examining measuring and testing any work and the quality weight or quantity of any materials used and shall supply samples of materials before incorporation in the Works for testing as may be selected and required by the Engineer. **Quality of Materials and Workmanship and Tests.**

(2) All samples shall be supplied by the Contractor at his own cost if the supply thereof is clearly intended by or provided for in the Contract but if not then at the cost of the Employer. **Cost of Samples.**

(3) The cost of making any test shall be borne by the Contractor if such test is clearly intended by or provided for in the Contract and (in the cases only of a test under load or of a test to ascertain whether the design of any finished or partially finished work is appropriate for the purposes which it was intended to fulfil) is particularised in the Specification or Bill of Quantities in sufficient detail to enable the Contractor to have priced or allowed for the same in his Tender. If any test is ordered by the Engineer which is either:— **Cost of Tests.**

(a) not so intended by or provided for; or
(b) (in the cases above mentioned) is not so particularised;

then the cost of such test shall be borne by the Contractor if the test shows the workmanship or materials not to be in accordance with the provisions of the Contract or the Engineer's instructions but otherwise by the Employer.

37. The Engineer and any person authorised by him shall at all times have access to the Works and to the Site and to all workshops and places where work is being prepared or whence materials manufactured articles and machinery are being obtained for the Works and the Contractor shall afford every facility for and every assistance in or in obtaining the right to such access. **Access to Site.**

38. (1) No work shall be covered up or put out of view without the approval of the Engineer and the Contractor shall afford full opportunity for the Engineer to examine and measure any work which is about to be covered up or put out of view and to examine foundations before permanent work is placed thereon. The Contractor shall give due notice to the Engineer whenever any such work or foundations is or are ready or about to be ready for examination and the Engineer shall without unreasonable delay unless he considers it unnecessary and advises the Contractor accordingly attend for the purpose of examining and measuring such work or of examining such foundations. **Examination of Work before Covering up.**

(2) The Contractor shall uncover any part or parts of the Works or make openings in or through the same as the Engineer may from time to time direct and shall reinstate and make good such part or parts to the satisfaction of the Engineer. If any such part or parts have been covered up or put out of view after compliance with the requirements of sub-clause (1) of this Clause and are found to be executed in accordance with the Contract the cost of uncovering making openings in or through reinstating and making good the same shall be borne by the Employer but in any other case all such cost shall be borne by the Contractor. **Uncovering and Making Openings.**

39. (1) The Engineer shall during the progress of the Works have power to order in writing:— **Removal of Improper Work and Materials.**

(a) the removal from the Site within such time or times as may be specified in the order of any materials which in the opinion of the Engineer are not in accordance with the Contract;
(b) the substitution of proper and suitable materials; and
(c) the removal and proper re-execution (notwithstanding any previous test thereof or interim payment therefor) of any work which in respect of materials or workmanship is not in the opinion of the Engineer in accordance with the Contract.

(2) In case of default on the part of the Contractor in carrying out such order the Employer shall be entitled to employ and pay other persons to carry out the same and all expenses consequent thereon or incidental thereto shall be borne by the Contractor and shall be recoverable from him by the Employer or may be deducted by the Employer from any monies due or which may become due to the Contractor. **Default of Contractor in Compliance.**

(3) Failure of the Engineer or any person acting under him pursuant to Clause 2 to disapprove any work or materials shall not prejudice the power of the Engineer or any of them subsequently to disapprove such work or materials. **Failure to Disapprove.**

Suspension of Work.

40. (1) The Contractor shall on the written order of the Engineer suspend the progress of the Works or any part thereof for such time or times and in such manner as the Engineer may consider necessary and shall during such suspension properly protect and secure the work so far as is necessary in the opinion of the Engineer. Subject to Clause 52(4) the Contractor shall be paid in accordance with Clause 60 the extra cost (if any) incurred in giving effect to the Engineer's instructions under this Clause except to the extent that such suspension is:—

(a) otherwise provided for in the Contract; or
(b) necessary by reason of weather conditions or by some default on the part of the Contractor; or
(c) necessary for the proper execution of the work or for the safety of the Works or any part thereof inasmuch as such necessity does not arise from any act or default of the Engineer or the Employer or from any of the Excepted Risks defined in Clause 20.

The Engineer shall take any delay occasioned by a suspension ordered under this Clause (including that arising from any act or default of the Engineer or the Employer) into account in determining any extension of time to which the Contractor is entitled under Clause 44 except when such suspension is otherwise provided for in the Contract or is necessary by reason of some default on the part of the Contractor.

Suspension lasting more than Three Months.

(2) If the progress of the Works or any part thereof is suspended on the written order of the Engineer and if permission to resume work is not given by the Engineer within a period of 3 months from the date of suspension then the Contractor may unless such suspension is otherwise provided for in the Contract or continues to be necessary by reason of some default on the part of the Contractor serve a written notice on the Engineer requiring permission within 28 days from the receipt of such notice to proceed with the Works or that part thereof in regard to which progress is suspended. If within the said 28 days the Engineer does not grant such permission the Contractor by a further written notice so served may (but is not bound to) elect to treat the suspension where it affects part only of the Works as an omission of such part under Clause 51 or where it affects the whole Works as an abandonment of the Contract by the Employer.

COMMENCEMENT TIME AND DELAYS

Commencement of Works.

41. The Contractor shall commence the Works on or as soon as is reasonably possible after the Date for Commencement of the Works to be notified by the Engineer in writing which date shall be within a reasonable time after the date of acceptance of the Tender. Thereafter the Contractor shall proceed with the Works with due expedition and without delay in accordance with the Contract.

Possession of Site.

42. (1) Save in so far as the Contract may prescribe the extent of portions of the Site of which the Contractor is to be given possession from time to time and the order in which such portions shall be made available to him and subject to any requirement in the Contract as to the order in which the Works shall be executed the Employer will at the Date for Commencement of the Works notified under Clause 41 give to the Contractor possession of so much of the Site as may be required to enable the Contractor to commence and proceed with the construction of the Works in accordance with the programme referred to in Clause 14 and will from time to time as the Works proceed give to the Contractor possession of such further portions of the Site as may be required to enable the Contractor to proceed with the construction of the Works with due despatch in accordance with the said programme. If the Contractor suffers delay or incurs cost from failure on the part of the Employer to give possession in accordance with the terms of this Clause then the Engineer shall take such delay into account in determining any extension of time to which the Contractor is entitled under Clause 44 and the Contractor shall subject to Clause 52(4) be paid in accordance with Clause 60 the amount of such cost as may be reasonable.

Wayleaves, etc.

(2) The Contractor shall bear all expenses and charges for special or temporary wayleaves required by him in connection with access to the Site. The Contractor shall also provide at his own cost any additional accommodation outside the Site required by him for the purposes of the Works.

Time for Completion.

43. The whole of the Works and any Section required to be completed within a particular time as stated in the Appendix to the Form of Tender shall be completed within the time so stated (or such extended time as may be allowed under Clause 44) calculated from the Date for Commencement of the Works notified under Clause 41.

Extension of Time for Completion.

44. (1) Should any variation ordered under Clause 51(1) or increased quantities referred to in Clause 51(3) or any other cause of delay referred to in these Conditions or exceptional adverse weather conditions or other special circumstances of any kind whatsoever which may occur be such as fairly to entitle the Contractor to an extension of time for the completion of the Works or (where different periods for completion of different Sections are provided for in the Appendix to the Form of Tender) of the relevant Section the Contractor shall within 28 days after the cause of the delay has arisen or as soon thereafter as is reasonable in all the circumstances deliver to the Engineer full and detailed particulars of any claim to extension of time to which he may consider himself entitled in order that such claim may be investigated at the time.

Interim Assessment of Extension.

(2) The Engineer shall upon receipt of such particulars or if he thinks fit in the absence of any such claim consider all the circumstances known to him at that time and make an assessment of the extension of time (if any) to which he considers the Contractor entitled for the completion of the Works or relevant Section and shall by notice in writing to the Contractor grant such extension of time for completion. In the event that the Contractor shall have made a claim for an extension of time but the Engineer considers the Contractor not entitled thereto the Engineer shall so inform the Contractor.

Assessment at Due Date for Completion.

(3) The Engineer shall at or as soon as possible after the due date or extended date for completion (and whether or not the Contractor shall have made any claim for an extension of time) consider all the circumstances known to him at that time and take action similar to that provided for in sub-clause (2) of this Clause. Should the Engineer consider that the Contractor is not entitled to an extension of time he shall so notify the Employer and the Contractor.

Final Determination of Extension.

(4) The Engineer shall upon the issue of the Certificate of Completion of the Works or of the relevant Section review all the circumstances of the kind referred to in sub-clause (1) of this Clause and shall finally determine and certify to the Contractor the overall extension of time (if any) to which he considers the Contractor entitled in respect of the Works or any relevant Section. No such final review of the circumstances shall result in a decrease in any extension of time already granted by the Engineer pursuant to sub-clauses (2) or (3) of this Clause.

Night and Sunday Work.

45. Subject to any provision to the contrary contained in the Contract none of the Works shall be executed during the night or on Sundays without the permission in writing of the Engineer save when the work is unavoidable or absolutely necessary for the saving of life or property or for the safety of the Works in which case the Contractor shall immediately advise the Engineer or the Engineer's Representative. Provided always that this Clause shall not be applicable in the case of any work which it is customary to carry out outside normal working hours or by rotary or double shifts.

Rate of Progress.

46. If for any reason which does not entitle the Contractor to an extension of time the rate of progress of the Works or any Section is at any time in the opinion of the Engineer too slow to ensure completion by the prescribed time or extended time for completion the Engineer shall so notify the Contractor in writing and the Contractor shall thereupon take such steps as are necessary and the Engineer may approve to expedite progress so as to complete the Works or such Section by the prescribed time or extended time. The Contractor shall not be entitled to any additional payment for taking such steps. If as a result of any notice given by the Engineer under this Clause the Contractor shall seek the Engineer's permission to do any work at night or on Sundays such permission shall not be unreasonably refused.

LIQUIDATED DAMAGES AND LIMITATION OF DAMAGES FOR DELAYED COMPLETION

Liquidated Damages for Whole of Works.

47. (1) (a) In the Appendix to the Form of Tender under the heading " Liquidated Damages for Delay " there is stated in column 1 the sum which represents the Employer's genuine pre-estimate (expressed as a rate per week or per day as the case may be) of the damages likely to be suffered by him in the event that the whole of the Works shall not be completed within the time prescribed by Clause 43.

Provided that in lieu of such sum there may be stated such lesser sum as represents the limit of the Contractor's liability for damages for failure to complete the whole of the Works within the time for completion therefor or any extension thereof granted under Clause 44.

(b) If the Contractor should fail to complete the whole of the Works within the prescribed time or any extension thereof granted under Clause 44 the Contractor shall pay to the Employer for such default the sum stated in column 1 aforesaid for every week or day as the case may be which shall elapse between the date on which the prescribed time or any extension thereof expired and the date of completion of the whole of the Works. Provided that if any part of the Works not being a Section or part of a Section shall be certified as complete pursuant to Clause 48 before completion of the whole of the Works the sum stated in column 1 shall be reduced by the proportion which the value of the part completed bears to the value of the whole of the Works.

Liquidated Damages for Sections.

(2) (a) In cases where any Section shall be required to be completed within a particular time as stated in the Appendix to the Form of Tender there shall also be stated in the said Appendix under the heading " Liquidated Damages for Delay " in column 2 the sum by which the damages stated in column 1 or the limit of the Contractor's

said liability as the case may be shall be reduced upon completion of each such Section and in column 3 the sum which represents the Employer's genuine pre-estimate (expressed as aforesaid) of any specific damage likely to be suffered by him in the event that such Section shall not be completed within that time.

Provided that there may be stated in column 3 in lieu of such sum such lesser sum as represents the limit of the Contractor's liability for failure to complete the relevant Section within the relevant time.

(b) If the Contractor should fail to complete any Section within the relevant time for completion or any extension thereof granted under Clause 44 the Contractor shall pay to the Employer for such default the sum stated in column 3 aforesaid for every week or day as the case may be which shall elapse between the date on which the relevant time or any extension thereof expired and the date of completion of the relevant Section. Provided that:—

(i) if completion of a Section shall be delayed beyond the due date for completion of the whole of the Works the damages payable under sub-clauses (1) and (2) of this Clause until completion of that Section shall be the sum stated in column 1 plus in respect of that Section the sum stated in column 3 less the sum stated in column 2;

(ii) if any part of a Section shall be certified as complete pursuant to Clause 48 before completion of the whole thereof the sums stated in columns 2 and 3 in respect of that Section shall be reduced by the proportion which the value of the part bears to the value of the Section and the sum stated in column 1 shall be reduced by the same amount as the sum in column 2 is reduced; and

(iii) upon completion of any such Section the sum stated in column 1 shall be reduced by the sum stated in column 2 in respect of that Section at the date of such completion.

Damages not a Penalty.

(3) All sums payable by the Contractor to the Employer pursuant to this Clause shall be paid as liquidated damages for delay and not as a penalty.

Deduction of Liquidated Damages.

(4) If the Engineer shall under Clause 44 (3) or (4) have determined and certified any extension of time to which he considers the Contractor entitled and shall have notified the Employer and the Contractor that he is of the opinion that the Contractor is not entitled to any or any further extension of time the Employer may deduct and retain from any sum otherwise payable by the Employer to the Contractor hereunder the amount which in the event that the Engineer's said opinion should not be subsequently revised would be the amount of the liquidated damages payable by the Contractor under this Clause.

Reimbursement of Liquidated Damages.

(5) If upon a subsequent or final review of the circumstances causing delay the Engineer shall grant an extension or further extension of time or if an arbitrator appointed under Clause 66 shall decide that the Engineer should have granted such an extension or further extension of time the Employer shall no longer be entitled to liquidated damages in respect of the period of such extension of time. Any sums in respect of such period which may have been recovered pursuant to sub-clause (3) of this Clause shall be reimbursable forthwith to the Contractor together with interest at the rate provided for in Clause 60(6) from the date on which such liquidated damages were recovered from the Contractor.

COMPLETION CERTIFICATE

Certificate of Completion of Works.

48. (1) When the Contractor shall consider that the whole of the Works has been substantially completed and has satisfactorily passed any final test that may be prescribed by the Contract he may give a notice to that effect to the Engineer or to the Engineer's Representative accompanied by an undertaking to finish any outstanding work during the Period of Maintenance. Such notice and undertaking shall be in writing and shall be deemed to be a request by the Contractor for the Engineer to issue a Certificate of Completion in respect of the Works and the Engineer shall within 21 days of the date of delivery of such notice either issue to the Contractor (with a copy to the Employer) a Certificate of Completion stating the date on which in his opinion the Works were substantially completed in accordance with the Contract or else give instructions in writing to the Contractor specifying all the work which in the Engineer's opinion requires to be done by the Contractor before the issue of such certificate. If the Engineer shall give such instructions the Contractor shall be entitled to receive such Certificate of Completion within 21 days of completion to the satisfaction of the Engineer of the work specified by the said instructions.

Completion of Sections and Occupied Parts.

(2) Similarly in accordance with the procedure set out in sub-clause (1) of this Clause the Contractor may request and the Engineer shall issue a Certificate of Completion in respect of:—

(a) any Section in respect of which a separate time for completion is provided in the Appendix to the Form of Tender; and

(b) any substantial part of the Works which has been both completed to the satisfaction of the Engineer and occupied or used by the Employer.

Completion of Other Parts of Works.

(3) If the Engineer shall be of the opinion that any part of the Works shall have been substantially completed and shall have satisfactorily passed any final test that may be prescribed by

the Contract he may issue a Certificate of Completion in respect of that part of the Works before completion of the whole of the Works and upon the issue of such certificate the Contractor shall be deemed to have undertaken to complete any outstanding work in that part of the Works during the Period of Maintenance.

Reinstatement of Ground.

(4) Provided always that a Certificate of Completion given in respect of any Section or part of the Works before completion of the whole shall not be deemed to certify completion of any ground or surfaces requiring reinstatement unless such certificate shall expressly so state.

MAINTENANCE AND DEFECTS

Definition of " Period of Maintenance ".

49. (1) In these Conditions the expression " Period of Maintenance " shall mean the period of maintenance named in the Appendix to the Form of Tender calculated from the date of completion of the Works or any Section or part thereof certified by the Engineer in accordance with Clause 48 as the case may be.

Execution of Work of Repair, etc.

(2) To the intent that the Works and each Section and part thereof shall at or as soon as practicable after the expiration of the relevant Period of Maintenance be delivered up to the Employer in the condition required by the Contract (fair wear and tear excepted) to the satisfaction of the Engineer the Contractor shall finish the work (if any) outstanding at the date of completion as certified under Clause 48 as soon as may be practicable after such date and shall execute all such work of repair amendment reconstruction rectification and making good of defects imperfections shrinkages or other faults as may during the Period of Maintenance or within 14 days after its expiration be required of the Contractor in writing by the Engineer as a result of an inspection made by or on behalf of the Engineer prior to its expiration.

Cost of Execution of Work of Repair, etc.

(3) All such work shall be carried out by the Contractor at his own expense if the necessity thereof shall in the opinion of the Engineer be due to the use of materials or workmanship not in accordance with the Contract or to neglect or failure on the part of the Contractor to comply with any obligation expressed or implied on the Contractor's part under the Contract. If in the opinion of the Engineer such necessity shall be due to any other cause the value of such work shall be ascertained and paid for as if it were additional work.

Remedy on Contractor's Failure to Carry out Work Required.

(4) If the Contractor shall fail to do any such work as aforesaid required by the Engineer the Employer shall be entitled to carry out such work by his own workmen or by other contractors and if such work is work which the Contractor should have carried out at the Contractor's own cost shall be entitled to recover from the Contractor the cost thereof or may deduct the same from any monies due or that become due to the Contractor.

Temporary Reinstatement.

(5) Provided always that if in the course or for the purposes of the execution of the Works or any part thereof any highway or other road or way shall have been broken into then notwithstanding anything herein contained:—

(a) If the permanent reinstatement of such highway or other road or way is to be carried out by the appropriate Highway Authority or by some person other than the Contractor (or any sub-contractor to him) the Contractor shall at his own cost and independently of any requirement of or notice from the Engineer be responsible for the making good of any subsidence or shrinkage or other defect imperfection or fault in the temporary reinstatement of such highway or other road or way and for the execution of any necessary repair or amendment thereof from whatever cause the necessity arises until the end of the Period of Maintenance in respect of the works beneath such highway or other road or way or until the Highway Authority or other person as aforesaid shall have taken possession of the Site for the purpose of carrying out permanent reinstatement (whichever is the earlier) and shall indemnify and save harmless the Employer against and from any damage or injury to the Employer or to third parties arising out or in consequence of any neglect or failure of the Contractor to comply with the foregoing obligations or any of them and against and from all claims demands proceedings damages costs charges and expenses whatsoever in respect thereof or in relation thereto. As from the end of such Period of Maintenance or the taking of possession as aforesaid (whichever shall first happen) the Employer shall indemnify and save harmless the Contractor against and from any damage or injury as aforesaid arising out or in consequence of or in connection with the said permanent reinstatement or any defect imperfection or failure of or in such work of permanent reinstatement and against and from all claims demands proceedings damages costs charges and expenses whatsoever in respect thereof or in relation thereto.

(b) Where the Highway Authority or other person as aforesaid shall take possession of the Site as aforesaid in sections or lengths the responsibility of the Contractor under paragraph (a) of this sub-clause shall cease in regard to any such section or length at the time possession thereof is so taken but shall during the continuance of the said Period of Maintenance continue in regard to any length of which possession has not been so taken and the indemnities given by the Contractor and the Employer respectively under the said paragraph shall be construed and have effect accordingly.

Contractor to Search.

50. The Contractor shall if required by the Engineer in writing carry out such searches tests or trials as may be necessary to determine the cause of any defect imperfection or fault under the directions of the Engineer. Unless such defect imperfection or fault shall be one for which the Contractor is liable under the Contract the cost of the work carried out by the Contractor as aforesaid shall be borne by the Employer. But if such defect imperfection or fault shall be one for which the Contractor is liable the cost of the work carried out as aforesaid shall be borne by the Contractor and he shall in such case repair rectify and make good such defect imperfection or fault at his own expense in accordance with Clause 49.

ALTERATIONS ADDITIONS AND OMISSIONS

Ordered Variations.

51. (1) The Engineer shall order any variation to any part of the Works that may in his opinion be necessary for the completion of the Works and shall have power to order any variation that for any other reason shall in his opinion be desirable for the satisfactory completion and functioning of the Works. Such variations may include additions omissions substitutions alterations changes in quality form character kind position dimension level or line and changes in the specified sequence method or timing of construction (if any).

Ordered Variations to be in Writing.

(2) No such variation shall be made by the Contractor without an order by the Engineer. All such orders shall be given in writing provided that if for any reason the Engineer shall find it necessary to give any such order orally in the first instance the Contractor shall comply with such oral order. Such oral order shall be confirmed in writing by the Engineer as soon as is possible in the circumstances. If the Contractor shall confirm in writing to the Engineer any oral order by the Engineer and such confirmation shall not be contradicted in writing by the Engineer forthwith it shall be deemed to be an order in writing by the Engineer. No variation ordered or deemed to be ordered in writing in accordance with sub-clauses (1) and (2) of this Clause shall in any way vitiate or invalidate the Contract but the value (if any) of all such variations shall be taken into account in ascertaining the amount of the Contract Price.

Changes in Quantities.

(3) No order in writing shall be required for increase or decrease in the quantity of any work where such increase or decrease is not the result of an order given under this Clause but is the result of the quantities exceeding or being less than those stated in the Bill of Quantities.

Valuation of Ordered Variations.

52. (1) The value of all variations ordered by the Engineer in accordance with Clause 51 shall be ascertained by the Engineer after consultation with the Contractor in accordance with the following principles. Where work is of similar character and executed under similar conditions to work priced in the Bill of Quantities it shall be valued at such rates and prices contained therein as may be applicable. Where work is not of a similar character or is not executed under similar conditions the rates and prices in the Bill of Quantities shall be used as the basis for valuation so far as may be reasonable failing which a fair valuation shall be made. Failing agreement between the Engineer and the Contractor as to any rate or price to be applied in the valuation of any variation the Engineer shall determine the rate or price in accordance with the foregoing principles and he shall notify the Contractor accordingly.

Engineer to fix Rates.

(2) Provided that if the nature or amount of any variation relative to the nature or amount of the whole of the contract work or to any part thereof shall be such that in the opinion of the Engineer or the Contractor any rate or price contained in the Contract for any item of work is by reason of such variation rendered unreasonable or inapplicable either the Engineer shall give to the Contractor or the Contractor shall give to the Engineer notice before the varied work is commenced or as soon thereafter as is reasonable in all the circumstances that such rate or price should be varied and the Engineer shall fix such rate or price as in the circumstances he shall think reasonable and proper.

Daywork.

(3) The Engineer may if in his opinion it is necessary or desirable order in writing that any additional or substituted work shall be executed on a daywork basis. The Contractor shall then be paid for such work under the conditions set out in the Daywork Schedule included in the Bill of Quantities and at the rates and prices affixed thereto by him in his Tender and failing the provision of a Daywork Schedule he shall be paid at the rates and prices and under the conditions contained in the " Schedules of Dayworks carried out incidental to Contract Work " issued by The Federation of Civil Engineering Contractors current at the date of the execution of the Daywork.

The Contractor shall furnish to the Engineer such receipts or other vouchers as may be necessary to prove the amounts paid and before ordering materials shall submit to the Engineer quotations for the same for his approval.

In respect of all work executed on a daywork basis the Contractor shall during the continuance of such work deliver each day to the Engineer's Representative an exact list in duplicate of the names occupation and time of all workmen employed on such work and a statement also in duplicate showing the description and quantity of all materials and plant used thereon or therefor (other than plant which is included in the percentage addition in accordance with the Schedule under which payment for daywork is made). One copy of each list and statement will if correct or when agreed be signed by the Engineer's Representative and returned to the Contractor. At the end of each month the Contractor shall deliver to the Engineer's Representative a priced statement of the labour material and plant (except as aforesaid) used and the Contractor shall not be entitled to any payment unless such lists and statements have been fully and punctually rendered. Provided always that if the Engineer shall consider that for any reason the sending of such list or statement by the Contractor in accordance with the foregoing provision was impracticable he shall nevertheless be entitled to authorise payment for such work either as daywork (on being satisfied as to the time employed and plant and materials used on such work) or at such value therefor as he shall consider fair and reasonable.

Notice of Claims.

(4) (a) If the Contractor intends to claim a higher rate or price than one notified to him by the Engineer pursuant to sub-clauses (1) and (2) of this Clause or Clause 56(2) the Contractor shall within 28 days after such notification give notice in writing of his intention to the Engineer.

(b) If the Contractor intends to claim any additional payment pursuant to any Clause of these Conditions other than sub-clauses (1) and (2) of this Clause he shall give notice in writing of his intention to the Engineer as soon as reasonably possible after the happening of the events giving rise to the claim. Upon the happening of such events the Contractor shall keep such contemporary records as may reasonably be necessary to support any claim he may subsequently wish to make.

(c) Without necessarily admitting the Employer's liability the Engineer may upon receipt of a notice under this Clause instruct the Contractor to keep such contemporary records or further contemporary records as the case may be as are reasonable and may be material to the claim of which notice has been given and the Contractor shall keep such records. The Contractor shall permit the Engineer to inspect all records kept pursuant to this Clause and shall supply him with copies thereof as and when the Engineer shall so instruct.

(d) After the giving of a notice to the Engineer under this Clause the Contractor shall as soon as is reasonable in all the circumstances send to the Engineer a first interim account giving full and detailed particulars of the amount claimed to that date and of the grounds upon which the claim is based. Thereafter at such intervals as the Engineer may reasonably require the Contractor shall send to the Engineer further up to date accounts giving the accumulated total of the claim and any further grounds upon which it is based.

(e) If the Contractor fails to comply with any of the provisions of this Clause in respect of any claim which he shall seek to make then the Contractor shall be entitled to payment in respect thereof only to the extent that the Engineer has not been prevented from or substantially prejudiced by such failure in investigating the said claim.

(f) The Contractor shall be entitled to have included in any interim payment certified by the Engineer pursuant to Clause 60 such amount in respect of any claim as the Engineer may consider due to the Contractor provided that the Contractor shall have supplied sufficient particulars to enable the Engineer to determine the amount due. If such particulars are insufficient to substantiate the whole of the claim the Contractor shall be entitled to payment in respect of such part of the claim as the particulars may substantiate to the satisfaction of the Engineer.

PROPERTY IN MATERIALS AND PLANT

Plant, etc.—Definitions.

53. (1) For the purpose of this Clause:—

(a) the expression " Plant " shall mean any Constructional Plant Temporary Works and materials for Temporary Works but shall exclude any vehicles engaged in transporting any labour plant or materials to or from the Site;

(b) the expression " agreement for hire " shall be deemed not to include an agreement for hire purchase.

Vesting of Plant.

(2) All Plant goods and materials owned by the Contractor or by any company in which the Contractor has a controlling interest shall when on the Site be deemed to be the property of the Employer.

Conditions of Hire of Plant.

(3) With a view to securing in the event of a forfeiture under Clause 63 the continued availability for the purpose of executing the Works of any hired Plant the Contractor shall not bring on to the Site any hired Plant unless there is an agreement for the hire thereof which contains a provision that the owner thereof will on request in writing made by the Employer within 7 days after the date on which any forfeiture has become effective and on the Employer undertaking to pay all hire charges in respect thereof from such date hire such Plant to the Employer on the same terms in all respects as the same was hired to the Contractor save that the Employer shall be entitled to permit the use thereof by any other contractor employed by him for the purpose of completing the Works under the terms of the said Clause 63.

Costs for Purposes of Clause 63.

(4) In the event of the Employer entering into any agreement for the hire of Plant pursuant to sub-clause (3) of this Clause all sums properly paid by the Employer under the provisions of any such agreement and all expenses incurred by him (including stamp duties) in entering into such agreement shall be deemed for the purpose of Clause 63 to be part of the cost of completing the Works.

Notification of Plant Ownership.

(5) The Contractor shall upon request made by the Engineer at any time in relation to any item of Plant forthwith notify to the Engineer in writing the name and address of the owner thereof and shall in the case of hired Plant certify that the agreement for the hire thereof contains a provision in accordance with the requirements of sub-clause (3) of this Clause.

Irremovability of Plant, etc.

(6) No Plant (except hired Plant) goods or materials or any part thereof shall be removed from the Site without the written consent of the Engineer which consent shall not be unreasonably withheld where the same are no longer immediately required for the purposes of the completion of the Works but the Employer will permit the Contractor the exclusive use of all such Plant goods and materials in and for the completion of the Works until the occurrence of any event which gives the Employer the right to exclude the Contractor from the Site and proceed with the completion of the Works.

Revesting and Removal of Plant.

(7) Upon the removal of any such Plant goods or materials as have been deemed to have become the property of the Employer under sub-clause (2) of this Clause with the consent as aforesaid the property therein shall be deemed to revest in the Contractor and upon completion of the Works the property in the remainder of such Plant goods and materials as aforesaid shall subject to Clause 63 be deemed to revest in the Contractor.

Disposal of Plant.

(8) If the Contractor shall fail to remove any Plant goods or materials as required pursuant to Clause 33 within such reasonable time after completion of the Works as may be allowed by the Engineer then the Employer may:—

(a) sell any which are the property of the Contractor; and
(b) return any not the property of the Contractor to the owner thereof at the Contractor's expense;

and after deducting from any proceeds of sale the costs charges and expenses of and in connection with such sale and of and in connection with return as aforesaid shall pay the balance (if any) to the Contractor but to the extent that the proceeds of any sale are insufficient to meet all such costs charges and expenses the excess shall be a debt due from the Contractor to the Employer and shall be deductible or recoverable by the Employer from any monies due or that may become due to the Contractor under the contract or may be recovered by the Employer from the Contractor at law.

Liability for Loss or Injury to Plant.

(9) The Employer shall not at any time be liable for the loss of or injury to any of the Plant goods or materials which have been deemed to become the property of the Employer under sub-clause (2) of this Clause save as mentioned in Clauses 20 and 65.

Incorporation of Clause in Sub-contracts.

(10) The Contractor shall where entering into any sub-contract for the execution of any part of the Works incorporate in such sub-contract (by reference or otherwise) the provisions of this Clause in relation to Plant goods or materials brought on to the Site by the sub-contractor.

No Approval by Vesting.

(11) The operation of this Clause shall not be deemed to imply any approval by the Engineer of the materials or other matters referred to herein nor shall it prevent the rejection of any such materials at any time by the Engineer.

Vesting of Goods and Materials not on Site.

54. (1) The Contractor may with a view to securing payment under Clause 60(1)(c) in respect of goods and materials listed in the Appendix to the Form of Tender before the same are delivered to the Site transfer the property in the same to the Employer before delivery to the Site provided:—

(a) that such goods and materials have been manufactured or prepared and are substantially ready for incorporation in the Works; and
(b) that the said goods and materials are the property of the Contractor or the contract for the supply of the same expressly provides that the property therein shall pass unconditionally to the Contractor upon the Contractor taking the action referred to in sub-clause (2) of this Clause.

Action by Contractor.

(2) The intention of the Contractor to transfer the property in any goods or materials to the Employer in accordance with this Clause shall be evidenced by the Contractor taking or causing the supplier of the said goods or materials to take the following action:—

(a) provide to the Engineer documentary evidence that the property in the said goods or materials has vested in the Contractor;
(b) suitably mark or otherwise plainly identify the said goods and materials so as to show that their destination is the Site that they are the property of the Employer and (where they are not stored at the premises of the Contractor) to whose order they are held;
(c) set aside and store the said goods and materials so marked or identified to the satisfaction of the Engineer; and
(d) send to the Engineer a schedule listing and giving the value of every item of the goods and materials so set aside and stored and inviting him to inspect the same.

(3) Upon the Engineer approving in writing the said goods and materials for the purposes of this Clause the same shall vest in and become the absolute property of the Employer and thereafter shall be in the possession of the Contractor for the sole purpose of delivering them to the Employer and incorporating them in the Works and shall not be within the ownership control or disposition of the Contractor. **Vesting in Employer.**

Provided always that:—

(a) approval by the Engineer for the purposes of this Clause or any payment certified by him in respect of goods and materials pursuant to Clause 60 shall be without prejudice to the exercise of any power of the Engineer contained in this Contract to reject any goods or materials which are not in accordance with the provisions of the Contract and upon any such rejection the property in the rejected goods or materials shall immediately revest in the Contractor;

(b) the Contractor shall be responsible for any loss or damage to such goods and materials and for the cost of storing handling and transporting the same and shall effect such adiitional insurance as may be necessary to cover the risk of such loss or damage from any cause.

(4) Neither the Contractor nor a sub-contractor nor any other person shall have a lien on any goods or materials which have vested in the Employer under sub-clause (3) of this Clause for any sum due to the Contractor sub-contractor or other person and the Contractor shall take all such steps as may reasonably be necessary to ensure that the title of the Employer and the exclusion of any such lien are brought to the notice of sub-contractors and other persons dealing with any such goods or materials. **Lien on Goods or Materials.**

(5) Upon cessation of the employment of the Contractor under this contract before the completion of the Works whether as a result of the operation of Clause 63 or otherwise the Contractor shall deliver to the Employer any goods or materials the property in which has vested in the Employer by virtue of sub-clause (3) of this Clause and if he shall fail to do so the Employer may enter any premises of the Contractor or of any sub-contractor and remove such goods and materials and recover the cost of so doing from the Contractor. **Delivery to the Employer of Vested Goods or Materials.**

(6) The Contractor shall incorporate provisions equivalent to those provided in this Clause in every sub-contract in which provision is to be made for payment in respect of goods or materials before the same have been delivered to the Site. **Incorporation in Sub-contracts.**

MEASUREMENT

55. (1) The quantities set out in the Bill of Quantities are the estimated quantities of the work but they are not to be taken as the actual and correct quantities of the Works to be executed by the Contractor in fulfilment of his obligations under the Contract. **Quantities.**

(2) Any error in description in the Bill of Quantities or omission therefrom shall not vitiate the Contract nor release the Contractor from the execution of the whole or any part of the Works according to the Drawings and Specification or from any of his obligations or liabilities under the Contract. Any such error or omission shall be corrected by the Engineer and the value of the work actually carried out shall be ascertained in accordance with Clause 52. Provided that there shall be no rectification of any errors omissions or wrong estimates in the descriptions rates and prices inserted by the Contractor in the Bill of Quantities. **Correction of Errors.**

56. (1) The Engineer shall except as otherwise stated ascertain and determine by admeasurement the value in accordance with the Contract of the work done in accordance with the Contract. **Measurement and Valuation.**

(2) Should the actual quantities executed in respect of any item be greater or less than those stated in the Bill of Quantities and if in the opinion of the Engineer such increase or decrease of itself shall so warrant the Engineer shall after consultation with the Contractor determine an appropriate increase or decrease of any rates or prices rendered unreasonable or inapplicable in consequence thereof and shall notify the Contractor accordingly. **Increase or Decrease of Rate.**

(3) The Engineer shall when he requires any part or parts of the work to be measured give reasonable notice to the Contractor who shall attend or send a qualified agent to assist the Engineer or the Engineer's Representative in making such measurement and shall furnish all particulars required by either of them. Should the Contractor not attend or neglect or omit to send such agent then the measurement made by the Engineer or approved by him shall be taken to be the correct measurement of the work. **Attending for Measurement.**

57. Except where any statement or general or detailed description of the work in the Bill of Quantities expressly shows to the contrary Bills of Quantities shall be deemed to have been prepared and measurements shall be made according to the procedure set forth in the " Standard Method of Measurement of Civil Engineering Quantities " issued by the Institution of Civil Engineers and reprinted in 1973 or such later or amended edition thereof as may be stated in the Appendix to the Form of Tender to have been adopted in its preparation notwithstanding any general or local custom. **Method of Measurement.**

PROVISIONAL AND PRIME COST SUMS AND NOMINATED SUB-CONTRACTS

Provisional Sum.

58. (1) " Provisional Sum " means a sum included in the Contract and so designated for the execution of work or the supply of goods materials or services or for contingencies which sum may be used in whole or in part or not at all at the direction and discretion of the Engineer.

Prime Cost Item.

(2) " Prime Cost (PC) Item " means an item in the Contract which contains (either wholly or in part) a sum referred to as Prime Cost (PC) which will be used for the execution of work or for the supply of goods materials or services for the Works.

Design Requirements to be Expressly Stated.

(3) If in connection with any Provisional Sum or Prime Cost Item the services to be provided include any matter of design or specification of any part of the Permanent Works or of any equipment or plant to be incorporated therein such requirement shall be expressly stated in the Contract and shall be included in any Nominated Sub-contract. The obligation of the Contractor in respect thereof shall be only that which has been expressly stated in accordance with this sub-clause.

Use of Prime Cost Items.

(4) In respect of every Prime Cost Item the Engineer shall have power to order the Contractor to employ a sub-contractor nominated by the Engineer for the execution of any work or the supply of any goods materials or services included therein. The Engineer shall also have power with the consent of the Contractor to order the Contractor to execute any such work or to supply any such goods materials or services in which event the Contractor shall be paid in accordance with the terms of a quotation submitted by him and accepted by the Engineer or in the absence thereof the value shall be determined in accordance with Clause 52.

Nominated Sub-contractors—Definition.

(5) All specialists merchants tradesmen and others nominated in the Contract for a Prime Cost Item or ordered by the Engineer to be employed by the Contractor in accordance with sub-clause (4) or sub-clause (7) of this Clause for the execution of any work or the supply of any goods materials or services are referred to in this Contract as " Nominated Sub-contractors ".

Production of Vouchers, etc.

(6) The Contractor shall when required by the Engineer produce all quotations invoices vouchers sub-contract documents accounts and receipts in connection with expenditure in respect of work carried out by all Nominated Sub-contractors.

Use of Provisional Sums.

(7) In respect of every Provisional Sum the Engineer shall have power to order either or both of the following:—

(a) work to be executed or goods materials or services to be supplied by the Contractor the value of such work executed or goods materials or services supplied being determined in accordance with Clause 52 and included in the Contract Price;
(b) work to be executed or goods materials or services to be supplied by a Nominated Sub-contractor in accordance with Clause 59A.

Nominated Sub-contractors—Objection to Nomination.

59A. (1) Subject to sub-clause (2)(c) of this Clause the Contractor shall not be under any obligation to enter into any sub-contract with any Nominated Sub-contractor against whom the Contractor may raise reasonable objection or who shall decline to enter into a sub-contract with the Contractor containing provisions:—

(a) that in respect of the work goods materials or services the subject of the sub-contract the Nominated Sub-contractor will undertake towards the Contractor such obligations and liabilities as will enable the Contractor to discharge his own obligations and liabilities towards the Employer under the terms of the Contract;
(b) that the Nominated Sub-contractor will save harmless and indemnify the Contractor against all claims demands and proceedings damages costs charges and expenses whatsoever arising out of or in connection with any failure by the Nominated Sub-contractor to perform such obligations or fulfil such liabilities;
(c) that the Nominated Sub-contractor will save harmless and indemnify the Contractor from and against any negligence by the Nominated Sub-contractor his agents workmen and servants and against any misuse by him or them of any Constructional Plant or Temporary Works provided by the Contractor for the purposes of the Contract and for all claims as aforesaid;
(d) equivalent to those contained in Clause 63.

Engineer's Action upon Objection.

(2) If pursuant to sub-clause (1) of this Clause the Contractor shall not be obliged to enter into a sub-contract with a Nominated Sub-contractor and shall decline to do so the Engineer shall do one or more of the following:—

(a) nominate an alternative sub-contractor in which case sub-clause (1) of this Clause shall apply;
(b) by order under Clause 51 vary the Works or the work goods materials or services the subject of the Provisional Sum or Prime Cost Item including if necessary the omission of any such work goods materials or services so that they may be provided by workmen contractors or suppliers as the case may be employed by the Employer either concurrently with the Works (in which case Clause 31 shall apply) or at

some other date. Provided that in respect of the omission of any Prime Cost Item there shall be included in the Contract Price a sum in respect of the Contractor's charges and profit being a percentage of the estimated value of such work goods material or services omitted at the rate provided in the Bill of Quantities or inserted in the Appendix to the Form of Tender as the case may be;

(c) subject to the Employer's consent where the Contractor declines to enter into a contract with the Nominated Sub-contractor only on the grounds of unwillingness of the Nominated Sub-contractor to contract on the basis of the provisions contained in paragraphs (a) (b) (c) or (d) of sub-clause (1) of this Clause direct the Contractor to enter into a contract with the Nominated Sub-contractor on such other terms as the Engineer shall specify in which case sub-clause (3) of this Clause shall apply;

(d) in accordance with Clause 58 arrange for the Contractor to execute such work or to supply such goods materials or services.

Direction by Engineer.

(3) If the Engineer shall direct the Contractor pursuant to sub-clause (2) of this Clause to enter into a sub-contract which does not contain all the provisions referred to in sub-clause (1) of this Clause:—

(a) the Contractor shall not be bound to discharge his obligations and liabilities under the Contract to the extent that the sub-contract terms so specified by the Engineer are inconsistent with the discharge of the same;

(b) in the event of the Contractor incurring loss or expense or suffering damage arising out of the refusal of the Nominated Sub-contractor to accept such provisions the Contractor shall subject to Clause 52(4) be paid in accordance with Clause 60 the amount of such loss expense or damage as the Contractor could not reasonably avoid.

Contractor Responsible for Nominated Sub-contracts.

(4) Except as otherwise provided in this Clause and in Clause 59B the Contractor shall be as responsible for the work executed or goods materials or services supplied by a Nominated Sub-contractor employed by him as if he had himself executed such work or supplied such goods materials or services or had sub-let the same in accordance with Clause 4.

Payments.

(5) For all work executed or goods materials or services supplied by Nominated Sub-contractors there shall be included in the Contract Price:—

(a) the actual price paid or due to be paid by the Contractor in accordance with the terms of the sub-contract (unless and to the extent that any such payment is the result of a default of the Contractor) net of all trade and other discounts rebates and allowances other than any discount obtainable by the Contractor for prompt payment;

(b) the sum (if any) provided in the Bill of Quantities for labours in connection therewith or if ordered pursuant to Clause 58(7)(b) as may be determined by the Engineer;

(c) in respect of all other charges and profit a sum being a percentage of the actual price paid or due to be paid calculated (where provision has been made in the Bill of Quantities for a rate to be set against the relevant item of prime cost) at the rate inserted by the Contractor against that item or (where no such provision has been made) at the rate inserted by the Contractor in the Appendix to the Form of Tender as the percentage for adjustment of sums set against Prime Cost Items.

Breach of Sub-contract.

(6) In the event that the Nominated Sub-contractor shall be in breach of the sub-contract which breach causes the Contractor to be in breach of contract the Employer shall not enforce any award of any arbitrator or judgment which he may obtain against the Contractor in respect of such breach of contract except to the extent that the Contractor may have been able to recover the amount thereof from the Sub-contractor. Provided always that *if* the Contractor shall not comply with Clause 59B (6) the Employer may enforce any such award or judgment in full.

Forfeiture of Sub-contract.

59B. (1) Subject to Clause 59A(2)(c) the Contractor shall in every sub-contract with a Nominated Sub-contractor incorporate provisions equivalent to those provided in Clause 63 and such provisions are hereinafter referred to as " the Forfeiture Clause ".

Termination of Sub-contract.

(2) If any event arises which in the opinion of the Contractor would entitle the Contractor to exercise his right under the Forfeiture Clause (or in the event that there shall be no Forfeiture Clause in the sub-contract his right to treat the sub-contract as repudiated by the Nominated Sub-contractor) he shall at once notify the Engineer in writing and if he desires to exercise such right by such notice seek the Employer's consent to his so doing. The Engineer shall by notice in writing to the Contractor inform him whether or not the Employer does so consent and if the Engineer does not give notice withholding consent within 7 days of receipt of the Contractor's notice the Employer shall be deemed to have consented to the exercise of the said right. If notice is given by the Contractor to the Engineer under this sub-clause and has not been withdrawn then notwithstanding that the Contractor has not sought the Employer's consent as aforesaid the Engineer may with the Employer's consent direct the Contractor to give notice to the Nominated Sub-contractor expelling the Nominated Sub-contractor from the sub-contract Works pursuant

to the Forfeiture Clause or rescinding the sub-contract as the case may be. Any such notice given to the Nominated Sub-contractor is hereinafter referred to as a notice enforcing forfeiture of the sub-contract.

Engineer's Action upon Termination.

(3) If the Contractor shall give a notice enforcing forfeiture of the sub-contract whether under and in accordance with the Forfeiture Clause in the sub-contract or in purported exercise of his right to treat the sub-contract as repudiated the Engineer shall do any one or more of the things described in paragraphs (a) (b) and (d) of Clause 59A(2).

Delay and Extra Cost.

(4) If a notice enforcing forfeiture of the sub-contract shall have been given with the consent of the Employer or by the direction of the Engineer or if it shall have been given without the Employer's consent in circumstances which entitled the Contractor to give such a notice:—

(a) there shall be included in the Contract Price:—

(i) the value determined in accordance with Clause 52 of any work the Contractor may have executed or goods or materials he may have provided subsequent to the forfeiture taking effect and pursuant to the Engineer's direction;

(ii) such amount calculated in accordance with paragraph (a) of Clause 59A(5) as may be due in respect of any work goods materials or services provided by an alternative Nominated Sub-contractor together with reasonable sums for labours and for all other charges and profit as may be determined by the Engineer;

(iii) any such amount as may be due in respect of the forfeited sub-contract in accordance with Clause 59A(5);

(b) the Engineer shall take any delay to the completion of the Works consequent upon the forfeiture into account in determining any extension of time to which the Contractor is entitled under Clause 44 and the Contractor shall subject to Clause 52(4) be paid in accordance with Clause 60 the amount of any additional cost which he may have necessarily and properly incurred as a result of such delay;

(c) the Employer shall subject to Clause 60(7) be entitled to recover from the Contractor upon the certificate of the Engineer issued in accordance with Clause 60(3):—

(i) the amount by which the total sum to be included in the Contract Price pursuant to paragraphs (a) and (b) of this sub-clause exceeds the sum which would but for the forfeiture have been included in the Contract Price in respect of work materials goods and services done supplied or performed under the forfeited sub-contract;

(ii) all such other loss expense and damage as the Employer may have suffered in consequence of the breach of the sub-contract;

all of which are hereinafter collectively called " the Employer's loss ".

Provided always that if the Contractor shall show that despite his having complied with sub-clause (6) of this Clause he has been unable to recover the whole or any part of the Employer's loss from the Sub-contractor the Employer shall allow or (if he has already recovered the same from the Contractor) shall repay to the Contractor so much of the Employer's loss as was irrecoverable from the Sub-contractor except and to the extent that the same was irrecoverable by reason of some breach of the sub-contract or other default towards the Sub-contractor by the Contractor or except to the extent that any act or default of the Contractor may have caused or contributed to any of the Employer's loss. Any such repayment by the Employer shall carry interest at the rate stipulated in Clause 60(6) from the date of the recovery by the Employer from the Contractor of the sum repaid.

Termination Without Consent.

(5) If notice enforcing forfeiture of the sub-contract shall have been given without the consent of the Employer and in circumstances which did not entitle the Contractor to give such a notice:—

(a) there shall be included in the Contract Price in respect of the whole of the work covered by the Nominated Sub-contract only the amount that would have been payable to the Nominated Sub-contractor on due completion of the sub-contract had it not been terminated;

(b) the Contractor shall not be entitled to any extension of time because of such termination nor to any additional expense incurred as a result of the work having been carried out and completed otherwise than by the said Sub-contractor;

(c) the Employer shall be entitled to recover from the Contractor any additional expense he may incur beyond that which he would have incurred had the sub-contract not been terminated.

Recovery of Employer's Loss.

(6) The Contractor shall take all necessary steps and proceedings as may be required by the Employer to enforce the provisions of the sub-contract and/or all other rights and/or remedies available to him so as to recover the Employer's loss from the Sub-contractor. Except in the case where notice enforcing forfeiture of the sub-contract shall have been given without the consent

of the Employer and in circumstances which did not entitle the Contractor to give such a notice the Employer shall pay to the Contractor so much of the reasonable costs and expenses of such steps and proceedings as are irrecoverable from the Sub-contractor provided that if the Contractor shall seek to recover by the same steps and proceedings any loss damage or expense additional to the Employer's loss the said irrecoverable costs and expenses shall be borne by the Contractor and the Employer in such proportions as may be fair in all the circumstances.

Payment to Nominated Sub-contractors.

59C. Before issuing any certificate under Clause 60 the Engineer shall be entitled to demand from the Contractor reasonable proof that all sums (less retentions provided for in the sub-contract) included in previous certificates in respect of the work executed or goods or materials or services supplied by Nominated Sub-contractors have been paid to the Nominated Sub-contractors or discharged by the Contractor in default whereof unless the Contractor shall:—

(a) give details to the Engineer in writing of any reasonable cause he may have for withholding or refusing to make such payment; and

(b) produce to the Engineer reasonable proof that he has so informed such Nominated Sub-contractor in writing;

the Employer shall be entitled to pay to such Nominated Sub-contractor direct upon the certification of the Engineer all payments (less retentions provided for in the sub-contract) which the Contractor has failed to make to such Nominated Sub-contractor and to deduct by way of set-off the amount so paid by the Employer from any sums due or which become due from the Employer to the Contractor. Provided always that where the Engineer has certified and the Employer has paid direct as aforesaid the Engineer shall in issuing any further certificate in favour of the Contractor deduct from the amount thereof the amount so paid direct as aforesaid but shall not withhold or delay the issue of the certificate itself when due to be issued under the terms of the Contract.

CERTIFICATES AND PAYMENT

Monthly Statements.

60. (1) The Contractor shall submit to the Engineer after the end of each month a statement (in such form if any as may be prescribed in the Specification) showing:—

(a) the estimated contract value of the Permanent Works executed up to the end of that month;

(b) a list of any goods or materials delivered to the Site for but not yet incorporated in the Permanent Works and their value;

(c) a list of any goods or materials listed in the Appendix to the Form of Tender which have not yet been delivered to the Site but of which the property has vested in the Employer pursuant to Clause 54 and their value;

(d) the estimated amounts to which the Contractor considers himself entitled in connection with all other matters for which provision is made under the Contract including any Temporary Works or Constructional Plant for which separate amounts are included in the Bill of Quantities;

unless in the opinion of the Contractor such values and amounts together will not justify the issue of an interim certificate.

Amounts payable in respect of Nominated Sub-contractors are to be listed separately.

Monthly Payments.

(2) Within 28 days of the date of delivery to the Engineer or Engineer's Representative in accordance with sub-clause (1) of this Clause of the Contractor's monthly statement the Engineer shall certify and the Employer shall pay to the Contractor (after deducting any previous payments on account):—

(a) the amount which in the opinion of the Engineer on the basis of the monthly statement is due to the Contractor on account of sub-clause (1)(a) and (d) of this Clause less a retention as provided in sub-clause (4) of this Clause;

(b) such amounts (if any) as the Engineer may consider proper (but in no case exceeding the percentage of the value stated in the Appendix to the Form of Tender) in respect of (b) and (c) of sub-clause (1) of this Clause which amounts shall not be subject to a retention under sub-clause (4) of this Clause.

The amounts certified in respect of Nominated Sub-contracts shall be shown separately in the certificate. The Engineer shall not be bound to issue an interim certificate for a sum less than that named in the Appendix to the Form of Tender.

Final Account.

(3) Not later than 3 months after the date of the Maintenance Certificate the Contractor shall submit to the Engineer a statement of final account and supporting documentation showing in detail the value in accordance with the Contract of the work done in accordance with the Contract together with all further sums which the Contractor considers to be due to him under the Contract up to the date of the Maintenance Certificate. Within 3 months after receipt of this final account and of all information reasonably required for its verification the Engineer shall issue a final certificate stating the amount which in his opinion is finally due under the Contract up to the date

of the Maintenance Certificate and after giving credit to the Employer for all amounts previously paid by the Employer and for all sums to which the Employer is entitled under the Contract up to the date of the Maintenance Certificate the balance if any due from the Employer to the Contractor or from the Contractor to the Employer as the case may be. Such balance shall subject to Clause 47 be paid to or by the Contractor as the case may require within 28 days of the date of the certificate.

Retention.

(4) The retention to be made pursuant to sub-clause (2)(a) of this Clause shall be a sum equal to 5 per cent of the amount due to the Contractor until a reserve shall have accumulated in the hand of the Employer up to the following limits:—

(a) where the Tender Total does not exceed £50,000 5 per cent of the Tender Total but not exceeding £1,500; or

(b) where the Tender Total exceeds £50,000 3 per cent of the Tender Total;

except that the limit shall be reduced by the amount of any payment that shall have been made pursuant to sub-clause (5) of this Clause.

Payment of Retention Money.

(5) (a) If the Engineer shall issue a Certificate of Completion in respect of any Section or part of the Works pursuant to Clause 48(2) or (3) there shall become due on the date of issue of such certificate and shall be paid to the Contractor within 14 days thereof a sum equal to $1\frac{1}{2}$ per cent of the amount due to the Contractor at that date in respect of such Section or part as certified for payment pursuant to sub-clause (2) of this Clause.

(b) One half of the retention money less any sums paid pursuant to sub-clause (5)(a) of this Clause shall be paid to the Contractor within 14 days after the date on which the Engineer shall have issued a Certificate of Completion for the whole of the Works pursuant to Clause 48(1).

(c) The other half of the retention money shall be paid to the Contractor within 14 days after the expiration of the Period of Maintenance notwithstanding that at such time there may be outstanding claims by the Contractor against the Employer. Provided always that if at such time there shall remain to be executed by the Contractor any outstanding work referred to under Clause 48 or any works ordered during such period pursuant to Clauses 49 and 50 the Employer shall be entitled to withhold payment until the completion of such works of so much of the second half of retention money as shall in the opinion of the Engineer represent the cost of the works so remaining to be executed.

Provided further that in the event of different maintenance periods having become applicable to different Sections or parts of the Works pursuant to Clause 48 the expression " expiration of the Period of Maintenance " shall for the purposes of this sub-clause be deemed to mean the expiration of the latest of such periods.

Interest on Overdue Payments.

(6) In the event of failure by the Engineer to certify or the Employer to make payment in accordance with sub-clauses (2) (3) and (5) of this Clause the Employer shall pay to the Contractor interest upon any payment overdue thereunder at a rate per annum equivalent to $\frac{3}{4}$ per cent plus the minimum rate at which the Bank of England will lend to a discount house having access to the Discount Office of the Bank current on the date upon which such payment first becomes overdue. In the event of any variation in the said Bank Rate being announced whilst such payment remains overdue the interest payable to the Contractor for the period that such payment remains overdue shall be correspondingly varied from the date of each such variation.

Correction and Withholding of Certificates.

(7) The Engineer shall have power to omit from any certificate the value of any work done goods or materials supplied or services rendered with which he may for the time being be dissatisfied and for that purpose or for any other reason which to him may seem proper may by any certificate delete correct or modify any sum previously certified by him.

Provided always that:—

(a) the Engineer shall not in any interim certificate delete or reduce any sum previously certified in respect of work done goods or materials supplied or services rendered by a Nominated Sub-contractor if the Contractor shall have already paid or be bound to pay that sum to the Nominated Sub-contractor;

(b) if the Engineer in the final certificate shall delete or reduce any sum previously certified in respect of work done goods or materials supplied or services rendered by a Nominated Sub-contractor which sum shall have been already paid by the Contractor to the Nominated Sub-contractor the Employer shall reimburse to the Contractor the amount of any sum overpaid by the Contractor to the Sub-contractor in accordance with the certificates issued under sub-clause (2) of this Clause which the Contractor despite compliance with Clause 59B(6) shall be unable to recover from the Nominated Sub-contractor together with interest thereon at the rate stated in Clause 60(6) from 28 days after the date of the final certificate issued under sub-clause (3) of this Clause until the date of such reimbursement.

(8) Every certificate issued by the Engineer pursuant to this Clause shall be sent to the Employer and at the same time a copy thereof shall be sent to the Contractor. **Copy Certificate for Contractor.**

61. (1) Upon the expiration of the Period of Maintenance or where there is more than one such period upon the expiration of the latest period and when all outstanding work referred to under Clause 48 and all work of repair amendment reconstruction rectification and making good of defects imperfections shrinkages and other faults referred to under Clauses 49 and 50 shall have been completed the Engineer shall issue to the Employer (with a copy to the Contractor) a Maintenance Certificate stating the date on which the Contractor shall have completed his obligations to construct complete and maintain the Works to the Engineer's satisfaction. **Maintenance Certificate.**

(2) The issue of the Maintenance Certificate shall not be taken as relieving either the Contractor or the Employer from any liability the one towards the other arising out of or in any way connected with the performance of their respective obligations under the Contract. **Unfulfilled Obligations.**

REMEDIES AND POWERS

62. If by reason of any accident or failure or other event occurring to in or in connection with the Works or any part thereof either during the execution of the Works or during the Period of Maintenance any remedial or other work or repair shall in the opinion of the Engineer be urgently necessary and the Contractor is unable or unwilling at once to do such work or repair the Employer may by his own or other workmen do such work or repair as the Engineer may consider necessary. If the work or repair so done by the Employer is work which in the opinion of the Engineer the Contractor was liable to do at his own expense under the Contract all costs and charges properly incurred by the Employer in so doing shall on demand be paid by the Contractor to the Employer or may be deducted by the Employer from any monies due or which may become due to the Contractor. Provided always that the Engineer shall as soon after the occurrence of any such emergency as may be reasonably practicable notify the Contractor thereof in writing. **Urgent Repairs.**

63. (1) If the Contractor shall become bankrupt or have a receiving order made against him or shall present his petition in bankruptcy or shall make an arrangement with or assignment in favour of his creditors or shall agree to carry out the Contract under a committee of inspection of his creditors or (being a corporation) shall go into liquidation (other than a voluntary liquidation for the purposes of amalgamation or reconstruction) or if the Contractor shall assign the Contract without the consent in writing of the Employer first obtained or shall have an execution levied on his goods or if the Engineer shall certify in writing to the Employer that in his opinion the Contractor:— **Forfeiture.**

(a) has abandoned the Contract; or

(b) without reasonable excuse has failed to commence the Works in accordance with Clause 41 or has suspended the progress of the Works for 14 days after receiving from the Engineer written notice to proceed; or

(c) has failed to remove goods or materials from the Site or to pull down and replace work for 14 days after receiving from the Engineer written notice that the said goods materials or work have been condemned and rejected by the Engineer; or

(d) despite previous warning by the Engineer in writing is failing to proceed with the Works with due diligence or is otherwise persistently or fundamentally in breach of his obligations under the Contract; or

(e) has to the detriment of good workmanship or in defiance of the Engineer's instruction to the contrary sub-let any part of the Contract;

then the Employer may after giving 7 days' notice in writing to the Contractor enter upon the Site and the Works and expel the Contractor therefrom without thereby avoiding the Contract or releasing the Contractor from any of his obligations or liabilities under the Contract or affecting the rights and powers conferred on the Employer or the Engineer by the Contract and may himself complete the Works or may employ any other contractor to complete the Works and the Employer or such other contractor may use for such completion so much of the Constructional Plant Temporary Works goods and materials which have been deemed to become the property of the Employer under Clauses 53 and 54 as he or they may think proper and the Employer may at any time sell any of the said Constructional Plant Temporary Works and unused goods and materials and apply the proceeds of sale in or towards the satisfaction of any sums due or which may become due to him from the Contractor under the Contract.

(2) By the said notice or by further notice in writing within 14 days of the date thereof the Engineer may require the Contractor to assign to the Employer and if so required the Contractor shall forthwith assign to the Employer the benefit of any agreement for the supply of any goods or materials and/or for the execution of any work for the purposes of this Contract which the Contractor may have entered into. **Assignment to Employer.**

Valuation at Date of Forfeiture.

(3) The Engineer shall as soon as may be practicable after any such entry and expulsion by the Employer fix and determine *ex parte* or by or after reference to the parties or after such investigation or enquiries as he may think fit to make or institute and shall certify what amount (if any) had at the time of such entry and expulsion been reasonably earned by or would reasonably accrue to the Contractor in respect of work then actually done by him under the Contract and what was the value of any unused or partially used goods and materials any Constructional Plant and any Temporary Works which have been deemed to become the property of the Employer under Clauses 53 and 54.

Payment after Forfeiture.

(4) If the Employer shall enter and expel the Contractor under this Clause he shall not be liable to pay to the Contractor any money on account of the Contract until the expiration of the Period of Maintenance and thereafter until the costs of completion and maintenance damages for delay in completion (if any) and all other expenses incurred by the Employer have been ascertained and the amount thereof certified by the Engineer. The Contractor shall then be entitled to receive only such sum or sums (if any) as the Engineer may certify would have been due to him upon due completion by him after deducting the said amount. But if such amount shall exceed the sum which would have been payable to the Contractor on due completion by him then the Contractor shall upon demand pay to the Employer the amount of such excess and it shall be deemed a debt due by the Contractor to the Employer and shall be recoverable accordingly.

FRUSTRATION

Payment in Event of Frustration.

64. In the event of the Contract being frustrated whether by war or by any other supervening event which may occur independently of the will of the parties the sum payable by the Employer to the Contractor in respect of the work executed shall be the same as that which would have been payable under Clause 65(5) if the Contract had been determined by the Employer under Clause 65.

WAR CLAUSE

Works to Continue for 28 Days on Outbreak of War.

65. (1) If during the currency of the Contract there shall be an outbreak of war (whether war is declared or not) in which Great Britain shall be engaged on a scale involving general mobilisation of the armed forces of the Crown the Contractor shall for a period of 28 days reckoned from midnight on the date that the order for general mobilisation is given continue so far as is physically possible to execute the Works in accordance with the Contract.

Effect of Completion Within 28 Days.

(2) If at any time before the expiration of the said period of 28 days the Works shall have been completed or completed so far as to be usable all provisions of the Contract shall continue to have full force and effect save that:—

(a) the Contractor shall in lieu of fulfilling his obligations under Clauses 49 and 50 be entitled at his option to allow against the sum due to him under the provisions hereof the cost (calculated at the prices ruling at the beginning of the said period of 28 days) as certified by the Engineer at the expiration of the Period of Maintenance of repair rectification and making good any work for the repair rectification or making good of which the Contractor would have been liable under the said Clauses had they continued to be applicable;

(b) the Employer shall not be entitled at the expiration of the Period of Maintenance to withhold payment under Clause 60(5)(c) of the second half of the retention money or any part thereof except such sum as may be allowable by the Contractor under the provisions of the last preceding paragraph which sum may (without prejudice to any other mode of recovery thereof) be deducted by the Employer from such second half.

Right of Employer to Determine Contract.

(3) If the Works shall not have been completed as aforesaid the Employer shall be entitled to determine the Contract (with the exception of this Clause and Clauses 66 and 68) by giving notice in writing to the Contractor at any time after the aforesaid period of 28 days has expired and upon such notice being given the Contract shall (except as above mentioned) forthwith determine but without prejudice to the claims of either party in respect of any antecedent breach thereof.

Removal of Plant on Determination.

(4) If the Contract shall be determined under the provisions of the last preceding sub-clause the Contractor shall with all reasonable despatch remove from the Site all his Constructional Plant and shall give facilities to his sub-contractors to remove similarly all Constructional Plant belonging to them and in the event of any failure so to do the Employer shall have the like powers as are contained in Clause 53(8) in regard to failure to remove Constructional Plant on completion of the Works but subject to the same condition as is contained in Clause 53(9).

Payment on Determination.

(5) If the Contract shall be determined as aforesaid the Contractor shall be paid by the Employer (insofar as such amounts or items shall not have been already covered by payment on

account made to the Contractor) for all work executed prior to the date of determination at the rates and prices provided in the Contract and in addition:—

(a) the amounts payable in respect of any preliminary items so far as the work or service comprised therein has been carried out or performed and a proper proportion as certified by the Engineer of any such items the work or service comprised in which has been partially carried out or performed;

(b) the cost of materials or goods reasonably ordered for the Works which shall have been delivered to the Contractor or of which the Contractor is legally liable to accept delivery (such materials or goods becoming the property of the Employer upon such payment being made by him);

(c) a sum to be certified by the Engineer being the amount of any expenditure reasonably incurred by the Contractor in the expectation of completing the whole of the Works in so far as such expenditure shall not have been covered by the payments in this sub-clause before mentioned;

(d) any additional sum payable under sub-clause (6)(b)(c) and (d) of this Clause;

(e) the reasonable cost of removal under sub-clause (4) of this Clause.

Provisions to Apply as from Outbreak of War.

(6) Whether the Contract shall be determined under the provisions of sub-clause (3) of this Clause or not the following provisions shall apply or be deemed to have applied as from the date of the said outbreak of war notwithstanding anything expressed in or implied by the other terms of the Contract *viz*:—

(a) The Contractor shall be under no liability whatsoever whether by way of indemnity or otherwise for or in respect of damage to the Works or to property (other than property of the Contractor or property hired by him for the purposes of executing the Works) whether of the Employer or of third parties or for or in respect of injury or loss of life to persons which is the consequence whether direct or indirect of war hostilities (whether war has been declared or not) invasion act of the Queen's enemies civil war rebellion revolution insurrection military or usurped power and the Employer shall indemnify the Contractor against all such liabilities and against all claims demands proceedings damages costs charges and expenses whatsoever arising thereout or in connection therewith.

(b) If the Works shall sustain destruction or any damage by reason of any of the causes mentioned in the last preceding paragraph the Contractor shall nevertheless be entitled to payment for any part of the Works so destroyed or damaged and the Contractor shall be entitled to be paid by the Employer the cost of making good any such destruction or damage so far as may be required by the Engineer or as may be necessary for the completion of the Works on a cost basis plus such profit as the Engineer may certify to be reasonable.

(c) In the event that the Contract includes the Contract Price Fluctuations Clause the terms of that Clause shall continue to apply but if subsequent to the outbreak of war the index figures therein referred to shall cease to be published or in the event that the contract shall not include a Price Fluctuations Clause in that form the following paragraph shall have effect:—

If under decision of the Civil Engineering Construction Conciliation Board or of any other body recognised as an appropriate body for regulating the rates of wages in any trade or industry other than the Civil Engineering Construction Industry to which Contractors undertaking works of civil engineering construction give effect by agreement or in practice or by reason of any Statute or Statutory Instrument there shall during the currency of the Contract be any increase or decrease in the wages or the rates of wages or in the allowances or rates of allowances (including allowances in respect of holidays) payable to or in respect of labour of any kind prevailing at the date of outbreak of war as then fixed by the said Board or such other body as aforesaid or by Statute or Statutory Instrument or any increase in the amount payable by the Contractor by virtue or in respect of any Scheme of State Insurance or if there shall be any increase or decrease in the cost prevailing at the date of the said outbreak of war of any materials consumable stores fuel or power (and whether for permanent or temporary works) which increase or increases decrease or decreases shall result in an increase or decrease of cost to the Contractor in carrying out the Works the net increase or decrease of cost shall form an addition or deduction as the case may be to or from the Contract Price and be paid to or allowed by the Contractor accordingly.

(d) If the cost of the Works to the Contractor shall be increased or decreased by reason of the provisions of any Statute or Statutory Instrument or other Government or Local Government Order or Regulation becoming applicable to the Works after the date of the said outbreak of war or by reason of any trade or industrial agreement entered into after such date to which the Civil Engineering Construction Conciliation Board or any other body as aforesaid is party or gives effect or by reason of any amendment of whatsoever nature of the Working Rule Agreement of the said Board or of any other body as aforesaid or by reason of any other circumstance or thing attributable to or consequent on such outbreak of war such increase or decrease of cost as certified by the Engineer shall be reimbursed by the Employer to the Contractor or allowed by the Contractor as the case may be.

(e) Damage or injury caused by the explosion whenever occurring of any mine bomb shell grenade or other projectile missile or munition of war and whether occurring before or after the cessation of hostilities shall be deemed to be the consequence of any of the events mentioned in sub-clause (6)(a) of this Clause.

SETTLEMENT OF DISPUTES

Settlement of Disputes—Arbitration.

66. (1) If any dispute or difference of any kind whatsoever shall arise between the Employer and the Contractor in connection with or arising out of the Contract or the carrying out of the Works including any dispute as to any decision opinion instruction direction certificate or valuation of the Engineer (whether during the progress of the Works or after their completion and whether before or after the determination abandonment or breach of the Contract) it shall be referred to and settled by the Engineer who shall state his decision in writing and give notice of the same to the Employer and the Contractor. Unless the Contract shall have been already determined or abandoned the Contractor shall in every case continue to proceed with the Works with all due diligence and he shall give effect forthwith to every such decision of the Engineer unless and until the same shall be revised by an arbitrator as hereinafter provided. Such decisions shall be final and binding upon the Contractor and the Employer unless either of them shall require that the matter be referred to arbitration as hereinafter provided. If the Engineer shall fail to give such decision for a period of 3 calendar months after being requested to do so or if either the Employer or the Contractor be dissatisfied with any such decision of the Engineer then and in any such case either the Employer or the Contractor may within 3 calendar months after receiving notice of such decision or within 3 calendar months after the expiration of the said period of 3 months (as the case may be) require that the matter shall be referred to the arbitration of a person to be agreed upon between the parties or (if the parties fail to appoint an arbitrator within one calendar month of either party serving on the other party a written notice to concur in the appointment of an arbitrator) a person to be appointed on the application of either party by the President for the time being of the Institution of Civil Engineers. If an arbitrator declines the appointment or after appointment is removed by order of a competent court or is incapable of acting or dies and the parties do not within one calendar month of the vacancy arising fill the vacancy then the President for the time being of the Institution of Civil Engineers may on the application of either party appoint an arbitrator to fill the vacancy. Any such reference to arbitration shall be deemed to be a submission to arbitration within the meaning of the Arbitration Act 1950 or the Arbitration (Scotland) Act 1894 as the case may be or any statutory re-enactment or amendment thereof for the time being in force. Any such reference to arbitration may be conducted in accordance with the Institution of Civil Engineers' Arbitration Procedure (1973) or any amendment or modification thereof being in force at the time of the appointment of the arbitrator and in cases where the President of the Institution of Civil Engineers is requested to appoint the arbitrator he may direct that the arbitration is conducted in accordance with the aforementioned Procedure or any amendment or modification thereof. Such arbitrator shall have full power to open up review and revise any decision opinion instruction direction certificate or valuation of the Engineer and neither party shall be limited in the proceedings before such arbitrator to the evidence or arguments put before the Engineer for the purpose of obtaining his decision above referred to. The award of the arbitrator shall be final and binding on the parties. Save as provided for in sub-clause (2) of this Clause no steps shall be taken in the reference to the arbitrator until after the completion or alleged completion of the Works unless with the written consent of the Employer and the Contractor. Provided always:—

(a) that the giving of a Certificate of Completion under Clause 48 shall not be a condition precedent to the taking of any step in such reference;

(b) that no decision given by the Engineer in accordance with the foregoing provisions shall disqualify him from being called as a witness and giving evidence before the arbitrator on any matter whatsoever relevant to the dispute or difference so referred to the arbitrator as aforesaid.

Interim Arbitration.

(2) In the case of any dispute or difference as to any matter arising under Clause 12 or the withholding by the Engineer of any certificate or the withholding of any portion of the retention money under Clause 60 to which the Contractor claims to be entitled or as to the exercise of the Engineer's power to give a certificate under Clause 63(1) the reference to the arbitrator may proceed notwithstanding that the Works shall not then be or be alleged to be complete.

(3) In any case where the President for the time being of the Institution of Civil Engineers is not able to exercise the functions conferred on him by this Clause the said functions may be exercised on his behalf by a Vice-President for the time being of the said Institution. **Vice-President to Act.**

APPLICATION TO SCOTLAND

67. If the Works are situated in Scotland the Contract shall in all respects be construed and operate as a Scottish contract and shall be interpreted in accordance with Scots law. **Application to Scotland.**

NOTICES

68. (1) Any notice to be given to the Contractor under the terms of the Contract shall be served by sending the same by post to or leaving the same at the Contractor's principal place of business (or in the event of the Contractor being a Company to or at its registered office). **Service of Notice on Contractor.**

(2) Any notice to be given to the Employer under the terms of the Contract shall be served by sending the same by post to or leaving the same at the Employer's last known address (or in the event of the Employer being a Company to or at its registered office). **Service of Notice on Employer.**

TAX MATTERS

69. (1) The rates and prices contained in the Bill of Quantities take account of the levels and incidence at the date for return of tenders (hereinafter called " the relevant date") of the taxes levies and contributions (including national insurance contributions but excluding income tax and any levy payable under the Industrial Training Act 1964) which are by law payable by the Contractor in respect of his workpeople and the premiums and refunds (if any) which are by law payable to the Contractor in respect of his workpeople. Any such matter is hereinafter called " a labour-tax matter ". **Tax Fluctuations.**

The rates and prices contained in the Bill of Quantities do not take account of any level or incidence of the aforesaid matters where at the relevant date such level or incidence does not then have effect but although then known is to take effect at some later date. The taking effect of any such level or incidence at the later date shall for the purposes of sub-clause (2) of this Clause be treated as the occurrence of an event.

(2) If after the relevant date there shall occur any of the events specified in sub-clause (3) of this Clause and as a consequence thereof the cost to the Contractor of performing his obligations under the Contract shall be increased or decreased then subject to the provisions of sub-clause (4) of this Clause the net amount of such increase or decrease shall constitute an addition to or deduction from the sums otherwise payable to the Contractor under the Contract as the case may require.

(3) The events referred to in the preceding sub-clause are as follows:—

(a) any change in the level of any labour-tax matter;
(b) any change in the incidence of any labour-tax matter including the imposition of any new such matter or the abolition of any previously existing such matter.

(4) In this Clause workpeople means persons employed by the Contractor on manual labour whether skilled or unskilled but for the purpose of ascertaining what if any additions or deductions are to be paid or allowed under this Clause account shall not be taken of any labour-tax matter in relation to any workpeople of the Contractor unless at the relevant time their normal place of employment is the Site.

(5) Subject to the provisions of the Contract as to the placing of sub-contracts with Nominated Sub-contractors the Contractor may incorporate in any sub-contract made for the purpose of performing his obligations under the Contract provisions which are *mutatis mutandis* the same as the provisions of this Clause and in such event additions or deductions to be made in accordance with any such sub-contract shall also be made under the Contract as if the increase or decrease of cost to the sub-contractor had been directly incurred by the Contractor.

(6) As soon as practicable after the occurrence of any of the events specified in sub-clause (3) of this Clause the Contractor shall give the Engineer notice thereof. The Contractor shall keep such contemporary records as are necessary for the purpose of ascertaining the amount of any addition or deduction to be made in accordance with this Clause and shall permit the Engineer to inspect such records. The Contractor shall submit to the Engineer with his monthly statements full details of every addition or deduction to be made in accordance with this Clause. All certificates for payment issued after submission of such details shall take due account of the additions or deductions to which such details relate. Provided that the Engineer may if the Contractor fails to submit full details of any deduction nevertheless take account of such deduction when issuing any certificate for payment.

Value Added Tax

70. (1) In this Clause " exempt supply " " invoice " " tax " " taxable person " and " taxable supply " have the same meanings as in Part I of the Finance Act 1972 (hereinafter referred to as " the Act ") including any amendment or re-enactment thereof and any reference to the Value Added Tax (General) Regulations 1972 (S.I. 1972/1147) (hereinafter referred to as the V.A.T. Regulations) shall be treated as a reference to any enactment corresponding to those regulations for the time being in force in consequence of any amendment or re-enactment of those regulations.

(2) The Contractor shall be deemed not to have allowed in his tender for the tax payable by him as a taxable person to the Commissioners of Customs and Excise being tax chargeable on any taxable supplies to the Employer which are to be made under the Contract.

(3) (a) The Contractor shall not in any statement submitted under Clause 60 include any element on account of tax in any item or claim contained in or submitted with the statement.

(b) The Contractor shall concurrently with the submission of the statement referred to in sub-clause (3)(a) of this Clause furnish the Employer with a written estimate showing those supplies of goods and services and the values thereof included in the said statement and on which tax will be chargeable under Regulation 21 of the V.A.T. Regulations at a rate other than zero.

(4) At the same time as payment (other than payment in accordance with this sub-clause) for goods or services which were the subject of a taxable supply provided by the Contractor as a taxable person to the Employer is made in accordance with the Contract there shall also be paid by the Employer a sum (separately identified by the Employer and in this Clause referred to as " the tax payment ") equal to the amount of tax payable by the Contractor on that supply. Within seven days of each payment the Contractor shall:—

(a) if he agrees with that tax payment or any part thereof issue to the Employer an authenticated receipt of the kind referred to in Regulation 21(2) of the V.A.T. Regulations in respect of that payment or that part; and

(b) if he disagrees with that tax payment or any part thereof notify the Employer in writing stating the grounds of his disagreement.

(5) (a) If any dispute difference or question arises between the Employer and the Contractor in relation to any of the matters specified in Section 40(1) of the Act then:—

(i) if the Employer so requires the Contractor shall refer the matter to the said Commissioners for their decision on it

(ii) if the Contractor refers the matter to the said Commissioners (whether or not in pursuance of sub-paragraph (i) above) and the Employer is dissatisfied with their decision on the matter the Contractor shall at the Employer's request refer the matter to a Value Added Tax Tribunal by way of appeal under Section 40 of the Act whether the Contractor is so dissatisfied or not

(iii) a sum of money equal to the amount of tax which the Contractor in making a deposit with the said Commissioners under Section 40(3)(a) of the Act is required so to deposit shall be paid to the Contractor; and

(iv) if the Employer requires the Contractor to refer such a matter to the Tribunal in accordance with sub-paragraph (ii) above then he shall reimburse the Contractor any costs and any expenses reasonably and properly incurred in making that reference less any costs awarded to the Contractor by the Tribunal and the decision of the Tribunal shall be binding on the Employer to the same extent as it binds the Contractor.

(b) Clause 66 shall not apply to any dispute difference or question arising under paragraph (a) of this sub-clause.

(6) (a) The Employer shall without prejudice to his rights under any other Clause hereof be entitled to recover from the Contractor:—

(i) any tax payment made to the Contractor of a sum which is in excess of the sum (if any) which in all the circumstances was due in accordance with sub-clause (4) of this Clause

(ii) in respect of any sum of money deposited by the Contractor pursuant to sub-clause (5)(a)(iii) of this Clause a sum equal to the amount repaid under Section 40(4) of the Act together with any interest thereon which may have been determined thereunder.

(b) If the Contractor shall establish that the Commissioners have charged him in respect of a taxable supply for which he has received payment under this Clause tax greater in amount than the sum paid to him by the Employer the Employer shall subject to the provisions of sub-clause (5) of this Clause pay to the Contractor a sum equal to the difference between the tax previously paid and the tax charged to the Contractor by the Commissioners.

(7) If after the date for return of tenders the descriptions of any supplies of goods or services which at the date of tender are taxable or exempt supplies are with effect after the date for return of tenders modified or extended by or under the Act and that modification or extension shall result in the Contractor having to pay either more or less tax or greater or smaller amounts attributable to tax and that tax or those amounts as the case may be shall be a direct expense or direct saving to the Contractor in carrying out the Works and not recoverable or allowable under the Contract or otherwise then there shall be paid to or allowed by the Contractor as appropriate a sum equivalent to that tax or amounts as the case may be.

Provided always that before that tax is included in any payment by the Employer or those amounts are included in any certificate by the Engineer as the case may be the Contractor shall supply all the information the Engineer requires to satisfy himself as to the Contractor's entitlement under this sub-clause.

(8) The Contractor shall upon demand pay to the Employer the amount of any sum due in accordance with sub-clauses (6) and (7) of this Clause and it shall be deemed a debt due by the Contractor to the Employer and shall be recoverable accordingly.

METRICATION

Metrication.

71. (1) If any materials described in the Contract or ordered by the Engineer are described by dimensions in the metric or imperial measure and having used his best endeavours the Contractor cannot without undue delay or additional expense or at all procure such materials in the measure specified in the Contract but can obtain such materials in the other measure to dimensions approximating to those described in the Contract or ordered by the Engineer then the Contractor shall forthwith give written notice to the Engineer of these facts stating the dimensions to which such materials are procurable in the other measure. Such notice shall where practicable be given in sufficient time to enable the Engineer to consider and if necessary give effect to any design change which may be required and to avoid delay in the performance of the Contractor's other obligations under the Contract. Any additional cost or expense incurred by the Contractor as a result of any delay arising out of the Contractor's default under this sub-clause shall be borne by the Contractor.

(2) As soon as practicable after the receipt of any such notice under the preceding sub-clause the Engineer shall if he is satisfied that the Contractor has used his best endeavours to obtain materials to the dimensions described in the Contract or ordered by the Engineer and that they are not obtainable without undue delay or without putting the Contractor to additional expense either:—

(a) instruct the Contractor pursuant to Clause 13 to supply such materials (despite such delay or expense) in the dimensions described in the Contract or originally ordered by the Engineer; or

(b) give an order to the Contractor pursuant to Clause 51:—

(i) to supply such materials to the dimensions stated in his said notice to be procurable instead of to the dimensions described in the Contract or originally ordered by the Engineer; or

(ii) to make some other variation whereby the need to supply such materials to the dimensions described in the Contract or originally ordered by the Engineer will be avoided.

(3) This Clause shall apply irrespective of whether the materials in question are to be supplied in accordance with the Contract directly by the Contractor or indirectly by a Nominated Sub-contractor.

SPECIAL CONDITIONS

Special Conditions.

72. The following special conditions form part of the Conditions of Contract.

(Note: Any special conditions which it is desired to incorporate in the conditions of contract should be numbered consecutively with the foregoing conditions of contract.)

The Institution of Civil Engineers	The Association of Consulting Engineers	The Federation of Civil Engineering Contractors

This clause has been prepared by the Institution of Civil Engineers, the Association of Consulting Engineers and the Federation of Civil Engineering Contractors, in consultation with the Government, for use in appropriate cases as a Special Condition of the Conditions of Contract for use in connection with Works of Civil Engineering Construction FIFTH EDITION dated June 1973.

CONTRACT PRICE FLUCTUATIONS

(1) The amount payable by the Employer to the Contractor upon the issue by the Engineer of an interim certificate pursuant to Clause 60 (2) or of the final certificate pursuant to Clause 60 (3) (other than amounts due under this Clause) shall be increased or decreased in accordance with the provisions of this Clause if there shall be any changes in the following Index Figures compiled by the Department of the Environment and published by Her Majesty's Stationery Office (HMSO) in the Monthly Bulletin of Construction Indices (Civil Engineering Works):—

(a) the Index of the Cost of Labour in Civil Engineering Construction;

(b) the Index of the Cost of Providing and Maintaining Constructional Plant and Equipment;

(c) the Indices of Constructional Material Prices applicable to those materials listed in sub-clause (4) of this Clause.

The net total of such increases and decreases shall be given effect to in determining the Contract Price.

(2) For the purpose of this Clause:—

(a) " Final Index Figure " shall mean any Index Figure appropriate to sub-clause (1) of this Clause not qualified in the said Bulletin as provisional;

(b) " Base Index Figure " shall mean the appropriate Final Index Figure applicable to the date 42 days prior to the date for the return of tenders;

(c) " Current Index Figure " shall mean the appropriate Final Index Figure to be applied in respect of any certificate issued or due to be issued by the Engineer pursuant to Clause 60 and shall be the appropriate Final Index Figure applicable to the date 42 days prior to:—

(i) the due date (or extended date) for completion; or

(ii) the date certified pursuant to Clause 48 of completion of the whole of the Works; or

(iii) the last day of the period to which the certificate relates:

whichever is the earliest.

Provided that in respect of any work the value of which is included in any such certificate and which work forms part of a Section for which the due date (or extended date) for completion or the date certified pursuant to Clause 48 of completion of such Section precedes the last day of the period to which the certificate relates the Current Index Figure shall be the Final Index Figure applicable to the date 42 days prior to whichever of these dates is the earliest.

(d) The " Effective Value " in respect of the whole or any Section of the Works shall be the difference between:—

(i) the amount which in the opinion of the Engineer is due to the Contractor under Clause 60 (2) (before deducting retention) or the amount due to the Contractor under Clause 60 (3) (but in each case before deducting sums previously paid on account) less any amounts for Dayworks Nominated Sub-contractors or any other items based on actual cost or current prices and any sums for increases or decreases in the Contract Price under this Clause;

and:—

(ii) the amount calculated in accordance with (i) above and included in the last preceding interim certificate issued by the Engineer in accordance with Clause 60.

Provided that in the case of the first certificate the Effective Value shall be the amount calculated in accordance with sub-paragraph (i) above.

(3) The increase or decrease in the amounts otherwise payable under Clause 60 pursuant to sub-clause (1) of this Clause shall be calculated by multiplying the Effective Value by a Price Fluctuation Factor which shall be the net sum of the products obtained by multiplying each of the proportions given in (a) (b) and (c) of sub-clause (4) of this Clause by a fraction the numerator of which is the relevant Current Index Figure minus the relevant Base Index Figure and the denominator of which is the relevant Base Index Figure.

(4) For the purpose of calculating the Price Fluctuation Factor the proportions referred to in sub-clause (3) of this Clause shall (irrespective of the actual constituents of the work) be as follows and the total of such proportions shall amount to unity:—

(a) 0. _____ * in respect of labour and supervision costs subject to adjustment by reference to the Index referred to in sub-clause (1)(a) of this Clause;

(b) 0. _____ * in respect of costs of provision and use of all civil engineering plant road vehicles etc. which shall be subject to adjustment by reference to the Index referred to in sub-clause (1)(b) of this Clause;

(c) the following proportions in respect of the materials named which shall be subject to adjustment by reference to the relevant indices referred to in sub-clause (1)(c) of this Clause:—

0. _____ * in respect of Aggregates
0. _____ * in respect of Bricks and Clay Products generally
0. _____ * in respect of Cements
0. _____ * in respect of Cast Iron products
0. _____ * in respect of Coated Roadstone for road pavements and bituminous products generally
0. _____ * in respect of Fuel for plant generally
0. _____ * in respect of Timber generally
0. _____ * in respect of Reinforcing steel and other metal sections
0. _____ * in respect of Fabricated Structural Steel;

(d) 0.15 in respect of all other costs which shall not be subject to any adjustment;

Total 1.00 .

(5) Provisional Index Figures in the Bulletin referred to in sub-clause (1) of this Clause may be used for the provisional adjustment of interim valuations but such adjustments shall be subsequently recalculated on the basis of the corresponding Final Index Figures.

(6) Clause 69 – Tax Fluctuations – shall not apply except to the extent that any matter dealt with therein is not covered by the Index of the Cost of Labour in Civil Engineering Construction.

* To be filled in by the Employer prior to inviting tenders.

SHORT DESCRIPTION
OF WORKS:—

All Permanent and Temporary Works in connection with*..

....

Form of Tender

(NOTE: The Appendix forms part of the Tender)

To ....

....

....

GENTLEMEN,

Having examined the Drawings, Conditions of Contract, Specification and Bill of Quantities for the construction of the above-mentioned Works (and the matters set out in the Appendix hereto), we offer to construct and complete the whole of the said Works and maintain the Permanent Works in conformity with the said Drawings, Conditions of Contract, Specification and Bill of Quantities for such sum as may be ascertained in accordance with the said Conditions of Contract.

We undertake to complete and deliver the whole of the Permanent Works comprised in the Contract within the time stated in the Appendix hereto.

If our tender is accepted we will, when required, provide two good and sufficient sureties or obtain the guarantee of a Bank or Insurance Company (to be approved in either case by you) to be jointly and severally bound with us in a sum equal to the percentage of the Tender Total as defined in the said Conditions of Contract for the due performance of the Contract under the terms of a Bond in the form annexed to the Conditions of Contract.

Unless and until a formal Agreement is prepared and executed this Tender, together with your written acceptance thereof, shall constitute a binding Contract between us.

We understand that you are not bound to accept the lowest or any tender you may receive.

† To the best of our knowledge and belief we have complied with the general conditions required by the Fair Wages Resolution for the three months immediately preceding the date of this tender.

We are, Gentlemen,

Yours faithfully,

Signature..

Address..

....

Date ....

* Complete as appropriate
† Delete if not required

FORM OF TENDER (APPENDIX)

APPENDIX

NOTE: Relevant Clause numbers are shown in brackets following the description

Amount of Bond (if any)	(10)	........% of Tender Total	
Minimum Amount of Insurance	(23 (2))	£........	
Time for Completion	(43)	Liquidated Damages for Delay (47)	
		Column 1 (see Clause 47 (1)	
For the Whole of the Works——[a]Weeks		£........[b]	per Day/Week[c]
For the following Sections		Column 2 (see Clause 47 (2))	Column 3
Section[d]		£........	£........
.... ——Weeks		Per Day/Week[c]	per Day/Week[c]
Section[d]		£........	£........
.... ——Weeks		per Day/Week[c]	per Day/Week[c]
Section[d]		£........	£........
.... ——Weeks		per Day/Week[c]	per Day/Week[c]
Section[d]		£........	£........
.... ——Weeks		per Day/Week[c]	per Day/Week[c]

Period of Maintenance (49 (1)) ....Weeks

Vesting of Materials not on Site (54 (1) and 60 (1))[e]

1........ 4........

2........ 5........

3........ 6........

Standard Method of Measurement adopted in preparation of Bills of Quantities (57)[f]........

....

Percentage for adjustment of P.C. Sums (59A (2)(b) and (5) (c)) ....%

Percentage of the Value of Goods and Materials to be included in Interim Certificates (60 (2)(b)) ....%

Minimum Amount of Interim Certificates (60 (2)) £ ....

(a) To be completed in every case (by Contractor if not already stipulated).
(b) To be completed by Engineer in every case.
(c) Delete which not required.
(d) To be completed if required, with brief description.
(e) (If used) materials to which clauses apply are to be filled in by Engineer prior to inviting tenders.
(f) Insert here any amendment or modification adopted if different from that stated in Clause 57.

Form of Agreement

THIS AGREEMENT made the .... day of ....

19.......... BETWEEN ....

of .... in the

County of .... (hereinafter called " the Employer ") of the one part and

.... of ....

in the County of ....

.... (hereinafter called " the Contractor ") of the other part WHEREAS the Employer is desirous that certain Works should be constructed, viz. the Permanent and Temporary Works in connection with ....

.... and has accepted a Tender by the Contractor for the construction and completion of such Works and maintenance of the Permanent Works NOW THIS AGREEMENT WITNESSETH as follows:—

1. In this Agreement words and expressions shall have the same meanings as are respectively assigned to them in the Conditions of Contract hereinafter referred to.

2. The following documents shall be deemed to form and be read and construed as part of this Agreement, viz:—

(a) The said Tender.
(b) The Drawings.
(c) The Conditions of Contract.
(d) The Specification.
(e) The Priced Bill of Quantities.

3. In consideration of the payments to be made by the Employer to the Contractor as hereinafter mentioned the Contractor hereby covenants with the Employer to construct and complete the Works and maintain the Permanent Works in conformity in all respects with the provisions of the Contract.

4. The Employer hereby covenants to pay to the Contractor in consideration of the construction and completion of the Works and maintenance of the Permanent Works the Contract Price at the times and in the manner prescribed by the Contract.

IN WITNESS whereof the parties hereto have caused their respective Common Seals to be hereunto affixed (or have hereunto set their respective hands and seals) the day and year first above written

The Common Seal of ....

.... Limited

was hereunto affixed in the presence of:—

or

SIGNED SEALED AND DELIVERED by the

said ....

....

in the presence of:—

....

....

Form of Bond

1 Is appropriate to an individual, 2 to a Limited Company and 3 to a Firm. Strike out whichever two are inappropriate.

4 Is appropriate where there are two individual Sureties, 5 where the Surety is a Bank or Insurance Company. Strike out whichever is inappropriate.

BY THIS BOND [1]We .... of .... in the County of .... [2]We .... Limited whose registered office is at .... in the County of .... [3]We .... and ....carrying on business in partnership under the name or style of .... at .... in the County of ....(hereinafter called " the Contractor ") [4]and .... of .... in the County of .... and .... of ....in the County of .... [5]and .... Limited whose registered office is at .... in the County of .... (hereinafter called " the [4]Sureties/Surety ") are held and firmly bound unto .... (hereinafter called " the Employer ") in the sum of .... pounds (£........................) for the payment of which sum the Contractor and the [4]Sureties/Surety bind themselves their successors and assigns jointly and severally by these presents.

Sealed with our respective seals and dated this........................ day of .... 19........

WHEREAS the Contractor by an Agreement made between the Employer of the one part and the Contractor of the other part has entered into a Contract (hereinafter called "the said Contract ") for the construction and completion of the Works and maintenance of the Permanent Works as therein mentioned in conformity with the provisions of the said Contract.

NOW THE CONDITION of the above-written Bond is such that if the Contractor shall duly perform and observe all the terms provisions conditions and stipulations of the said Contract on the Contractor's part to be performed and observed according to the true purport intent and meaning thereof or if on default by the Contractor the Sureties/Surety shall satisfy and discharge the damages sustained by the Employer thereby up to the amount of the above-written Bond then this obligation shall be null and void but otherwise shall be and remain in full force and effect but no alteration in terms of the said Contract made by agreement between the Employer and the Contractor or in the extent or nature of the Works to be constructed completed and maintained thereunder and no allowance of time by the Employer or the Engineer under the said Contract nor any forbearance or forgiveness in or in respect of any matter or thing concerning the said Contract on the part of the Employer or the said Engineer shall in any way release the Sureties/Surety from any liability under the above-written Bond.

Signed Sealed and Delivered by the said
in the presence of:— }

The Common Seal of
LIMITED
was hereunto affixed in the presence of:— }

(Similar forms of Attestation Clause for the Sureties or Surety)

APPENDIX B

FORM OF SUB-CONTRACT

AN AGREEMENT made the..day of ....19.....................

BETWEEN ....of/whose

registered office is at..

....(hereinafter called "The Contractor") of.....................

the one part and.. of/whose

registered office is at..

....(hereinafter called "the Sub-Contractor") of the other part.

WHEREAS the Contractor has entered into a Contract (hereinafter called "the Main Contract") particulars of which are set out in the First Schedule hereto:

AND WHEREAS the Sub-Contractor having been afforded the opportunity to read and note the provisions of the Main Contract (other than details of the Contractor's prices thereunder), has agreed to execute upon the terms hereinafter appearing the works which are described in the documents specified in the Second Schedule hereto and which form part of the works to be executed by the Contractor under the Main Contract:

NOW IT IS HEREBY AGREED as follows:

Definitions.

1. In this Sub-Contract (as hereinafter defined) the following expressions shall have the meanings hereby respectively assigned to them, except where the context otherwise requires:

"the Main Contract" means the contract, particulars of which are given in the First Schedule hereto.

"the Sub-Contract" means this Agreement together with such other documents as are specified in the Second Schedule hereto, but excluding any standard printed conditions that may be included in such other documents.

"the Sub-Contract Works" means the works described in the documents specified in the Second Schedule hereto.

"the Main Works" mean the Works as defined by the Main Contract.

The expressions "Employer", "Engineer", "Engineer's Representative", "Constructional Plant", "Temporary Works" and "Site" have the meanings respectively assigned to them by the Main Contract.

"the Price" means the sum specified in the Third Schedule hereto as payable to the Sub-Contractor for the Sub-Contract Works or such other sum as may become payable under the Sub-Contract by reason of any authorised variation of the Sub-Contract Works.

General.

2. (1) The Sub-Contractor shall execute, complete and maintain the Sub-Contract Works in accordance with the Sub-Contract and to the reasonable satisfaction of the Contractor and of the Engineer.

(2) Subject to Clause 4 (Contractor's Facilities), the Sub-Contractor shall provide all labour, materials, Constructional Plant, Temporary Works and everything whether of a permanent or temporary nature required for the execution, completion and maintenance of the Sub-Contract Works.

(3) The Sub-Contractor shall not assign the whole or any part of the benefit of this Sub-Contract nor shall he sub-let the whole or any part of the Sub-Contract Works without the previous written consent of the Contractor.

Provided always that the Sub-Contractor may without such consent assign either absolutely or by way of charge any sum which is or may become due to him under this Sub-Contract.

Main Contract.

3. (1) The Sub-Contractor shall be deemed to have full knowledge of the provisions of the Main Contract (other than the details of the Contractor's prices thereunder as stated in the bills of quantities or schedules of rates and prices as the case may be), and the Contractor shall, if so requested by the Sub-Contractor, provide the Sub-Contractor with a true copy of the Main Contract (less such details), at the Sub-Contractor's expense.

(2) Save where the provisions of the Sub-Contract otherwise require, the Sub-Contractor shall so execute, complete and maintain the Sub-Contract Works that no act or omission of his in relation thereto shall constitute, cause or contribute to any breach by the Contractor of any of his obligations under the Main Contract and the Sub-Contractor shall, save as aforesaid, assume and perform hereunder all the obligations and liabilities of the Contractor under the Main Contract in relation to the Sub-Contract Works.

Nothing herein shall be construed as creating any privity of contract between the Sub-Contractor and the Employer.

(3) The Sub-Contractor shall indemnify the Contractor against every liability which the Contractor may incur to any other person whatsoever and against all claims, demands, proceedings, damages, costs and expenses made against or incurred by the Contractor by reason of any breach by the Sub-Contractor of the Sub-Contract.

(4) The Sub-Contractor hereby acknowledges that any breach by him of the Sub-Contract may result in the Contractor's committing breaches of and becoming liable in damages under the Main Contract and other contracts made by him in connection with the Main Works and may occasion further loss or expense to the Contractor in connection with the Main Works and all such damages loss and expense are hereby agreed to be within the contemplation of the parties as being probable results of any such breach by the Sub-Contractor.

Contractor's Facilities.

4. (1) The Contractor shall permit the Sub-Contractor for the purpose of executing and completing the Sub-Contract Works to use such scaffolding as is from time to time provided by the Contractor in connection with the Main Works, but the Contractor shall not be bound to provide or retain any such scaffolding for the Sub-Contractor's use. No such permission shall imply any warranty by the Contractor as to the fitness, condition or suitability of such scaffolding, nor shall it impose any liability upon the Contractor in respect of its use by the Sub-Contractor, his servants or agents, nor relieve the Sub-Contractor of any statutory or other obligation to test or inspect the scaffolding to be used by his servants or agents or to provide suitable scaffolding for their use.

(2) The Contractor shall provide at the Site the Constructional Plant and other facilities specified in the Fourth Schedule hereto and shall permit the Sub-Contractor, in common with such other contractors as the Contractor may allow, to have the use thereof for the purposes of executing and completing, but not of maintaining the Sub-Contract Works, upon such terms and conditions, if any, as are specified in the said Schedule, but the Contractor shall have no liability to the Sub-Contractor in respect of any failure to provide such Constructional Plant or facilities, if such failure is due to circumstances outside the Contractor's control, nor in respect of any inadequacy or unfitness for the Sub-Contractor's purposes of any Constructional Plant or facilities so provided.

Site Working and Access.

5. (1) The Sub-Contractor shall in the execution of the Sub-Contract Works on the Site observe the same hours of working as the Contractor and shall comply with all reasonable rules and regulations of the Contractor governing the execution of work, the arrival at and the departure from the Site of materials and Constructional Plant and the storage of materials and Constructional Plant on the Site.

(2) The Contractor shall from time to time make available to the Sub-Contractor such part or parts of the Site and such means of access thereto within the Site as shall be necessary to enable the Sub-Contractor to execute the Sub-Contract Works in accordance with the Sub-Contract, but the Contractor shall not be bound to give the Sub-Contractor possession or exclusive control of any part of the Site.

(3) The Sub-Contractor shall permit the Engineer, the Engineer's Representative and other the Engineer's servants and agents and the Contractor, his servants and agents (including any other sub-contractors engaged in the execution of the Main Works), during working hours to have reasonable access to the Sub-Contract Works and to the places on the Site where any work or materials therefor are being executed prepared or stored and the Sub-Contractor shall also permit or procure reasonable access for the Engineer, his servants and agents and for the Contractor, his servants and agents to such places off the Site where work is being executed or prepared by or on behalf of the Sub-Contractor in connection with the Sub-Contract Works.

Commencement and Completion.

6. (1) Within 10 days of receipt of the Contractor's written instructions so to do, the Sub-Contractor shall enter upon the Site and commence the execution of the Sub-Contract Works and shall thereafter proceed with the same with due diligence and without any delay, except such as may be expressly sanctioned or ordered by the Contractor or be wholly beyond the control of the Sub-Contractor. Subject to the provisions of this clause, the Sub-Contractor shall complete the Sub-Contract Works within the Period for Completion specified in the Third Schedule hereto.

(2) If the Sub-Contractor shall be delayed in the execution of the Sub-Contract Works:

(a) by any circumstance or occurrence (other than a breach of this Sub-Contract by the Sub-Contractor), entitling the Contractor to an extension of his time for completion of the Main Works under the Main Contract; or

(b) by the ordering of any variation of the Sub-Contract Works to which paragraph (a) of this sub-clause does not apply; or

(c) by any breach of this Sub-Contract by the Contractor;
then in any such event the Sub-Contractor shall be entitled to such extension of the Period for Completion as may in all the circumstances be fair and reasonable.

Provided always that in any case to which paragraph (a) of this sub-clause applies, it shall be a condition precedent to the Sub-Contractor's right to an extension of the Period for Completion that he shall have given written notice to the Contractor of the circumstances or occurrence which is delaying him within 14 days of such delay first occurring and in any such case the extension shall not in any event exceed the extension of time to which the Contractor is properly entitled under the Main Contract.

(3) Where differing Periods of Completion are specified in the Third Schedule for different parts of the Sub-Contract Works, then for the purposes of the preceding provisions of this clause each such part shall be treated as if it were the whole of the Sub-Contract Works.

(4) Nothing in this clause shall be construed as preventing the Sub-Contractor from commencing off the Site any work necessary for the execution of the Sub-Contract Works at any time before receipt of the Contractor's written instructions under sub-clause (1) of this clause.

Instructions and Decisions.

7. (1) Subject to Clause 8 (Variations), the Sub-Contractor shall in relation to the Sub-Contract Works comply with all instructions and decisions of the Engineer and of the Engineer's Representative which are notified and confirmed in writing to him by the Contractor, irrespective of whether such instructions and decisions were validly given under the Main Contract. The Sub-Contractor shall have the like rights, (if any), to payment against the Contractor in respect of such compliance as the Contractor has against the Employer under the Main Contract. Further if any such instruction or decision notified and confirmed as aforesaid is invalidly and incorrectly given by the Engineer under the Main Contract, then the Sub-Contractor shall be entitled to recover from the Contractor his additional reasonable costs, (if any), of complying therewith after he has finally performed his obligations under Clause 14 (Maintenance and Defects), and provided that such costs were not caused or contributed to by any breach of this Sub-Contract by the Sub-Contractor.

(2) The Contractor shall have the like powers in relation to the Sub-Contract Works to give instructions and decisions as the Engineer has in relation to the Main Works under the Main Contract and the Sub-Contractor shall have the like obligations to abide by and comply therewith and the like rights in relation thereto as the Contractor has under the Main Contract. The said powers of the Contractor shall be exercisable in any case irrespective of whether the Engineer has exercised like powers in relation thereto under the Main Contract.

Variations.

8. (1) The Sub-Contractor shall make such variations of the Sub-Contract Works, whether by way of addition, modification or omission, as may be:

(a) ordered by the Engineer under the Main Contract and confirmed in writing to the Sub-Contractor by the Contractor; or

(b) agreed to be made by the Employer and the Contractor and confirmed in writing to the Sub-Contractor by the Contractor; or

(c) ordered in writing by the Contractor.

Any order relating to the Sub-Contract Works which is validly given by the Engineer under the Main Contract and constitutes a variation thereunder shall for the purposes of this clause be deemed to constitute a variation of the Sub-Contract Works, if confirmed by the Contractor in accordance with paragraph (a) hereof.

(2) The Sub-Contractor shall not act upon an unconfirmed order for the variation of the Sub-Contract Works which is directly received by him from the Employer or the Engineer. If the Sub-Contractor shall receive any such direct order, he shall forthwith inform the Contractor's agent or foreman in charge of the Main Works thereof and shall supply him with a copy of such direct order, if given in writing. The Sub-Contractor shall only act upon such order as directed in writing by the Contractor, but the Contractor shall give his directions thereon with all reasonable speed.

(3) Save as aforesaid the Sub-Contractor shall not make any alteration in or modification of the Sub-Contract Works.

Valuation of Variations.

9. (1) All authorised variations of the Sub-Contract Works shall be valued in the manner provided by this clause and the value thereof shall be added to or deducted from the sum specified in the Third Schedule hereto as the case may require.

(2) The value of all authorised variations shall be ascertained by reference to the rates and prices (if any), specified in this Sub-Contract for the like or analogous work, but if there are no such rates and prices, or if they are not applicable, then such value shall be such as is fair and reasonable in all the circumstances. In determining what is a fair and reasonable valuation, regard shall be had to any valuation made under the Main Contract in respect of the same variation.

(3) Where an authorised variation of the Sub-Contract Works, which also constitutes an authorised variation under the Main Contract is measured by the Engineer thereunder, then provided that the rates and prices in this Sub-Contract permit such variation to be valued by reference to measurement, the Contractor shall permit the Sub-Contractor to attend any measurement made on behalf of the Engineer and such measurement made under the Main Contract shall also constitute the measurement of the variation for the purposes of this Sub-Contract and it shall be valued accordingly.

(4) Save where the contrary is expressly stated in any bill of quantities forming part of this Sub-Contract, no quantity stated therein shall be taken to define or limit the extent of any work to be done by the Sub-Contractor in the execution and completion of the Sub-Contract Works, but any difference between the quantity so billed and the actual quantity executed shall be ascertained by measurement, valued under the clause as if it were an authorised variation and the necessary addition to or deduction from the sum specified in the Third Schedule hereto shall be made accordingly.

Notices and Claims.

10. (1) Without prejudice to the generality of Clause 3 (Main Contract), whenever the Contractor is required by the terms of the Main Contract to give any return, account or notice to the Engineer or to the Employer, the Sub-Contractor shall in relation to the Sub-Contract Works give a similar return, account or notice or such other information in writing to the Contractor as will enable the Contractor to comply with such terms of the Main Contract and shall do so in sufficient time to enable the Contractor to comply with such terms punctually.

Provided always that the Sub-Contractor shall be excused any non-compliance with this sub-clause for so long as he neither knew nor ought to have known of the Contractor's need of any such return, account, notice or information from him.

(2) Subject to the Sub-Contractor's complying with this sub-clause, the Contractor shall take all reasonable steps to secure from the Employer such financial benefits, if any, as may be claimable in accordance with the Main Contract on account of any adverse physical conditions or artificial obstructions or any other circumstances that may be encountered during the execution of the Sub-Contract Works and the Sub-Contractor shall in sufficient time afford the Contractor all information and assistance that may be requisite to enable the Contractor to claim such benefits. On receiving payment of any such financial benefits from the Employer, the Contractor shall in turn pay to the Sub-Contractor such proportion thereof as may in all the circumstances be fair and reasonable. Save as aforesaid the Contractor shall have no liability to the Sub-Contractor in respect of any condition, obstruction or circumstance that may affect the execution of the Sub-Contract Works and the Sub-Contractor shall be deemed to have satisfied himself as to the correctness and sufficiency of the Price to cover the provision and doing by him of all things necessary for the performance of his obligations under the Sub-Contract.

(3) If by reason of any breach by the Sub-Contractor of the provisions of sub-clause (1) of this clause the Contractor is prevented from recovering any sum from the Employer under the Main Contract in respect of the Main Works, then without prejudice to any other remedy of the Contractor for such breach, the Contractor may deduct such sum from monies otherwise due to the Sub-Contractor under this Sub-Contract.

Property in Materials and Plant.

11. (1) Where it is provided by the Main Contract that the property in any Constructional Plant, Temporary Works, materials or things whatsoever shall in certain events vest in the Employer or revest in the Contractor, then in so far as such Constructional Plant, Temporary Works, materials or things are to be provided by the Sub-Contractor in connection with the Sub-Contract Works, the property therein shall pass from the Sub-Contractor to the Contractor immediately before it is due to vest in the Employer in pursuance of the Main Contract and shall re-pass from the Contractor to the Sub-Contractor immediately after it has revested in the Contractor in pursuance of the Main Contract.

(2) Without prejudice to the generality of Clause 3 (Main Contract), the Sub-Contractor shall comply with the requirements of the Main Contract as to the bringing on to and removal from the Site of Constructional Plant, Temporary Works, materials and other things and in so far as any items thereof are hired by the Sub-Contractor, he shall comply with all the requirements of the Main Contract as to the terms of such hirings and as to the giving of information and certificates in relation thereto.

Indemnities.

12. (1) The Sub-Contractor shall at all times indemnify the Contractor against all liabilities to other persons (including the servants and agents of the Contractor or Sub-Contractor) for bodily injury, damage to property or other loss which may arise out of or in consequence of the execution, completion or maintenance of the Sub-Contract Works and against all costs, charges and expenses that may be occasioned to the Contractor by the claims of such persons.

Provided always that the Contractor shall not be entitled to the benefit of this indemnity in respect of any liability or claim if he is entitled by the terms of the Main Contract to be indemnified in respect thereof by the Employer.

Provided further that the Sub-Contractor shall not be bound to indemnify the Contractor against any such liability or claim if the injury, damage or loss in question was caused solely by the wrongful acts or omissions of the Contractor, his servants or agents.

(2) The Contractor shall indemnify the Sub-Contractor against all liabilities and claims against which the Employer by the terms of the Main Contract undertakes to indemnify the Contractor and to the like extent, but no further.

Insurances.

13. (1) The Sub-Contractor shall effect insurance against such risks as are specified in Part I of the Fifth Schedule hereto and in such sums and for the benefit of such persons as are specified therein and unless the said Fifth Schedule otherwise provides, shall maintain such insurance from the time that the Sub-Contractor first enters upon the Site for the purpose of executing the Sub-Contract Works until he has finally performed his obligations under Clause 14 (Maintenance and Defects).

(2) The Contractor shall maintain in force until such time as the Main Works have been completed or ceased to be at his risk under the Main Contract, the policy of insurance specified in Part II of the Fifth Schedule hereto. In the event of the Sub-Contract Works, or any Constructional Plant, Temporary Works, materials or other things belonging to the Sub-Contractor being destroyed or damaged during such period in such circumstances that a claim is established in respect thereof under the said policy, then the Sub-Contractor shall be paid the amount of such claim, or the amount of his loss, whichever is the less, and shall apply such sum in replacing or repairing that which was destroyed or damaged. Save as aforesaid the Sub-Contract Works shall be at the risk of the Sub-Contractor until the Main Works have been completed under the Main Contract, or if the Main Works are to be completed by sections, until the last of the sections in which the Sub-Contract Works are comprised has been completed, and the Sub-Contractor shall make good all loss of or damage occurring to the Sub-Contract Works prior thereto at his own expense.

(3) Where by virtue of this clause either party is required to effect and maintain insurance, then at any time until such obligation has fully been performed, he shall if so required by the other party produce for inspection the appropriate policy of insurance together with receipts for premiums payable thereunder and in the event of his failing to do so, the other party may himself effect such insurance and recover the cost of so doing from the party in default.

Maintenance and Defects.

14. (1) If the Sub-Contractor shall complete the Sub-Contract Works before the completion of the Main Works, or where under the Main Contract the Main Works are to be completed by sections, before the completion of the last of such sections in which the Sub-Contract Works are comprised, the Sub-Contractor shall maintain the Sub-Contract Works in perfect condition and shall make good every defect and imperfection therein from whatever cause arising until such completion of the Main Works or last section thereof is achieved and subject to Clause 13 (Insurance), shall not be entitled to any additional payment for so doing unless such defect or imperfection is caused by the act, neglect or default of the Employer, his servants or agents under the Main Contract or of the Contractor, his servants or agents under the Sub-Contract.

(2) After completion of the Main Works or of the last of the sections thereof in which the Sub-Contract Works are comprised, as the case may be, the Sub-Contractor shall maintain the Sub-Contract Works and shall make good such defects and imperfections therein as the Contractor is liable to make good under the Main Contract for the like period and otherwise upon the like terms as the Contractor is liable to do under the Main Contract.

Provided always that if any defect or imperfection made good by the Sub-Contractor under this sub-clause is caused by the act, neglect or default under the Sub-Contract of the Contractor, his servants or agents, then notwithstanding that the Contractor may have no corresponding right under the Main Contract, the Sub-Contractor shall be entitled to be paid by the Contractor his reasonable costs of making good such defect or imperfection.

Payment.

15. (1) From time to time during the execution of the Sub-Contract Works the Sub-Contractor shall within 7 days of the Contractor's request so to do, submit to the Contractor a written statement of the value of all work properly done under the Sub-Contract and of all materials delivered to the Site for incorporation in the Sub-Contract Works at such date as may be specified in the Contractor's request. Such written statement shall be in such form and contain such details as the Contractor may reasonably require and the value of work done shall be calculated in accordance with the rates and prices, if any, specified in the Sub-Contract, or if there are no such rates or prices, then by reference to the Price.

(2) The Contractor shall from time to time make prompt applications for payment under and in accordance with the Main Contract and subject to the Sub-Contractor's having complied with the preceding sub-clause, shall include in such applications claims for work done and, if allowable under the Main Contract, for materials delivered to the Site by the Sub-Contractor and the Contractor shall use his best endeavours to obtain prompt payment of all sums due to him in respect of the Sub-Contract Works under the Main Contract.

(3) Within 7 days of his receiving from the Employer on account of the Main Works any payment which includes a sum in respect of the Sub-Contract Works, the Contractor shall pay to the Sub-Contractor in respect of the work done or materials provided by the Sub-Contractor and allowed for in such payment under the Main Contract, a sum calculated in accordance with the rates and prices specified in this Sub-Contract, or by reference to the Price, as the case may require, but subject to a deduction of retention monies at the rate specified in the Third Schedule hereto until such time as the limit of retention, (if any), therein specified has been reached.

(4) Within 7 days of the Contractor's receipt of any payment under the Main Contract which is by way of release either of the first or second half of the retention monies for the Main Works of where under the Main Contract the Main Works are to be completed by sections, then for the last of such sections in which the Sub-Contract Works are comprised, the Contractor shall pay to the Sub-Contractor the first or second half as appropriate of the retention monies held under this Sub-Contract.

(5) Within three months after the Sub-Contractor has finally performed his obligations under Clause 14 (Maintenance and Defects), or within 14 days after the Contractor has recovered full payment under the Main Contract in respect of the Sub-Contract Works, whichever is the sooner, and provided that one month has expired since the submission by the Sub-Contractor of his final account to the Contractor, the Contractor shall pay to the Sub-Contractor the Price together with any other sums that may have become due to the Sub-Contractor under the Sub-Contract, less such sums as have already been received by the Sub-Contractor on account of the Price or of such other sums.

Provided always that if the Contractor shall have been required by the Main Contract to give to the Employer or to procure the Sub-Contractor to give to the Employer any undertaking as to the completion or maintenance of the Sub-Contract Works, the Sub-Contractor shall not be entitled to payment under this Sub-Contract until he has given a like undertaking to the Contractor, or has given the required undertaking to the Employer, as the case may be.

(6) The Contractor shall not be liable to the Sub-Contractor for any matter or thing arising out of or in connection with this Sub-Contract or the execution of the Sub-Contract Works unless the Sub-Contractor has made a written claim in respect thereof to the Contractor before the Engineer issues the Maintenance Certificate in respect of the Main Works, or, where under the Main Contract the Main Works are to be completed by sections, the Maintenance Certificate in respect of the last of such sections in which the Sub-Contract Works are comprised.

Determination of the Main Contract.

16. (1) If the Main Contract is determined for any reason whatsoever before the Sub-Contractor has fully performed his obligations under this Sub-Contract, then the Contractor may at any time thereafter by written notice to the Sub-Contractor forthwith determine the Sub-Contractor's employment under the Sub-Contract and thereupon the Sub-Contractor shall, subject to Clause 11 (Property in Materials), with all reasonable speed remove his men and Constructional Plant from the Site.

(2) Upon such a determination of the Sub-Contractor's employment, the other provisions of this Sub-Contract shall cease to have effect and subject to sub-clause (3) hereof, the Sub-Contractor shall be entitled to be paid the full value, calculated by reference to the Price and to the rates and prices contained in any bill of quantities or schedule forming part of this Sub-Contract, of all work properly done on the Site by the Sub-Contractor and of all materials properly bought and left on the Site by the Sub-Contractor, together with his reasonable costs of removing his Constructional Plant from the Site, but less such sums as the Sub-Contractor has already received on account of the Price. Furthermore if at the date of such determination the Sub-Contractor has properly prepared or fabricated off the Site any goods for subsequent incorporation in the Sub-Contract Works and he shall deliver such goods to the Site or to such other place as the Contractor may reasonably direct, then he shall be paid for such goods as for materials properly brought and left on the Site by him.

Provided always that nothing herein shall affect the rights of either party in respect of any breach of this Sub-Contract committed by the other prior to such determination, nor any right which accrued to the Sub-Contractor prior to such determination to receive any payment which is not in respect or on account of the Price.

(3) If the Main Contract is determined by the Employer in consequence of any breach of this Sub-Contract by the Sub-Contractor, then the provisions of the preceding sub-clause as to payment shall not apply, but the rights of the Contractor and the Sub-Contractor hereunder shall be the same as if the Sub-Contractor had by such breach repudiated this Sub-Contract and the Contractor had by his notice of determination under sub-clause (1) of this clause elected to accept such repudiation.

Sub-Contractor's Default.

17. (1) If the Sub-Contractor:

(a) fails to proceed with the Sub-Contract Works with due diligence after being required in writing so to do by the Contractor; or

(b) fails to execute the Sub-Contract Works or to perform his other obligations in accordance with the Sub-Contract after being required in writing so to do by the Contractor; or

(c) refuses or neglects to remove defective materials or make good defective work after being directed in writing so to do by the Contractor; or

(d) commits an act of bankruptcy or enters into a deed of arrangement with his creditors or, being a company goes into liquidation, (other than a voluntary liquidation for the purposes of reconstruction),

then in any such event and without prejudice to any other rights or remedies, the Contractor may by written notice to the Sub-Contractor forthwith determine the Sub-Contractor's employment under this Sub-Contract and thereupon the Contractor may take possession of all materials, Constructional Plant and other things whatsoever brought on to the Site by the Sub-Contractor and may use them for the purpose of executing, completing and maintaining the Sub-Contract Works and may, if he thinks fit, sell all or any of them and apply the proceeds in or towards the satisfaction of monies otherwise due to him from the Sub-Contractor.

(2) Upon such a determination, the rights and liabilities of the Contractor and the Sub-Contractor shall, subject to the preceding sub-clause, be the same as if the Sub-Contractor had repudiated this Sub-Contract and the Contractor had by his notice of determination under the preceding sub-clause elected to accept such repudiation.

(3) The Contractor may in lieu of giving a notice of determination under this clause take part only of the Sub-Contract Works out of the hands of the Sub-Contractor and may by himself, his servants or agents execute, complete and maintain such part and in such event the Contractor may recover his reasonable costs of so doing from the Sub-Contractor, or deduct such costs from monies otherwise becoming due to the Sub-Contractor.

Disputes.

18. (1) If any dispute arises between the Contractor and the Sub-Contractor in connection with this Sub-Contract, it shall, subject to the provisions of this clause, be referred to the arbitration and final decision of a person agreed between the parties, or failing such agreement, appointed upon the application of either of the parties by the President for the time being of the Institution of Civil Engineers.

(2) If any dispute arises in connection with the Main Contract and the Contractor is of opinion that such dispute touches or concerns the Sub-Contract Works, then provided that an arbitrator has not already been agreed or appointed in pursuance of the preceding sub-clause, the Contractor may by notice in writing to the Sub-Contractor require that any dispute under this Sub-Contract shall be referred to the arbitrator to whom the dispute under the Main Contract is referred and if such arbitrator (hereinafter called "the joint arbitrator") be willing so to act, such dispute under this Sub-Contract shall be so referred. In such event the joint arbitrator may, subject to the consent of the Employer, give such directions for the determination of the two said disputes either concurrently or consecutively as he may think just and convenient and provided that the Sub-Contractor is allowed to act as a party to the dispute between the Employer and the Contractor, the joint arbitrator may in determining the dispute under this Sub-Contract take account of all material facts proved before him in the dispute under the Main Contract.

(3) If at any time before an arbitrator has been agreed or appointed in pursuance of sub-clause (1) of this clause any dispute arising in connection with the Main Contract is made the subject of proceedings in any court between the Employer and the Contractor and the Contractor is of opinion that such dispute touches or concerns the Sub-Contract Works, he may by notice in writing to the Sub-Contractor abrogate the provisions of sub-clause (1) of this clause and thereafter no dispute under this Sub-Contract shall be referable to arbitration without further submission by the Contractor and Sub-Contractor.

*IN WITNESS whereof the parties hereto *have caused their respective Common Seals to be hereunto affixed*

have hereunto set their respective hands and Seals.

the day and year first above written

* *Strike out words not applicable and use appropriate execution clause on page 13. If the Sub-Contract is executed under Seal a ten shilling stamp must be affixed within 30 days of the date of the Sub-Contract. If the Sub-Contract is executed under hand a sixpenny stamp must be affixed and cancelled.*

FIRST SCHEDULE

PARTICULARS OF MAIN CONTRACT

Parties:

Date:

Brief Description of Main Works:

SECOND SCHEDULE

(A) Further Documents forming part of the Sub-Contract

(B) Sub-Contract Works

THIRD SCHEDULE

(A) The Price

(B) (i) Percentage of Retention

(ii) Limit of Retention

(C) Period for Completion

FOURTH SCHEDULE

Contractor's Facilities

(A) Constructional Plant	Terms and Conditions
(B) Other Facilities	

FIFTH SCHEDULE

INSURANCES

Part I Sub-Contractor's Insurances

Part II Contractor's Policy of Insurance

NOTES FOR THE GUIDANCE OF CONTRACTORS ON THE COMPLETION OF THE SCHEDULES

The First Schedule

This should identify the Main Contract and specify the documents of which it consists, e.g. The Agreement dated the between

and as Employer and Contractor for the construction

of

and incorporating the following documents:

General Conditions of Contract

Specification

Bills of Quantities Nos. 1– etc.

It is desirable to identify the Main Contract and the documents included in it as clearly as possible, but nothing further should be put in this Schedule.

The Second Schedule

There should be specified in this Schedule the further documents which define the Sub-Contract Works and which are intended to form part of the Sub-Contract. Thus where there are priced Bills of Quantities for the Sub-Contract Works, these should be specified in this Schedule: where there are Drawings of the Sub-Contract Works, these should be specified in the Schedule: so also with Specifications, Schedules of Rates and Prices, Quotations and Estimates.

It may sometimes be that the Sub-Contract Works will consist of all the work described in certain portions of the Bills of Quantities extracts of the Specification and Drawings under the Main Contract. In such cases these portions and extracts can be specified in this Schedule, but in the case of Bills of Quantities so incorporated, care should be taken to exclude the rates and prices therein unless such rates and prices are also to operate as between the Contractor and Sub-Contractor.

Where there are no priced Bills of Quantities for the Sub-Contract Works and it is decided to incorporate the Sub-Contractor's Quotation or Estimate for the Sub-Contract Works, care should be taken that these documents do not also contain conditions of contract or terms of payment inconsistent with the Sub-Contract. Although the definition of "the Sub-Contract" expressly excludes any standard printed conditions on such documents, it is nevertheless very desirable that any provisions in such documents which are inconsistent with the Sub-Contract should be deleted from those documents and such deletions initialled by both parties. The documents should then be specified in this Schedule "subject to the deletions therefrom as initialled therein on behalf of the Contractor and Sub-Contractor".

It is possible in this Schedule to incorporate supplementary conditions of Sub-Contract. For special reasons this may be necessary, but the Sub-Contract is intended to provide a comprehensive code for all normal circumstances and therefore in general supplementary conditions should not be included, because their inclusion may well lead to doubt and inconsistencies in the Sub-Contract as a whole.

Care should be taken to ensure that the extent of the work to be done for the lump sum specified in the Third Schedule is clearly defined in these further documents. In particular it should be noted that unless any Bill of Quantities incorporated in the Sub-Contract expressly provides that the quantities are only provisional and are subject to re-measurement, the Bills do not define or limit the extent of the work to be done by the Sub-Contractor for the lump sum: see sub-clause (4) of clause 9 (Valuation of Variations).

The Third Schedule

(a) *The Sum:* This should be a simple lump sum: the definition of "the Price" in the Sub-Contract provides for its adjustment to take account of authorised variations. Where there are Bills of Quantities this lump sum will normally be the total of the prices in such Bill.

This form of Sub-Contract is not however, adapted for use where there is merely a schedule of rates and prices for varying types of work, but no defined quantity of any such work, because in these circumstances there can be no lump sum.

(b) *The Period for Completion:* This should be stated as a simple period of weeks or months. No attempt should be made to define it by dates. The Sub-Contract permits differing periods of completion to be specified for differing parts of the Sub-Contract Works. When it is desired so to provide then this part of the Schedule should specify the various parts of the Sub-Contract Works and the periods of completion appropriate to each of them.

(c) *Percentage of Retention Monies:* This should be expressed as a simple percentage.

(d) *Limit of Retention:* If there is a limit, this should be expressed as a simple sum of money.

The Fourth Schedule

Reference should be made to clause 4 (Contractor's Facilities) of the Sub-Contract. Any facilities such as water, lighting or Constructional Plant which the Contractor is prepared to provide for the Sub-Contractor's use should be listed in this Schedule. The Schedule should specify any conditions subject to which any such facilities will be provided, e.g., the provision of specified items of Constructional Plant such as cranes for the purpose of enabling the Sub-Contractor to perform certain operations only. If the Contractor proposes to charge the Sub-Contractor for the provision of any such facilities, the Schedule should specify these charges, the rates, if any, at which they are to be calculated and how and when they are to be paid by the Sub-Contractor. Normally it will be appropriate to provide that such charges shall be set off against payments otherwise becoming due to the Sub-Contractor under the Sub-Contract.

The Fifth Schedule

Reference should be made to clause 13 (Insurances) of the Sub-Contract. In completing the two Parts of this Schedule the parties should take care to ensure that all insurances required by the Main Contract are effected by one or other of them and that there is no unnecessary duplication of insurance.

Part 1 should specify insurances to be effected by the Sub-Contractor.

Part 2 should specify the policy of insurance which the Contractor is effecting in pursuance of clause 21 of the Main Contract Conditions, if it is intended that the Sub-Contractor shall have the benefit thereof. In such cases his interest should be noted either generally or specifically on the policy and this Part of the Schedule should so state. If the Sub-Contractor is not to have any benefit under this policy of the Contractor, then that Part can be left blank.

THE COMMON SEAL *of the above-named Contractor was hereunto affixed in the presence of:—*

L.S.

....

....

THE COMMON SEAL *of the above-named Sub-Contractor was hereunto affixed in the presence of:—*

L.S.

....

....

OR

SIGNED SEALED AND DELIVERED *by the above-named Contractor in the presence of:—*

....

....

SIGNED SEALED AND DELIVERED *by the above-named Sub-Contractor in the presence of:—*

....

....

VALUE ADDED TAX CLAUSE FOR INCORPORATION IN FEDERATION OF CIVIL ENGINEERING CONTRACTORS FORM OF SUB-CONTRACT

This form is for inclusion in all Sub-Contracts where this Form of Sub-Contract is used.

19. (1) In this Clause references to "the Act" mean the Finance Act 1972, Part I, as amended from time to time and the expressions "tax" "taxable person" and "taxable supply" have the same meaning as in the Act. **Value Added Tax.**

(2) The Sub-Contractor shall be deemed not to have allowed in the Price for any tax payable by him as a taxable person to the Commissioners of Customs and Excise being tax chargeable on any taxable supplies to the Contractor which are to be provided under the Sub-Contract.

(3) In any return account notice statement of work done application for payment or any document submitted with any of the aforesaid the Sub-Contractor shall not include any amount of money on account of tax as a separate item or claim.

(4) (a) There shall be added to the amount of every payment made by the Contractor to the Sub-Contractor pursuant to Clause 15 (Payment) and paid by the Contractor a sum separately identified equal to the amount of tax properly payable by the Sub-Contractor as a taxable person to the Commissioners in respect of the taxable supply to which the payment made under Clause 15 (3) relates.

(b) Where the Contractor has been authorised by H.M. Customs and Excise to operate self-billing procedures on terms and conditions acceptable to the Sub-Contractor the Contractor shall with every payment made pursuant to Clause 15 issue a tax invoice on behalf of the Sub-Contractor and despatch a Sub-Contractor's record copy of such invoice to the Sub-Contractor with that payment. The Contractor shall not issue a tax invoice except as aforesaid, and shall immediately notify the Sub-Contractor in the event of the terms of the approval given by H.M. Customs and Excise being varied or withdrawn.

(5) (a) Upon receipt of the amounts referred to in sub-clause (4) the Sub-Contractor shall, except where self-billing arrangements under sub-clause (4) (b) apply, forthwith issue to the Contractor an authenticated receipt of the kind referred to in Regulation 21 (2) of the Value Added Tax (General) Regulations 1971 (S.I. 1972/1147) or any amendment thereof in respect of those amounts.

(b) Upon receipt of a record copy of a self-billing invoice under sub-clause (4) (b) the Sub-Contractor shall not issue an authenticated receipt but shall account to H.M. Customs and Excise for output tax in accordance with the tax invoice issued by the Contractor on behalf of the Sub-Contractor and shall not at any time issue any other document which constitutes a tax invoice.

(6) Where the Sub-Contractor is bound under the Sub-Contract to issue an authenticated receipt and he shall fail to comply with sub-clause (5) (a) the Contractor may after notifying the Sub-Contractor in writing of his failure and requesting the Sub-Contractor to issue authenticated receipts in respect of amounts received from the Contractor by the Sub-Contractor withhold further payments including payment of retention monies to the Sub-Contractor equivalent to the amount for which the receipt or receipts should have been given.

Provided that any payments withheld pursuant to this sub-clause shall be released to the Sub-Contractor upon full compliance with the aforesaid notification and request and the provisions of this Clause shall apply to the release of those payments.

(7) If the Sub-Contractor shall establish that the Commissioners have charged him in respect of a taxable supply for which he has received payment under the Sub-Contract tax greater than the sum paid to him by the Contractor the Contractor shall forthwith pay to the Sub-Contractor a sum equal to the difference between the tax previously paid and the tax charged to the Sub-Contractor by the Commissioners.

(8) Without prejudice to any other remedies available to either the Contractor or the Sub-Contractor the Contractor shall be entitled to withhold from the Sub-Contractor an amount of money equal to the amount of any tax paid to the Sub-Contractor in exess of the amount which in all the circumstances should have been paid to the Sub-Contractor.

(9) Where the Contractor makes any provision pursuant to Clause 4 (Contractors' Facilities) and that provision is a taxable supply to the Sub-Contractor by the Contractor the Sub-Contractor shall pay tax to the Contractor in accordance with the requirements of the Contractor at the rate properly payable by the Contractor to the Commissioners.

30th March 1973

APPENDIX C

FORMS

FORM "A"

(*Name of Employer*)

No. . . . .

Contract

Order for Variation in the work under Clause 51 (2) of the Conditions of Contract

To:

I hereby order the following variation in the Works comprised in the above Contract:

(*Description of Variation*)

Date . . . .

Engineer

FORM "B."
Clause 52 (4)

No...............

Contract..

To.. *Engineer to*..

Variation Order No.............

Please note that .... intend to claim payment for work carried out in accordance with the above Order.

Date ....

Contractor

FORM "C."

(*Name of Employer*)

No. . . . .

Contract

Contractor's monthly return of extra and additional work under Clause 52 (4) of the Conditions of Contract.

Date of Order. . . . . .19. . . .	*Month ending* . . . . .19. . . .
No. of Order.	

Metres	*No.*	*Description of Work*	*Rate*	£	*p*
			£		

Date. . . . .

. . . .
Contractor

No. . . . .
Contract

Contractor

Date

On A/c of Works at
. . . .
. . . .

Now certified £
Previously certified £

TOTAL . . . . £

FORM "D."
(*Name of Employer*)
ENGINEER'S CERTIFICATE

No. of Certificate. . . . . *Contract* . . . .

Contractor. *Date* . . . . .19. . . .

I hereby certify that the sum of. . . . . .is due to. . . . . on account of Works at. . . . .

Now certified . . £. . . . .
Previously certified £. . . . . *Engineer*

TOTAL . . £

Received from . . . . of . . . . the above sum of . . . .

Date . . . .
Contractor

FORM "E."

(*Name of Employer*)

ENGINEER'S MAINTENANCE CERTIFICATE.

Clause 61 (1)

Contract.................................... *Date* ....19....

Contractor....................................

I hereby certify that the Works comprised in the above contract have been completed and maintained to my satisfaction and that the contractor is entitled to be paid the sum of.. being the balance of the retention money under the contract.

....

Engineer

APPENDIX D

THE DUODECIMAL SYSTEM

In the past, when feet and inches were used for measuring purposes the general unit for payment of engineering works was the yard, although the physical dimensions were measured on the ground in the smaller units. Rather than reducing all lengths to inches and obtaining areas in square inches, or using awkward decimal or vulgar fractions if lengths were kept in feet, surveyors developed the habit of multiplying the feet and inches together and obtaining answers in units, twelfths, one hundred and forty fourths, etc. The ordinary principles of long multiplication applied, with the exception that each column, instead of representing one tenth of that on its left, represented one twelfth. Once this basic consideration is grasped, the whole system becomes strictly analogous to ordinary decimal fractions. Examples may make this clearer.

Ex. 1.—Determine the floor area of a room whose length and breadth are 14′ 2″ and 12′ 4″ respectively.

These two dimensions were written down beneath each other as shown, with a full stop between the feet and inches. Multiplying the 2″ by 4″, we have 8 square inches, which is $^{8}/_{144}$ of a square foot; this 8 is entered in the third column. $4 \times 14 = 56$; this should go into the second column, but with the limit of 12 in any column the 56 is divided by twelve and the integer of the answer goes forward into the first column, and the remainder is put in the second column. The 12 and the 2 are multiplied in the same way to be entered in the second column, but since $^{24}/_{12}$ is really 2, this number is put straight into the first column. The 12 and the 14 are multiplied and the answer is written directly into the first column. The columns are then added, and we obtain the answer $174 + {}^{8}/_{12} + {}^{8}/_{144}$. Rigorously the answer can be reduced to $174\,^{13}/_{18}$ ft^2, but for all practical purposes the $^{8}/_{144}$ would be struck out and the $^{8}/_{12}$ rounded up to $\frac{3}{4}$.

14.	2	
12.	4	
		8
4.	8.	
2.		
168.		
174.	8.	8

When a volume is required, the area is multiplied by the height in exactly the same way.

Ex. 2.—If the height of this room is 8′ 10″, determine its volumetric capacity.

Set out the figures as shown and proceed as before.

	174. 8. 8
	8. 10.
$^{10}/_{12} \times {}^{8}/_{144} = {}^{80}/_{1728} = {}^{6}/_{144} + {}^{8}/_{1728}$	6.
$^{10}/_{12} \times {}^{8}/_{12} = {}^{80}/_{144} = {}^{6}/_{12} + {}^{8}/_{144}$	6. 8. 8
$174 \times {}^{10}/_{12} = 145$	145.
$8 \times {}^{8}/_{144} = {}^{64}/_{144} = {}^{5}/_{12} + {}^{4}/_{144}$	5. 4.
$8 \times {}^{8}/_{12} = {}^{64}/_{12} = 5 + {}^{4}/_{12}$	5. 4.
$8 \times 174 = 1392$	1392.
	1543. 4. 6. 8

This result would normally be rounded off as 1543 ft^3.

In the former practice these figures would have been carried forward from the dimension sheets to the abstracts in these units. They would have been divided by 3, 9, or 27 to reduce them to yards, linear, square, or cubic respectively, when the actual bill was being written.

APPENDIX E

SQUARE AND ROUND STEEL

Masses, Areas and Circumferences

(Masses of Steel : 7·85 tonne/m³)

Side or Dia. in mm	Mass of ● Bar in kg/m	Mass of ■ Bar in kg/m	Area of ● Bar in mm²	Area of ■ Bar in mm²	Circumference of ● Bar in mm
5	0·154	0·196	19·635	25	15·7
6	0·222	0·283	28.274	36	18·9
7	0·302	0·385	38·485	49	22·0
8	0·395	0·503	50·266	64	25·1
9	0·499	0·636	63·617	81	28·3
10	0·616	0·785	78·540	100	31·4
11	0·746	0·950	95·033	121	34·6
12	0·888	1·130	113·097	144	37·7
13	1·042	1·326	132·732	169	40·8
14	1·208	1·538	153·938	196	44·0
15	1·387	1·766	176·715	225	47·1
16	1·578	2·010	201·062	256	50·3
17	1·782	2·268	226·980	289	53·4
18	1·998	2·543	254·469	324	56·5
19	2·225	2·834	283·529	361	59·7
20	2·466	3·142	314·159	400	62·8
21	2·719	3·461	346·361	441	66·0
22	2·984	3·799	380·133	484	69·1
23	3·261	4·152	415·476	529	72·3
24	3·551	4·521	452·389	576	75·4
25	3·853	4·906	490·874	625	78·5
26	4·168	5·306	530·929	676	81·7
27	4·494	5·722	572·555	729	84·8
28	4·833	6·154	615·752	784	88·0
29	5·184	6·601	660·520	841	91·1
30	5·548	7·064	706·858	900	94·2
31	5·925	7·54	754·768	961	97·4
32	6·313	8·04	804·248	1024	100·5
33	6·714	8·55	855·30	1089	103·7
34	7·127	9·07	907·92	1156	106·8
35	7·553	9·62	962·11	1225	110·0
36	7·990	10·17	1017·88	1296	113·1
37	8·440	10·75	1075·21	1369	116·2
38	8·903	11·33	1134·11	1444	119·4
39	9·378	11·94	1194·59	1521	122·5
40	9·865	12·56	1256·64	1600	125·7

Side or Dia. in mm	Mass of ● Bar in kg/m	Mass of ■ Bar in kg/m	Area of ● Bar in mm^2	Area of ■ Bar m mm^2	Circumference of ● Bar in mm
41	10·36	13·19	1320·25	1681	128·8
42	10·88	13·85	1385·44	1764	131·9
43	11·40	14·51	1452·20	1849	135·1
44	11·94	15·19	1520·53	1936	138·2
45	12·48	15·90	1590·43	2025	141·4
46	13·05	16·61	1661·90	2116	144·5
47	13·62	17·34	1734·94	2209	147·7
48	14·21	18·08	1809·56	2304	150·8
49	14·80	18·85	1885·74	2401	153·9
50	15·41	19·62	1963·50	2500	157·1

STEEL CUP-HEADED RIVETS

APPROXIMATE MASSES IN KILOGRAMS PER 1000 HEADS

DIAMETER OF RIVET IN MILLIMETRES						
10	**12**	**16**	**20**	**22**	**24**	**27**
6·1	9·7	23·6	50·6	66·8	95·5	116·2

BS 4190 ISO METRIC BLACK BOLTS WITH NUTS

APPROXIMATE MASSES IN KILOGRAMS PER 1000

Length under head in mm	DIAMETER OF BOLTS IN MILLIMETRES										
	6	**8**	**10**	**12**	**16**	**20**	**24**	**30**	**36**	**42**	**48**
25	8·97	18·7	36·6	52·5							
30	10·1	20·7	39·1	56·1	107	186					
35	11·2	22·7	42·2	59·7	114	196					
40	12·3	24·7	45·3	64·1	121	207	347				
45	13·4	26·7	48·4	68·5	128	217	362				
50	14·5	28·7	51·5	72·9	136	227	377				
55	15·6	30·7	54·6	77·3	144	238	392				
60	16·7	32·7	57·7	81·7	152	251	407				
65	17·8	34·7	60·8	86·1	160	264	422				
70	18·9	36·7	63·9	90·5	168	277	440				
75	20·0	38·7	67·0	95·0	176	290	458				
80	21·1	40·7	70·1	100	182	303	476	853			
90		44·7	76·3	109	198	329	511	908			
100		48·7	82·5	118	214	355	547	963	1520		
110			88·7	127	230	381					
120			94·9	136	246	407	618	1070	1680	2450	
130			101	145	262	433					
140			107	154	278	459	689	1180	1840	2670	
150			113	163	294	485	725	1230	1920	2780	3860
160			119	172	310	501	760	1290	2000	2890	4000
170			125	181	326	527					
180			131	190	342	553	831	1400	2160	3110	4280
190			137	199	358	579					
200			143	208	374	605	902	1510	2320	3330	4560
Approximate mass in kg of 1000 nuts	1·11	2·32	10·9	15·9	30·8	60·3	103	216	369	610	924

PROPORTIONS AND STRENGTH REQUIREMENTS FOR NOMINAL CONCRETE MIXES WITH PORTLAND CEMENT OR PORTLAND-BLASTFURNACE CEMENT AND WITH AGGREGATES COMPLYING WITH BS 882 OR BS 1047

(1)	(2)		(3)		(4)	
Mix proportions	Cubic metres of aggregate per 50 kg of cement		Cube strength within 28 days after mixing		Alternative cube strength within 7 days after mixing	
	Fine	Coarse	Preliminary test	Works test	Preliminary test	Works test
			N/mm^2	N/mm^2	N/mm^2	N/mm^2
1:1:2	0·035	0·70	40	30	26·7	20
1:1½:3	0·05	0·10	34	25·5	22·7	17
1:2:4	0·07	0·14	28	21	18·7	14

APPENDIX F

CHORD LENGTHS AND SEGMENT AREAS OF CIRCLES OF UNITY DIAMETER WITH ARGUMENTS IN CHORD HEIGHTS

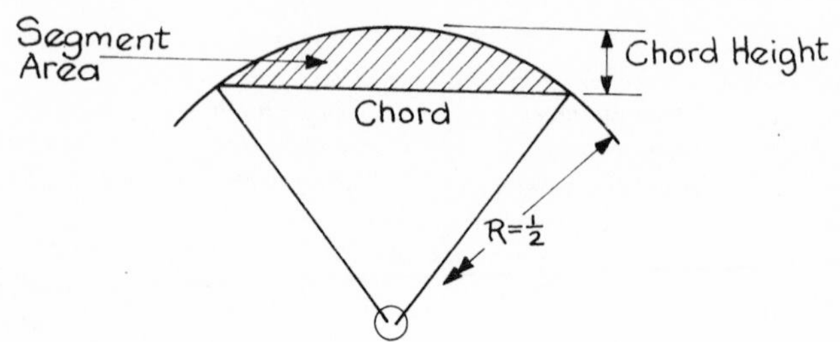

Height	*Chord*	*Segment*	*Height*	*Chord*	*Segment*
0·001	0·06321	0·00004	0·041	0·39658	0·01093
0·002	0·08935	0·00012	0·042	0·40118	0·01133
0·003	0·10938	0·00022	0·043	0·40571	0·01173
0·004	0·12624	0·00034	0·044	0·41019	0·01214
0·005	0·14107	0·00047	0·045	0·41461	0·01255
0·006	0·15445	0·00062	0·046	0·41897	0·01297
0·007	0·16675	0·00078	0·047	0·42328	0·01339
0·008	0·17817	0·00095	0·048	0·42753	0·01382
0·009	0·18888	0·00114	0·049	0·43174	0·01425
0·010	0·19900	0·00133	0·050	0·43589	0·01468
0·011	0·20860	0·00153	0·051	0·44000	0·01512
0·012	0·21777	0·00175	0·052	0·44405	0·01556
0·013	0·22655	0·00197	0·053	0·44807	0·01601
0·014	0·23498	0·00220	0·054	0·45204	0·01646
0·015	0·24310	0·00244	0·055	0·45596	0·01691
0·016	0·25095	0·00269	0·056	0·45984	0·01737
0·017	0·25854	0·00294	0·057	0·46369	0·01783
0·018	0·26590	0·00320	0·058	0·46749	0·01830
0·019	0·27305	0·00347	0·059	0·47125	0·01877
0·020	0·28000	0·00375	0·060	0·47497	0·01924
0·021	0·28677	0·00403	0·061	0·47866	0·01972
0·022	0·29337	0·00432	0·062	0·48231	0·02020
0·023	0·29981	0·00462	0·063	0·48593	0·02068
0·024	0·30610	0·00492	0·064	0·48951	0·02117
0·025	0·31225	0·00523	0·065	0·49305	0·02166
0·026	0·31827	0·00555	0·066	0·49656	0·02215
0·027	0·32417	0·00587	0·067	0·50004	0·02265
0·028	0·32995	0·00619	0·068	0·50349	0·02315
0·029	0·33561	0·00653	0·069	0·50691	0·02366
0·030	0·34117	0·00687	0·070	0·51029	0·02417
0·031	0·34664	0·00721	0·071	0·51365	0·02468

Height	*Chord*	*Segment*	*Height*	*Chord*	*Segment*
0·032	0·35200	0·00756	0·072	0·51698	0·02520
0·033	0·35727	0·00791	0·073	0·52027	0·02572
0·034	0·36246	0·00827	0·074	0·52354	0·02624
0·035	0·36756	0·00864	0·075	0·52678	0·02676
0·036	0·37258	0·00901	0·076	0·53000	0·02729
0·037	0·37752	0·00938	0·077	0·53318	0·02782
0·038	0·38239	0·00976	0·078	0·53634	0·02836
0·039	0·38719	0·01015	0·079	0·53948	0·02890
0·040	0·39192	0·01054	0·080	0·54259	0·02944
0·081	0·54567	0·02998	0·121	0·65225	0·05404
0·082	0·54873	0·03053	0·122	0·65457	0·05469
0·083	0·55176	0·03108	0·123	0·65687	0·05535
0·084	0·55478	0·03163	0·124	0·65916	0·05600
0·085	0·55776	0·03219	0·125	0·66144	0·05666
0·086	0·56073	0·03275	0·126	0·66370	0·05733
0·087	0·56367	0·03331	0·127	0·66595	0·05799
0·088	0·56659	0·03387	0·128	0·66818	0·05866
0·089	0·56949	0·03444	0·129	0·67040	0·05933
0·090	0·57236	0·03501	0·130	0·67261	0·06000
0·091	0·57522	0·03558	0·131	0·67480	0·06067
0·092	0·57805	0·03616	0·132	0·67698	0·06135
0·093	0·58086	0·03674	0·133	0·67915	0·06203
0·094	0·58366	0·03732	0·134	0·68130	0·06271
0·095	0·58643	0·03791	0·135	0·68345	0·06339
0·096	0·58918	0·03850	0·136	0·68558	0·06407
0·097	0·59192	0·03909	0·137	0·68769	0·06476
0·098	0·59463	0·03968	0·138	0·68980	0·06545
0·099	0·59732	0·04028	0·139	0·69189	0·06614
0·100	0·60000	0·04088	0·140	0·69397	0·06683
0·101	0·60266	0·04148	0·141	0·69604	0·06753
0·102	0·60530	0·04208	0·142	0·69810	0·06823
0·103	0·60792	0·04269	0·143	0·70015	0·06893
0·104	0·61052	0·04330	0·144	0·70218	0·06963
0·105	0·61311	0·04391	0·145	0·70420	0·07033
0·106	0·61568	0·04452	0·146	0·70621	0·07103
0·107	0·61823	0·04514	0·147	0·70821	0·07174
0·108	0·62076	0·04576	0·148	0·71020	0·07245
0·109	0·62328	0·04638	0·149	0·71218	0·07316
0·110	0·62578	0·04701	0·150	0·71414	0·07387
0·111	0·62826	0·04763	0·151	0·71610	0·07459
0·112	0·63073	0·04826	0·152	0·71804	0·07531
0·113	0·63319	0·04889	0·153	0·71998	0·07603
0·114	0·63562	0·04953	0·154	0·72190	0·07675
0·115	0·63804	0·05017	0·155	0·72381	0·07747
0·116	0·64045	0·05081	0·156	0·72571	0·07819
0·117	0·64284	0·05145	0·157	0·72760	0·07892
0·118	0·64522	0·05209	0·158	0·72948	0·07965

Height	*Chord*	*Segment*	*Height*	*Chord*	*Segment*
0·119	0·64758	0·05274	0·159	0·73135	0·08038
0·120	0·64992	0·05339	0·160	0·73321	0·08111
0·161	0·73506	0·08185	0·201	0·80150	0·11262
0·162	0·73690	0·08258	0·202	0·80298	0·11343
0·163	0·73873	0·08332	0·203	0·80446	0·11423
0·164	0·70455	0·08406	0·204	0·80594	0·11504
0·165	0·74236	0·08480	0·205	0·80740	0·11584
0·166	0·74416	0·08554	0·206	0·80886	0·11665
0·167	0·74595	0·08629	0·207	0·81031	0·11746
0·168	0·74773	0·08704	0·208	0·81175	0·11827
0·169	0·74950	0·08779	0·209	0·81319	0·11908
0·170	0·75127	0·08854	0·210	0·81462	0·11990
0·171	0·75302	0·08929	0·211	0·81604	0·12071
0·172	0·75476	0·09004	0·212	0·81745	0·12153
0·173	0·75649	0·09080	0·213	0·81886	0·12235
0·174	0·75822	0·09155	0·214	0·82025	0·12317
0·175	0·75993	0·09231	0·215	0·82164	0·12399
0·176	0·76164	0·09307	0·216	0·82303	0·12481
0·177	0·76334	0·09384	0·217	0·82441	0·12563
0·178	0·76503	0·09460	0·218	0·82577	0·12646
0·179	0·76670	0·09537	0·219	0·82714	0·12729
0·180	0·76837	0·09613	0·220	0·82849	0·12811
0·181	0·77004	0·09690	0·221	0·82984	0·12894
0·182	0·77169	0·09767	0·222	0·83118	0·12977
0·183	0·77333	0·09845	0·223	0·83252	0·13061
0·184	0·77497	0·09922	0·224	0·83384	0·13144
0·185	0·77660	0·10000	0·225	0·83516	0·13227
0·186	0·77821	0·10077	0·226	0·83648	0·13311
0·187	0·77982	0·10155	0·227	0·83779	0·13395
0·188	0·78142	0·10233	0·228	0·83909	0·13478
0·189	0·78302	0·10312	0·229	0·84038	0·13562
0·190	0·78460	0·10390	0·230	0·84166	0·13646
0·191	0·78618	0·10469	0·231	0·84294	0·13731
0·192	0·78775	0·10547	0·232	0·84422	0·13815
0·193	0·78931	0·10626	0·233	0·84548	0·13900
0·194	0·79086	0·10705	0·234	0·84674	0·13984
0·195	0·79240	0·10784	0·235	0·84800	0·14069
0·196	0·79394	0·10864	0·236	0·84924	0·14154
0·197	0·79546	0·10943	0·237	0·85048	0·14239
0·198	0·79698	0·11023	0·238	0·85172	0·14324
0·199	0·79850	0·11102	0·239	0·85295	0·14409
0·200	0·80000	0·11182	0·240	0·85417	0·14494
0·241	0·85538	0·14580	0·281	0·89898	0·18092
0·242	0·85659	0·14666	0·282	0·89995	0·18182
0·243	0·85779	0·14751	0·283	0·90091	0·18272
0·244	0·85899	0·14837	0·284	0·90187	0·18362

Height	*Chord*	*Segment*	*Height*	*Chord*	*Segment*
0·245	0·86017	0·14923	0·285	0·90283	0·18452
0·246	0·86136	0·15009	0·286	0·90378	0·18543
0·247	0·86253	0·15095	0·287	0·90472	0·18633
0·248	0·86370	0·15182	0·288	0·90566	0·18723
0·249	0·86487	0·15268	0·289	0·90660	0·18814
0·250	0·86603	0·15355	0·290	0·90752	0·18905
0·251	0·86718	0·15441	0·291	0·90845	0·18996
0·252	0·86832	0·15528	0·292	0·90936	0·19086
0·253	0·86946	0·15615	0·293	0·91028	0·19177
0·254	0·87060	0·15702	0·294	0·91118	0·19269
0·255	0·87172	0·15789	0·295	0·91209	0·19360
0·256	0·87284	0·15876	0·296	0·91298	0·19451
0·257	0·87396	0·15964	0·297	0·91387	0·19542
0·258	0·87507	0·16051	0·298	0·91476	0·19634
0·259	0·87617	0·16139	0·299	0·91564	0·19725
0·260	0·87727	0·16226	0·300	0·91652	0·19817
0·261	0·87836	0·16314	0·301	0·91739	0·19909
0·262	0·87945	0·16402	0·302	0·91825	0·20000
0·263	0·88052	0·16490	0·303	0·91911	0·20092
0·264	0·88160	0·16578	0·304	0·91997	0·20184
0·265	0·88267	0·16666	0·305	0·92081	0·22760
0·266	0·88373	0·16755	0·306	0·92166	0·20368
0·267	0·88478	0·16843	0·307	0·92250	0·20461
0·268	0·88584	0·16932	0·308	0·92333	0·20553
0·269	0·88688	0·17020	0·309	0·92416	0·20645
0·270	0·88792	0·17109	0·310	0·92499	0·20738
0·271	0·88895	0·17198	0·311	0·92581	0·20830
0·272	0·88998	0·17287	0·312	0·92662	0·20923
0·273	0·89100	0·17376	0·313	0·92743	0·21015
0·274	0·89202	0·17465	0·314	0·92823	0·21108
0·275	0·89303	0·17554	0·315	0·92903	0·21201
0·276	0·89403	0·17644	0·316	0·92983	0·21294
0·277	0·89503	0·17733	0·317	0·93061	0·21387
0·278	0·89603	0·17823	0·318	0·93140	0·21480
0·279	0·89702	0·17912	0·319	0·93218	0·21573
0·280	0·89800	0·18002	0·320	0·93295	0·21667
0·321	0·93372	0·21760	0·361	0·96058	0·25551
0·322	0·93449	0·21853	0·362	0·96116	0·25647
0·323	0·93525	0·21947	0·363	0·96173	0·25743
0·324	0·93600	0·22040	0·364	0·96230	0·25840
0·325	0·93675	0·22134	0·365	0·96286	0·25936
0·326	0·93749	0·22228	0·366	0·96342	0·26032
0·327	0·93823	0·22322	0·367	0·96397	0·26128
0·328	0·93897	0·22415	0·368	0·96452	0·26225
0·329	0·93970	0·22509	0·369	0·96507	0·26321
0·330	0·94043	0·22603	0·370	0·96561	0·26418

Height	*Chord*	*Segment*	*Height*	*Chord*	*Segment*
0·331	0·94115	0·22697	0·371	0·96614	0·26514
0·332	0·94186	0·22792	0·372	0·96668	0·26611
0·333	0·94257	0·22886	0·373	0·96720	0·26708
0·334	0·94328	0·22980	0·374	0·96773	0·26805
0·335	0·94398	0·23074	0·375	0·96825	0·26901
0·336	0·94468	0·23169	0·376	0·96876	0·26998
0·337	0·94537	0·23263	0·377	0·96927	0·27095
0·338	0·94606	0·23358	0·378	0·96978	0·27192
0·339	0·94674	0·23543	0·379	0·97028	0·27289
0·340	0·94742	0·23547	0·380	0·97077	0·27386
0·341	0·94809	0·23642	0·381	0·97127	0·27483
0·342	0·94876	0·23737	0·382	0·97175	0·27580
0·343	0·94942	0·23832	0·383	0·97224	0·27678
0·344	0·95008	0·23927	0·384	0·97272	0·27775
0·345	0·95074	0·24022	0·385	0·97339	0·27872
0·346	0·95139	0·24117	0·386	0·97366	0·27969
0·347	0·95203	0·24212	0·387	0·97413	0·28067
0·348	0·95267	0·24307	0·388	0·97459	0·28164
0·349	0·95331	0·24403	0·389	0·97505	0·28262
0·350	0·95394	0·24498	0·390	0·97550	0·28359
0·351	0·95457	0·24593	0·391	0·97595	0·28457
0·352	0·95519	0·24689	0·392	0·97639	0·28554
0·353	0·95581	0·24785	0·393	0·97683	0·28642
0·354	0·95642	0·24880	0·394	0·97727	0·28750
0·355	0·95703	0·24976	0·395	0·97770	0·28848
0·356	0·95763	0·25072	0·396	0·97813	0·28945
0·357	0·95823	0·25167	0·397	0·97855	0·29043
0·358	0·95882	0·25263	0·398	0·97897	0·29141
0·359	0·95941	0·25359	0·399	0·97939	0·29239
0·360	0·96000	0·25455	0·400	0·97980	0·29337
0·401	0·98020	0·29435	0·441	0·99301	0·33384
0·402	0·98060	0·29533	0·442	0·99325	0·33483
0·403	0·98100	0·29631	0·443	0·99348	0·33582
0·404	0·98139	0·29729	0·444	0·99371	0·33682
0·405	0·98178	0·29827	0·445	0·99393	0·33781
0·406	0·98217	0·29926	0·446	0·99415	0·33880
0·407	0·98255	0·30024	0·447	0·99437	0·33980
0·408	0·98293	0·30122	0·448	0·99458	0·34079
0·409	0·98330	0·30220	0·449	0·99478	0·34179
0·410	0·98367	0·30319	0·450	0·99499	0·34278
0·411	0·98403	0·30417	0·451	0·99519	0·34378
0·412	0·98439	0·30516	0·452	0·99538	0·34477
0·413	0·98475	0·30614	0·453	0·99557	0·34577
0·414	0·98510	0·30712	0·454	0·99576	0·34676
0·415	0·98544	0·30811	0·455	0·99594	0·34776
0·416	0·98579	0·30910	0·456	0·99612	0·34876
0·417	0·98613	0·31008	0·456	0·99630	0·34975
0·418	0·98646	0·31107	0·458	0·99647	0·35075

Height	*Chord*	*Segment*	*Height*	*Chord*	*Segment*
0·419	0·98679	0·31205	0·459	0·99663	0·35175
0·420	0·98712	0·31304	0·460	0·99679	0·35274
0·421	0·98744	0·31403	0·461	0·99695	0·35374
0·422	0·98776	0·31502	0·462	0·99711	0·35474
0·423	0·98807	0·31600	0·463	0·99726	0·35573
0·424	0·98838	0·31700	0·464	0·99740	0·35673
0·425	0·98869	0·31798	0·465	0·99755	0·35733
0·426	0·98899	0·31897	0·466	0·99769	0·35873
0·427	0·98928	0·31996	0·467	0·99782	0·35972
0·428	0·98958	0·32095	0·468	0·99795	0·36072
0·429	0·98987	0·32194	0·469	0·99808	0·36172
0·430	0·99015	0·32293	0·470	0·99820	0·36272
0·431	0·99043	0·32392	0·471	0·99832	0·36372
0·432	0·99071	0·32491	0·472	0·99843	0·36471
0·433	0·99098	0·32590	0·473	0·99854	0·35471
0·434	0·99125	0·32689	0·474	0·99865	0·36671
0·435	0·99151	0·32788	0·475	0·99875	0·36771
0·436	0·99177	0·32887	0·476	0·99885	0·36871
0·437	0·99203	0·32987	0·477	0·99894	0·36971
0·438	0·99228	0·33086	0·478	0·99903	0·37071
0·439	0·99253	0·33185	0·479	0·99912	0·37171
0·440	0·99277	0·33284	0·480	0·99920	0·37270
0·481	0·99928	0·37370	0·491	0·99984	0·38370
0·482	0·99935	0·37470	0·492	0·99987	0·38470
0·483	0·99942	0·37570	0·493	0·99990	0·38570
0·484	0·99949	0·37670	0·494	0·99993	0·38670
0·485	0·99955	0·37770	0·495	0·99995	0·38770
0·486	0·99961	0·37870	0·496	0·99997	0·38870
0·487	0·99966	0·37970	0·497	0·99998	0·38970
0·488	0·99971	0·38070	0·498	0·99999	0·39070
0·489	0·99976	0·38170	0·499	1·00000	0·39170
0·490	0·99980	0·38270	0·500	1·00000	0·39270

APPENDIX G

EXTRACTS FROM BS 4466:1969

Shape code	Method of measurement of bending dimensions	Total length of bar (L) measured along centre line	Dimensions to be given in schedule
20	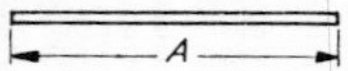	A	Straight
32	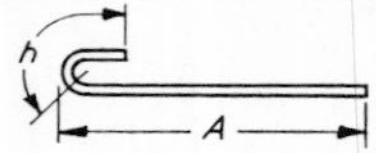	$A + h$	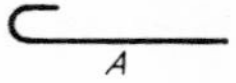
33	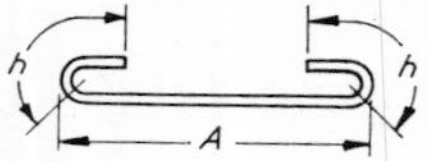	$A + 2h$	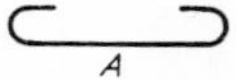
38*	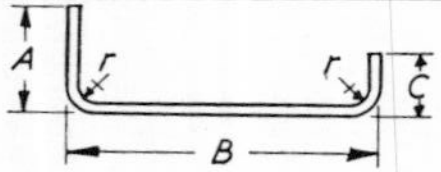 or 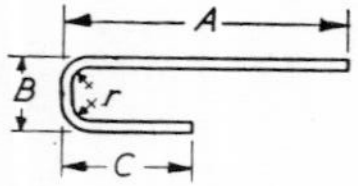	$A + B + C - r - 2d$ $A + B + C - r - 2d$	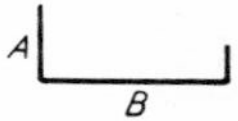 or 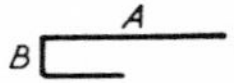
41*	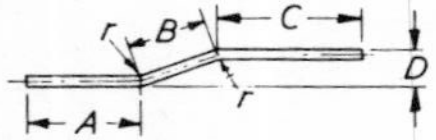 D shall be at least $2d$. or 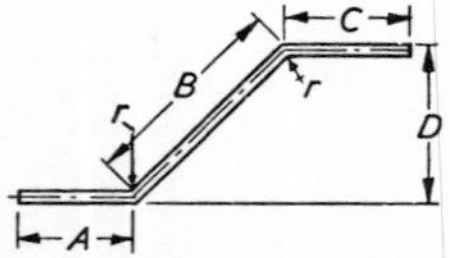	$A + B + C$	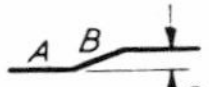 or 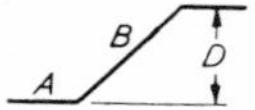

Shape code	Method of measurement of bending dimensions	Total length of bar (L) measured along centre line	Dimensions to be given in schedule
43*	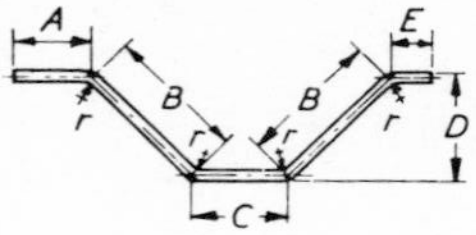	If angle with horizontal is 45° or less $A + 2B + C + E$	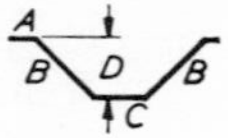
49*	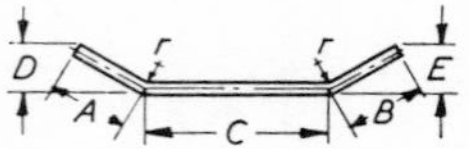	If angle with horizontal is 45° or less $A + B + C$	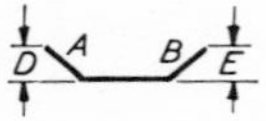
60	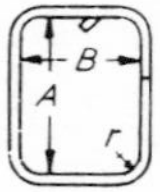 These dimensions shall be assumed to be internal unless noted otherwise by the use of arrows or the suffix 'O.D.'.	$2(A + B) + 20d$	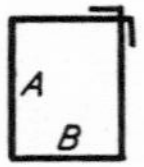
72	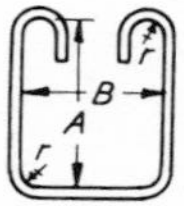 These dimensions shall be assumed to be internal unless noted otherwise by the use of arrows or the suffix 'O.D.'.	$2A + B + 25d$ ($25d$ permits the use of both mild steel and high yield steel bars).	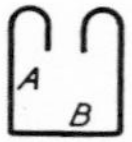
81	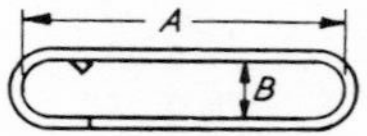 These dimensions shall be assumed to be internal unless noted otherwise by the use of arrows or the suffix 'O.D.'.	$2A + 3B + 22d$	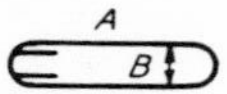

r = standard radius of bend (see Clause 7) unless otherwise stated.

* For these shapes in particular the effect of a positive cutting tolerance increasing the actual length of the 'free' leg or legs by up to 25 mm should be considered.

INDEX

(References are to Sections)